Speaking of Jersey

Reflections on the Island's past, present and future

Contributors: Charles Alluto, John Asbury, David Barlow,
Deputy Julian Bernstein, Betty Brooke, Josephine Cabot,
Sir Peter Crill, Maria da Silva, Revd John Dodd, Lee Durrell,
Andre Ferrari, Don Filleul OBE, Michael Halsey, Anne Herrod,
Madeline Jouanny, Mick Kavanagh, Philip Le Brocq, Francis Le Gresley,
Deputy Roy Le Hérissier, Christopher Le Quesne, Peter Le Rossignol,
Bob Le Sueur, Eileen Le Sueur, Wade Lewis, Robert Michel, Jack Minier,
Anne Perchard MBE, Jurat Henry Perrée, Revd Christina Price,
Colin Powell OBE, Louise Read, Carlos Santos-Costa, Andrew Syvret,
Michael Talibard, Daniel Tardivel, Dr Sarah Williams, Jack Worrall,
Gordon Young

Robin Pittman

With a foreword by General Sir Michael Wilkes KBE CBE
Lieutenant-Governor of Jersey 1996-2001

SEAFLOWER BOOKS

Published in 2003 by
SEAFLOWER BOOKS
1 The Shambles
Bradford on Avon
Wiltshire   BA15 1JS

Tel/Fax 01225 863595

www.ex-librisbooks.co.uk

Designed by Seaflower Books

Printed by Cromwell Press
Trowbridge, Wiltshire

ISBN 1 903341 14 0

Acknowledgments: Chris Thomas of Expressions Photography
Ltd. for all portrait photographs except Jack Minier and
Gordon Young (courtesy *Jersey Evening Post*), Lee Durrell and
Christopher Le Quesne.

Contents

Foreword
by General Sir Michael Wilkes
Lieutenant-Governor of Jersey 1996-2001

*T*he people of Jersey are a proud and resilient folk, independent of mind as befits an island race and instinctively resourceful in the face of less than generous neighbours. If one adds to this the gifts which nature has bestowed on the Island in terms of spectacular scenery and a geographically advantageous position in terms of the world's time zones, one has to recognise a formidable combination of assets.

The history of Jersey is both rich and varied, and it is unsurprising that circumstance has conspired to produce an almost natural rhythm of peaks and troughs in its development. In recent years the once-dominant staples of agriculture and tourism have been almost completely eclipsed by a vigorous financial services industry. To describe it as a 'cuckoo in the nest' would be to belittle the enormous advantages that have accrued from the revenue it has generated. Jersey's infrastructure and the service industries on which it relies have blossomed; standards of living have expanded exponentially as have the expectations of Islanders. The Island is at a peak.

As Jersey's position as a primary player in the offshore finance industry has taken on a greater profile, so has its status in the European scene come more into question. Hard decisions lie ahead concerning both the Island's internal management and its international relationships. To achieve satisfactory resolution to these looming and critical questions will require good government and cool heads, and opinions are divided as to whether either of these characteristics is evident as we face a new century and new challenges. By almost universal agreement Jersey stands at a crossroads.

And this is where Robin Pittman's series of recollections, garnered from a broad cross-section of Jersey people, some born in the Island and others not, comes into its own. It provides a fascinating backdrop to the events that I have mentioned as well as giving us some very personal glimpses into the past, present and future. We all tend to view our childhood days through rose-tinted spectacles, but through this book one is able to get a taste of the freedom and leisurely pace of life in early 20th century Jersey. The war years cannot have been easy, and the process of occupation has left a vivid scar on the memories of those who lived through that time. Post-war recovery took some time but eventually led to the birth of the finance industry that lies at the heart of the Island's present prosperity. All this *Speaking of Jersey* reveals.

The true interest of this book lies in Robin Pittman's ability to have persuaded his contributors, each from his or her own perspective, to look into the future, to reveal their reservations about the current situation and to suggest possible solutions. It is unusual in a small community for colours to have been so firmly nailed to the mast!

Certain themes recur through the book, but one fact above all shines through: the profound love for Jersey and the deep commitment to the Island shown by Robin's skilfully chosen subjects. I commend *Speaking of Jersey* to all those who share that passion.

Introduction

Those who read this book are likely to have at least some knowledge of Jersey and its history. A brief word may, however, be appropriate. Jersey became a possession of the English Crown in 1204. It is not directly subordinate to the Parliament of the United Kingdom but is instead directly answerable to the Crown. Increasingly over the years the Bailiff, who is the Chief Judge and Speaker of the Island's Parliament (the States), assumed the executive power of the Crown's major representative, the Lieutenant-Governor. The Bailiff's own office, however, has gradually been reduced in influence by the growth of the States. The States has steadily become more influential, emerging as a fully representative legislative body when the Jurats and the Rectors were removed from it in 1947.

In the twentieth century Jersey's three-pronged source of prosperity – agriculture, tourism and, to a lesser extent, light industry – carried the Island forward until the outbreak of the Second World War. After the German Occupation rehabilitation was swift, and a major development in the Island's growth was the arrival of the finance industry in the 1960s. With it came rapid population growth: 55,000 in the '60s and 90,000 in 2002. By the 1990s the Island was in the enviable position to many of having an over-heated economy. In the eyes of others, however, it was getting out of control and threatening to destroy the natural environment of the Island as more and more pressure arose for building and for expansion of the infrastructure. Thus in recent years Jersey has witnessed the demise of an agriculturally oriented society based on smallholdings, a decline in tourism and the establishment of a highly sophisticated finance industry (which itself now faces a degree of challenge from European and other moves against such offshore centres).

By the later 1990s pressure for change to its political system grew, and this led to the setting up by the States of a Review Panel on the Island's machinery of government. This body, the Clothier Commission, reported in December 2000 and recommended the replacement of the States' committee structure by a ministerial system with a Chief Minister.

The Island is thus – politically, socially and economically – at a crossroads, and this may be an opportune time to tap the opinions of a variety of those living in Jersey – older and younger, Jersey-born and originally from elsewhere, well-known and less well-known.

In compiling this book I have recorded, except in two instances, in-depth conversations with contributors; I gave all my subjects the freedom to alter and amend what I transcribed and wrote up following our meeting (in some cases more than one). What appear here are completely their own accounts and reflections.

My selection of contributors can hardly be termed scientific, but I have attempted, by choosing some with whom I am acquainted and others recommended to me, to achieve an interesting cross-section of Islanders. Readers will reach their own judgment as to whether I succeeded in this.

They will also have to make allowance for the fact that many months passed between the conducting of my first interview – in December 2001 – and the appearance of this book. In the meantime much has happened in Jersey as the States wrestled with the implications of the Clothier Report and with acceptance or otherwise of its various recommendations. Several comments in these pages may possibly have been overtaken by events. Despite that, there is value, I believe, in considering the thrust of observations made at a politically interesting time in the Island's history.

I am indebted to a number of people who have made this book possible. First, not unnaturally and also very sincerely, I give my warm thanks to all those who agreed to contribute (only one of those approached refused my request). I am grateful to Deputy Roy Le Hérissier, a contributor, who allowed me to rely, as the basis of my first paragraphs of this Introduction, on his paper concerning Jersey government which appeared in the journal *Public Administration and Development* (1998). I am especially grateful to Betty Brooke and Philip Le Brocq, both of them contributors, with each of whom I discussed my idea of this book and whose encouragement I greatly valued. Roger Jones of Seaflower Books, who so economically and skilfully has published various books of great quality about Jersey, has my special thanks as does my wife Laura who read through each contribution when completed and made very constructive suggestions. The advice of all the above-named has been extremely helpful, but the ultimate and full responsibility for what appears between these covers is necessarily mine.

Finally I wish to thank General Sir Michael Wilkes (whose admirable father, the late Jack Wilkes, was my Battery Commander when I was a Royal Artillery National Service subaltern) for so willingly agreeing to write a foreword. As a former Lieutenant-Governor he possesses a unique insight into the affairs and concerns of this special and beautiful Island.

RNP

Chapter One

Born in the 1910s

Eileen Le Sueur
John Dodd
Henry Perrée

Eileen Le Sueur

Eileen Le Sueur (née Le Marquand) was born in 1914 on her family's farm in St Ouen. She attended St Ouen Elementary School after which she worked on the farm before marrying her husband in 1938 and moving to Clair Val Farm, St Saviour, which has been her home since then. She has had a deep and continuing interest in the preservation of the Jersey-French language and has over the years been very active in the Island's amateur dramatics.

My first memories at the age of four are going with my mother to the Sunday evening service at St Ouen Methodist chapel and starting at the Sunday school. Here we were taught the *Notre Père* – the Lord's Prayer in French. We were given a line to learn each week and we returned the following Sunday to be tested in our knowledge of it. We were taught by Miss Florrie du Feu. She used to wear lovely big hats. One of them had a bunch of red cherries hanging on the side and I always wished that I could have a bite. At school we were not allowed to speak in Jersey-French. The headmaster, Mr Le Blanc, was firmly against it, claiming that it would spoil our ability to speak the 'good' French. In truth he thought that it was rather common to talk in Jersey-French which he considered slang. Now interestingly efforts are made to encourage its use and preserve it as part of Jersey's heritage.

When each day I returned from school I would change into old clothes and start on various odd jobs: polishing my mother's and father's shoes or cleaning the cutlery. I would help on the farm as well. It was a self-sufficient operation: a bit of everything. My father had ten or so head of cattle and used to grow turnips, swedes, mangolds, carrots, hay, wheat, oats and potatoes. Today one lifts the phone and orders a bag of dairy nuts or a bale of hay. Times past everything was grown on the farm; money was saved and spent only on essentials.

We were a fairly strict Methodist family; twice to chapel on Sundays. And there were the Sunday evenings when the Breton workers, over to dig the potatoes, would congregate at Le Marais and play their little French accordions and dance and sing. Sometimes after the chapel service we would join them.

Born in the 1910s...

When I left school, and with my father not in good health, I did what was expected and went to work on the farm. We used to have a little dairy and sell our milk through the parish. In the end we bought a van but I had no licence to drive. I went to the parish hall for one and the Constable, Francis Le Boutillier, said to me, 'I've seen you driving around the parish. Come and drive round my lawn.' So I reversed round his lawn and that satisfied him. This was my driving test. In the van we delivered milk up to L'Etacq and along the Five Mile Road (where in those days before the Germans came the well-to-do had bungalows and chalets). The milk was carried in a big dairy can and I used to have a pint measure with a long handle attached in order to fill customers' jugs. There was no pasteurisation; it was milk straight from the cow, and one can ask for nothing better.

My parents saved their money and I benefited during my childhood when they paid for me to have piano and singing lessons. I still have my certificates, and music has meant so much to me through my life. My mother also once paid for me to go by air to visit an uncle in London. I was 21 and my father gave me what was then a fortune, £5, as spending money. I flew in a Rapide from the beach at West Park (the planes had to wait for the tide to go out) and I still have the photo of myself going on board.

In many ways we were a happy community. The farmers helped each other: give me a hand with the ploughing and I'll come with my horse next week and help you with yours. I suppose the exception to this co-operation was in religion: church and chapel kept apart. Having said that, I gave up Methodism just before I married: the organist left and went to the parish church, and it was there that I married in January 1938.

It was not long after our marriage and our move to Clair Val that we were occupied by the Germans. My husband throughout the '30s had travelled frequently to America with Jersey cattle. This was now of course at an end and we made the decision just before the Occupation that, with our livestock to look after, we would stay.

One of the most frightening episodes for me at this bad time was to do with our hidden radio. Too many people would come and listen and in due course the Germans had their suspicions and arrived to search for it. Despite all my denials and with my heart beating 50 to the dozen they went through all our cupboards and up into the hay loft where it was secreted. I was probably saved by the use of Jersey-French, telling my young son in the patois to say nothing and pretend that he did not understand the Germans' harshly-spoken English. They went away and it was amazing that we were not caught. It was

Born in the 1910s...

a close-run thing.

Another alarming happening towards the end of the Occupation concerned the leaflets which the RAF used to air-drop. We gathered up a supply of them and put them in our loft to dry off. Once again the Germans came, both to check on cow numbers and to search. They found the pile of leaflets and ordered me to report to the Town Hall at eight o'clock the following morning. I cycled in and reported and was then taken to court. I was there all day facing questions about why we had picked up the leaflets. I managed to secure my freedom by saying to the Germans, 'When you came you emptied our shops, and we have no magazines. This paper is for the toilet.' They let me go at five o'clock.

On the whole we suffered less than did people in town who would walk out to us and beg us for just one egg. They would also come for milk. One lad came and helped out on the farm after he left school in order to have a bottle of milk each night to take home for his family. The Jersey cow saved many a life.

The Liberation was a great event. Some of the Germans were held back and put to work removing the barbed wire and other fortifications. I remember going up King Street and seeing this truck full of Germans in the back. One of them was the German who used to come and harshly check on the number of our cows. I saw him and shouted out, 'How many cows have you now got?' It was a proud moment for me but his head went down with shame as he looked away.

As life returned to normal I began to take up my interest in Jersey-French. We started a Jersey folk night and from this emerged L'Assembliée d'Jérriais of which for a time I was President. I have also been very active in local dramatics. This started during the Occupation and my involvement has been continuous ever since – in the Green Room Club and in the Amateur Dramatic Society. Other long-standing interests have been the St Saviour Social Club, the St Saviour Women's Institute and Eden Methodist chapel.

As I reflect on Jersey past and present I dislike the fact that there are rules for everything: too many regulations and too many committees. The old days of mutual help have given way to greed. People borrow money; they would not have done so in times past. Here is what happened not long after Jack and I married. There was a cart for sale in the *Evening Post*. It was advertised for £7 and we sorely needed it. When my husband approached the owner, Mr Kline of St Martin, and said that he could not afford it, Mr Kline generously gave him the cart. The following Saturday we cycled over to St Ouen and told my father of our good fortune.

'We've got a cart. For the mangolds,' I said.

'How did you get the cart,' he replied. 'I thought you had no money.'

'Mr Kline gave Jack £7.'

All hell broke loose – in Jersey-French and English: 'You should be ashamed of yourselves. If you borrow money, the farm will never be yours. Don't you borrow any more money. I never borrowed money; don't you start.'

We never slept that night, so great had been the telling-off. And we had not even borrowed the money; it had been Mr Kline's gift. Nevertheless there was a lesson here and this we have taught our children: if you haven't got it, do without. Today you can borrow money from the States and borrow from the banks. If the old folks could come back, they would not want to live here now. We have lived through the best century and God help those who follow us. We made our own lives; now our lives are made for us by others.

John Dodd

The Reverend John Dodd was born in 1915. In 1936 he gained first class honours in Classics, History and French at Liverpool University. He married in 1938 and was an educational missionary in the West Indies for five years before returning to England and taking in 1951 a Bachelor of Divinity honours degree at London University. In 1954 he studied at Westcott House, Cambridge, and was ordained an Anglican priest in the following year. From 1953 to 1961 he taught at Victoria College Prep. and from 1961 to 1968 at Jersey College for Girls. From 1954 to 1978 he was an assistant priest at St Helier parish church and from 1978 to 1993 Priest-in-Charge of Gouray church. From 1993 to 1995 he was a non-stipendiary priest at St Luke's church and is currently Chaplain at Glanville Home and at Jeanne Jugou Home.

Born in the 1910s...

I was born in Liverpool in 1915 and my father, who came from an old Liverpool and Cheshire family, was Permanent Secretary to the Lord Mayor of Liverpool. In fact he was rather embarrassed about his lineage: the house in which he was born had belonged to a slave-owning company and one of his ancestors had been a captain of a ship which transported slaves to the city. When I was doing missionary work in the West Indies my pupils and parishioners were the grandchildren of slaves. Perhaps it was God's plan for me to atone in small measure for the sins of my forebears.

In my youth little boys always went through a stage when they wanted to be engine drivers. For a time we lived near a railway line and some of my earliest memories are of collecting the numbers of passing locomotives and seeing the Flying Scotsman steaming by twice a day on its Glasgow-Liverpool run. Train-spotting was the start of my criminal career: older boys told me that, if one put a halfpenny on the line and let the train go over it, it would expand to a whole penny which could then be used in a slot machine in order to get a bar of chocolate. Sadly the experiment failed: the engine passed over it, but the halfpenny remained unexpanded.

After primary education I attended a newly-created grammar school called Quarry Bank, where the headmaster, who was an aristocrat and had been an Eton Scholar and a housemaster at Shrewsbury, successfully grafted together older traditions with the different requirements of our new establishment. I was happy there, was active in games and in the scouts and ended up as a prefect and head of house. One of my most vivid schoolboy memories was of a group of us being taken down a coal mine near Wigan and given a full conducted tour, an experience which made me realise how hard and dangerous was the miner's lot. One final reference to school: years later when teaching at Jersey College for Girls I gained a certain kudos when my pupils discovered that I had attended the same school as two of the Beatles.

My teachers had advised me to do an arts degree at Liverpool University. There were no grants in those days; you were either brilliant (which I was not) and gained a state scholarship or you were fortunate (as I was) to have a father who could afford the fees. As to my career aspirations, I was torn between teaching and the Church and in the end decided to work for qualifications relevant to both. As a consequence I had long and rewarding years of study, some of which were spent as an educational missionary in Trinidad and Guyana before going to theological college in Cambridge. (I had married Julia in 1938 and our daughter was born in 1943.)

Two factors then played their part in my decision to come to Jersey. I was

Born in the 1910s...

under the misapprehension that everyone in the Island spoke French – and I had fluency in the language. I was also assured that the climate was sub-tropical, not unlike my familiar West Indies and with palm trees as well. In fact, on the day we arrived it was pouring with rain and the wind was cold and cutting! But Jersey did provide me with the opportunity to follow both my vocations. I took up teaching at Victoria College Prep. and went on from there to teach Classics and Divinity at the Girls' College. At the same time I became assistant priest at the Town Church, helping out on Sundays and in the school holidays and retaining this responsibility for 24 years.

Such a happy state of affairs was sadly not to last: one Monday evening in 1966 I had completed my preparation and marking for the following day, had read my evening office and retired to bed. I woke the next morning to a silent world – I had become incurably deaf. All teachers have had their 'off days' when students, unstimulated by quadratic equations or the reform bill, have felt like calling out, 'Oh, shut up'. This of course happened to me when some of my pupils discovered my situation, and this spelt the end of my teaching career. How fortunate I was to have had my two-fold qualifications: I was now able to concentrate on my church work, and for 15 years I was Priest-in-Charge at Gouray. I finally retired in 1983 but now in my late 80s I am still working, taking services to cover for other clergy and acting as chaplain to two old people's homes.

I have now lived in Jersey for over half a century and have witnessed many changes. I shall leave the analysis of constitutional, economic and demographic matters to those more knowledgeable than myself. Likewise there will be others to expound on the Island's architecture, its tourism and the state of its agriculture. I can, however, comment on what makes me rejoice: the increasing co-operation between the various denominations and faiths. Thirty years ago I was asked by the Roman Catholic priest at St Aubin's to take part in a wedding of two of my former pupils; I was happy to do this but realised only later that I was actually initiating a trend. Today our ecumenism is a pleasant and helpful feature of Jersey's religious life. As to the Island's moral atmosphere today, there is so much that is worthy of praise: the contributions to so many charities is outstanding, and appeals by individual sufferers are so often met with generous and swift response; and many people give their time and talents voluntarily to a host of good causes.

Like all law-abiding and loyal citizens, however, I am distressed by the reports which I read nightly in the *Jersey Evening Post* of vandalism, theft, assault, drunkenness and drug abuse. The language of psychology and

Born in the 1910s...

psychiatry, the use of terms such as 'genes' and 'hormones', has become a jargon to conceal and explain away wrong-doing. It is as though in contemporary life the motto is 'You mustn't blame yourself'; sin has been replaced by sickness, and a virtue is made out of vice. A commentator in a recent weekly periodical listed the seven deadly sins and illustrated how they had now been diminished and explained away: *lust* – the use of God's gift of sex with a slight hormonal imbalance innate in us; *gluttony* – this is in our genes and often inherited; *sloth* – the cost of living today is so great that we have to work too hard and so need to relax completely; *envy* and *avarice* – why should I be poor or unemployed when others have so much, and why should others be more attractive or cleverer than me, since it's in the genes?; *anger* – this can be addictive or even inherited and surely protest begets progress; *pride* – this could be a disease but is today rehabilitated, it being good to feel pride in our words and actions. As to the seven virtues they are scorned: *humility* – lack of self-esteem; *kindness* – self-advertisement; *abstinence* – unnecessary, eat and drink what you want; *chastity* – outmoded; *patience* – an excuse for doing nothing; *liberality* – you can give too much to the wrong causes; *diligence* – a cover for trying or pretending to be perfect.

It is a depressing list but I am not at heart a pessimist. I hope and pray that true values and positive estimates of good and evil will prevail in this special island of ours.

Henry Perrée

Henry Perrée, the son of Francis John Perrée, farmer and for many years Constable of St Mary, was born at La Forêt, St Mary, in 1915. He was educated at Harleston House School, St Lawrence, and then as a weekly boarder at Victoria College. After he left school he farmed and then worked for his father's company, Jersey Farmers' (Trading) Union. He volunteered for the Army in January 1940, joined the Royal Army Service Corps and was evacuated from Dunkirk. He was later commissioned into the Royal Artillery and served in Burma and India. Back in Jersey he continued farming and then became General Manager and Secretary of Jersey Milk Marketing Board. He was appointed Secretary/Agent of the National Trust for Jersey in 1969, became a Jurat in 1974 and served as Lieutenant Bailiff from 1982 to 1987.

*A*s farmers' sons in those far off days we did little outside school. One might meet up with friends on a Sunday and play kick-tin in the yard and perhaps help bring in the cows at five o'clock. Your parents did not take you out, and transport at any rate was by horse and van. Going in to town meant a walk to Millbrook and then the train. On the way back we would return to Millbrook, cross over the bridge, cast an eye on the locomotive passing by underneath and then walk home up Mont Félard and back to St Mary with Mother carrying all her heavy shopping. There was a bus on Saturdays, a two-horse affair run by Mr Godel. It was enclosed, with steps at the back. The women and children would travel inside and the men used to be seated on the top. As it came up St Peter's Valley the men would get off and walk when the steep parts were reached in order to assist the horses. In time this was replaced by a Saturday motor bus, an open vehicle called the Scarlet Pimpernel. Perhaps once a year we would go out to Grouville where Mother had cousins. We would get to town and walk up Hill Street for the Gorey train, passing under the bridges and through the tunnels to Grouville. This was a special treat.

During my time at Victoria College my brother John and I were the only two local boarding boys; we came home at the weekends while the other

Born in the 1910s...

boarders, mostly from Service families, stayed at school. The College had a
fine reputation under its headmaster Mr Worrall and the standard of discipline
was high. I was a keen swimmer – we used the Havre des Pas pool – and was
even keener at rifle shooting, captaining the College VIII for two years. We
used to go to Bisley, these being my first visits to England. I was a bad sailor
and terribly sick (but I got my sea legs during the war on the trip through the
Mediterranean and the Suez Canal to India). I was senior prefect in my house,
a good cross-country runner and a sergeant in the Officers' Training Corps.
As I reflect on my youth I would say that the good discipline at school was
mirrored generally throughout the Island: rules were followed; children were
taught to be polite; we all went to Sunday school.

I left school in 1933 and came home to farm with my father. In fact Father
was running the JF(T)U and it was actually my brother John who managed
the farm. This was for me a frustrating experience. Father offered no advice,
no help, no suggestion that my brothers and I might pursue a professional
training. He had three farms and three sons, my eldest brother being Frank,
and, as far as he was concerned, his three sons would each in due course
inherit one of the farms. To him that was that. I look back now and reckon
that I would have liked to have become a civil engineer – bridges, dams,
railways and so on – but the opportunity was never on offer. Furthermore
Father never gave us a wage. Mother would provide us with some pocket
money, but I received not a penny for my two years on the farm.

My father was Constable of St Mary, and he and his friend Charles Billot,
Constable of St Martin, would go off to England selling cattle, usually in
groups of 30 head. In these years before the war I went to more than 20 of
these sales, sometimes with either or both of my brothers and sometimes on
my own. It was while I was on one of these forays that I wrote a letter to my
father expressing the wish for another job instead of the farm. His response
was, 'Right, put your overalls on and be at the store [the JF(T)U] on Monday
next week at half past seven and you'll get to work there.' I remember my first
morning and my first job, an extremely dirty one stacking bonemeal flour.
From working in the store I became a truck driver – I had always been keen
on motor engines – and then a salesman. I used to buy on the Weighbridge –
potatoes and tomatoes. It was not too different from trading on the Stock
Exchange: there would be the smallest rumour that fewer loads were on their
way to the Weighbridge and that you wanted so many tons, and therefore you
would nudge the price up by a few pence.

This was my life up to the outbreak of war, and then I joined up. I don't think that I had a great rush of patriotism. It was more like this: there was a war on and not much happening at the front and, partial in those youthful days to a drink or two, I probably had a couple of beers too many and decided to go along to the Army recruiting office. I joined the Royal Army Service Corps, no doubt in the fond belief that in a few months' time I would be driving down the Unter den Linden and chatting up the girls. Instead I found myself in a hotel in Margate where we had no uniforms, virtually no basic training and no cutlery. We would sit down for breakfast at tables for six, and the six of us would eat our food having to share one set of knife, fork and spoon. We were soon, however, on our way to Portsmouth and across the Channel to Cherbourg and then on by train to a base depot in western Brittany. After a few weeks I as a driver/mechanic was posted to a motor ambulance convoy in the area of the Somme.

By mid-May the Germans had begun their attack to the west and our unit of 75 ambulances and support vehicles moved north passing hordes of refugees, mostly with horse-drawn transport, coming south and being dive-bombed by German Stukas. We assisted with casualty work and moved on to Dunkirk. Our unit ended up just north of the town and my duty for the next few days was to drive into Dunkirk and bring out casualties to a nearby medical centre. We occupied the empty houses bordering the shore. A friend and I joined up with a French detachment. They had brought a live pig which was kept in the cellar. It was in due course slaughtered and we had some good pork and chips. Three days after our arrival we waded out into the sea but were not picked up. The following morning we made for a large ship's boat wallowing in the shallows and got away in it to deeper water. There we were picked up by a destroyer. The captain was determined not to sail before the last man had been taken off the beaches, but a ferocious German attack on the boats, with many casualties taken onto our ship, gave him no alternative but to sail for Dover. It was all a very tough experience; it took 30 years for Dunkirk no longer to be for me a recurring dream, and it still occasionally comes back.

After my return to England and eventually to Chipping Norton in the Cotswolds (just a few miles from Kingham where I used to take cattle for auction) we were all given 48 hours' leave and, as the boats and boat trains were still operating normally, I sailed home to Jersey. I have a clear memory of a very strange and sad episode on that mail-boat: on board was a group of 18-year old conscripts travelling for basic training to an artillery unit on Alderney. As we came through the Alderney race one of the youths jumped

Born in the 1910s...

overboard. A lifebuoy was thrown down alongside him. I saw him turning his head towards it, but he swam on. Cherbourg launched its lifeboat but he was never found.

Without too much of a thought for the future and conscious of my luck in being alive, Joan and I decided to get married. With the Dean's licence and dispensations from our parish rectors the wedding took place at St Brelade's church on 16 June just five days after my return to the Island. In fact by this date people were already evacuating Jersey but, with no immediate sailings, I stayed on until the 28th. Passing through Guernsey en route to England, I and a friend were in a pub on the St Peter Port waterfront when the Germans dropped their first bombs as a prelude to occupation. Everybody scattered, but my companion and I had been at Dunkirk and were accustomed to the odd explosion or two. We quickly drank down a couple of pints from the top shelf before seeking some shelter in the town. My mail-boat, along with two coal-boats crowded with evacuees, was the last sailing before the Germans arrived. I didn't see my wife again until December 1945, five and a half years later.

I returned to my old unit and in due course was recommended for a commission in the Royal Artillery. Our officer course was at Llandrindod Wells. All those in the front of the train taking us there went for light anti-aircraft training and those in the rear section for heavy ack-ack. After various postings in England I volunteered for service overseas. I sailed on the Empress of Canada through the Mediterranean; Geraldo and his orchestra were on board bound for Egypt. Eventually my regiment ended up in Burma and then we were sent back to Poona where, with training completed, the war finished. I returned to Jersey in December 1945 and was demobbed two months later.

I found that the post-war Island had changed little since before the Occupation. Farming and land values were unaffected. A significant development, however, was the constitutional reforms of 1948 which followed a Royal Commission and resulted in the removal of the Jurats and Rectors from the States and the creation of Senators with their all-Island election. As for myself I came back to La Fôret and farmed there for the next nine years before becoming in 1955 the first General Manager/Secretary of the newly formed Jersey Milk Marketing Board. During these years I took on other responsibilities as well: the parish rate assessment committee (for nearly 20 years); membership of the Board of Arbitrators concerning the compulsory purchase of land; I was a founder member of the Jersey Air Rifle Club and was president of the St Mary Rifle Club for 44 years, from 1953 to 1997.

By 1966 the Milk Marketing Board had acquired full control of all the Island's milk supplies and processing, and it was the right time for me to retire. New opportunities were to open up for me. In 1969 my wife spotted an advertisement for the post of Secretary/Agent of the National Trust for Jersey. I applied and was appointed. In the years following, and I served for a decade, I was instrumental in the Trust's development and restoration of Quetivel Mill. In March 1974 I was privileged to be appointed a Jurat. The sitting in court and listening to all sorts of criminal and civil cases I found straightforward; it requires a bit of common sense and one is well assisted by the Crown officers and Court officials. Other duties had also to be undertaken. One of these was acting as returning officer at elections. I wrote up notes to assist and these same notes were being used by succeeding Jurats for the next 20 years. From 1982 until my retirement as a Jurat in 1987 I filled the office of Lieutenant Bailiff.

From the vantage point of a long and full life I consider the Island today. I am not opposed to changes in our governmental system which would bring about improvement. The real improvement, however, should be in personalities and not necessarily in constitutional reform. Someone in England recently wrote that he had given up voting because of the poor calibre of current Members of Parliament. The same applies to the apathy of electors and disenchantment in our politicians here in Jersey. How do you attract a better quality of States Member? That is a difficult question.

As to Jersey's future I am an optimist. Mind you, the average islander is a pessimist. Take farming: farmers here and elsewhere are always pessimistic, grumbling about the returns on their cattle or their potatoes. That is the nature of farmers the world over. But Jersey has always been adaptable, able to surmount new problems. Go back to the days when everybody knitted garments, and then consider how the Island has always found something else. We have always met new challenges and I have faith that we will continue to do so.

Born in the 1910s...

Chapter Two

Born in the 1920s

Bob Le Sueur
Betty Brooke
Sir Peter Crill
Don Filleul
Jack Worrall

Bob Le Sueur

Bob Le Sueur was born in 1920 and was a pupil at Victoria College from 1932 to 1938. In Jersey throughout the Occupation, he worked for the insurance company, General Accident. After five years from 1947 with the Overseas Trading Corporation he undertook a two-year teacher-training course at St Luke's College, Exeter, returning to the Island in 1955 to take up his new profession in education. He was on the staff of Hautlieu School, teaching principally English but also Spanish to A-level, from then until his retirement in 1981. Since that year he has travelled extensively.

I was born in a house on Victoria Avenue at First Tower in sound and sight of the sea. My first memories are of the quietness of the area and being taught by my father to ride a fairy cycle on its as yet untarmaced surface. The trains had not at that time given way to the buses (which ran on solid tyres). Father at the time said that he would not put money in the latter, but within a few years the railway company was in dire financial trouble and went out of business. Another memory was the awe in which I held people from the mainland – from Britain. My mother used to generate a small income by letting some rooms to holiday-makers from the UK, and these were people whom one respected and invested with a degree of glamour and who would spoil me and take me out with them on their jaunts. In fact we were at that time, and using the word with some precision, insular, and our Christmas visits to an uncle in Guernsey were the extent of my travels until my teens.

After a dame school I went on to a boys' school in West Park Avenue. There were 40 or so of us, all taught by a Mr Cavey. He was a severe disciplinarian and, among his aberrations, did not tolerate left-handedness. One boy called Edwards, as we were writing, would move his pen from his right to his left hand. Mr Cavey would approach him quietly from behind with a black ebony ruler and suddenly smash it down on poor Edwards's left hand. Halfway through my first term we all arrived at school on a Monday morning and found no one there to let us in. Word was brought that Mr Cavey was unwell; and within a week he was dead. The whole school went to

Born in the 1920s...

the funeral, following the horse-drawn hearse up St John's Road. As a boy of 11 I had a somewhat simplistic notion of God and had been worried that He could read all our thoughts, particularly unclean ones. I felt some guilt that God would know how glad I was that Mr Cavey was dead. Would I be struck dead as a punishment? Would the lid of the coffin move and our headmaster emerge alive and well? Fortunately he didn't and the following term I moved to Victoria College.

The College under Mr Worrall's leadership had a more humane regime and my years there were on the whole happy. Weak eyesight caused me at one stage to miss two consecutive terms and I, a bookish youth, was forbidden both reading and the cinema. Later I reached the dizzy heights of corporal in the OTC, and the camps gave me my first experiences of crossing the Channel to England.

I left school in 1938. Jobs were hard to come by, with much unemployment, and I considered myself fortunate in becoming an office boy with General Accident. I was happy with my lot, beginning to work for my insurance exams, even spending a spell in our Southampton branch office. And then came the war.

At that time I had the idealistic notion that all fighting was wrong and my ambition was to get some non-combatant work with the Quakers in the Friends' Ambulance Unit. (It was fortunate for any wounded soldiers that this was never to come about; I would have been a disaster.) My boss at General Accident, anxious about staff shortages, counselled delay and, come June 1940 and the announcement that the Channel Islands were not to be defended, I had done nothing to further my plans. That night every household in Jersey was having the agonising discussion about staying or leaving. My father in his 50s did not relish being a penniless refugee, and so my parents decided to stay; I decided to go.

Now the evacuation procedure was to go to the Town Hall and get the requisite piece of paper. I rose early and bicycled to West Park and down the Parade, hoping to stop off, get the written authority and then seek my manager's permission to leave. When I reached the Town Hall I saw a vast line of people blocking the pavement along the Parade, down Gloucester Street, past the Opera House and round the corner onto the Esplanade. I decided not to queue – I would be late for work – and went on to the office at 27 Hill Street. When I reached it I found only one other member of staff, a heavily pregnant young woman of 19 and almost in tears. I presumed that the others were all queuing for their tickets. In the meantime the office was in

Born in the 1920s…

bedlam with phones ringing and clients demanding the daftest of requests. I tried to get through to our Southampton branch, of which we were a sub-office, an attempt that, because of blocked phone lines, took three days. Eventually I was able to speak to the manager there who, uninformed of the Island situation, was extremely brusque and asked me whether I had been drinking and evidently assumed that I was deranged. In the end he told me to stay at my post until the Resident Secretary returned, and this I did for the next five years: Acting Local Resident Secretary at the age of 19.

There then followed a strange few days, with German planes overhead, when a kind of normality resumed: potato exports restarted and the mail-boat did several round trips. On the very last boat into the Island arrived a Mr Rodd, a self-employed commercial traveller (whom I was later to employ in the office). Nobody in England had told him what the situation was and he landed with his suitcase and samples of Christmas novelties. He went straight to the British Hotel and asked for his usual stock room only to be informed of the circumstances, and he returned at once to the shipping office to secure a ticket back to the mainland. He managed to obtain a place on the 1 July sailing (I planned to be on that boat myself), but by then the Germans had arrived and the ship never sailed. Mr Rodd, in his early 60s and a veteran of the First War trenches, always wore a somewhat startled and affronted expression. Over the next five years he had much to be affronted about, eventually being deported from Jersey to an internment camp in Germany and fortunately surviving his experiences.

I had mixed feelings about my failure to leave. I was disappointed in not having the opportunity to do something useful for humanity, but here was a strange and new situation to absorb. I remember seeing my first Germans. I was standing outside a shop in Broad Street when a car drew up. Two German officers alighted, went in and bought stationery. They didn't seize it in armfuls but purchased what they wanted, saluted and drove off. Good heavens, I thought, this may not be quite as bad as one's worst fears.

On the whole the occupying forces were well disciplined. I recall, however, the moment when my eyes were opened and I reconsidered my pacifist principles. In 1942 the Germans began to fortify the Island and to bring in slave labour to carry out their plans. One summer afternoon a neighbour knocked at the door and told me to come out and look. Along Victoria Avenue was an unforgettable sight: a long column of men in tatters, their faces ashen-grey, no doubt having travelled across Europe in cattle-trucks. Some of them had rags round their feet and no shoes, and their guards occasionally hit out

Born in the 1920s...

to keep them in line. This, I thought, was what we had heard; this was what the Occupation could be like; ours hadn't been so to this point, but I now saw that people could be destroyed and dehumanised.

I am sometimes asked about collaboration during the Occupation. It is true that some young women, not large numbers of them, consorted with the Germans. The hormones were flowing, and some of the men were very good-looking, with their cult of physical fitness and their bronzed bodies and their exercises and handstands on the beach. But for most Islanders the Occupation forces were held in varying degrees of hostility, and those who were actively pro-German could be counted on the fingers of one hand. At home we listened to the BBC every day, legally until 1942 before radios were called in. When that happened my mother got our old discarded Pye battery wireless down from the loft and gave that over while our newer electric radio was secreted under the floorboards.

Privation caught up on us gradually – my father's weight went down from 17 to nine stone. In our small garden we grew vegetables and kept hens and one rabbit. Our reluctance to eat the rabbit was overcome by the expedient of swopping it with the next-door neighbour's. We killed each other's and ate with a clear conscience.

Towards the end of the Occupation I became involved in helping Russians who had escaped from Island labour camps. I knew a Mrs Gould from St Ouen who had insurance with us, and she harboured a Russian youth, called Bill by her, who masqueraded as a Frenchman. Sadly someone denounced her and, while Bill managed to get away first, her house was searched and the Germans discovered not only her radio but also a Russian dictionary. She was arrested, tried and sent, by one of the last boats in 1944 before communications were cut off, to France and then on to Ravensbrück concentration camp. There she was unable to sustain the workload, developed oedema and, expendable, went to the gas chamber. I had the task of finding hiding-places for Bill (and other Russians) and he spent his first weekend in the filing room of my office before being housed in a lock-up garage and other temporary shelters until given hospitality by two young conscientious objectors sharing a flat in Grosvenor Street. He stayed with them until the Liberation in May 1945.

The Liberation was both ecstatic and at the same time confusing. The huge numbers of Germans – one to every three of the population – meant that all could not be shipped off immediately. In the first week or so people were disconcerted to see a small number of Germans still driving cars round

Born in the 1920s...

the Island, these being officers connected with details of the handover. The whole repatriation process was carried out in a civilised fashion: St Helier's boundaries were the dividing line for a few days, and no British soldiers could cross the perimeter out and no Germans could enter, an arrangement made to avoid incidents. I remember going up Trinity Hill and coming to the barbed wire barricade with a British soldier on one side and a German on the other. The German was smoking and the cigarette must have come from the Tommy. I then went on to Bonne Nuit and there at the end of the harbour were German soldiers sunbathing and taking an early summer dip.

Perhaps our memories of the Occupation and of such matters as the Russian escapees should have been recorded nearer the time. Madeleine Bunting, author of *A Model Occupation* published in 1995, took the line in her book that we kept quiet because we must have all had guilty consciences with something to hide. But it was not like that: it was a psychological thing – these years had been an unpleasant experience, this chapter was finished and we wanted to get on with our lives in happier circumstances.

Fairly rapidly the Island returned to a kind of normality and life became easier. We were soon put on UK food rations. English people look back on that era and recall the small amount of butter and so on. Our reaction was different: our stomachs had shrunk through privation and we wondered how others could possibly indulge in such generous allocations. A final reflection on the Occupation: it sharpened personalities, and those who were by nature giving and good became saintly while those who were by nature selfish became unspeakably unpleasant.

After the war I continued working for General Accident for a further two years. My superiors in England had learned during the Occupation that the office was functioning: I used the Red Cross message facility which allowed communication only with one's relatives. I corresponded in this way with 'Uncle Eric', in fact my terrifying Southampton boss, telling him that I was still working in the same office and coping as well as possible. In fact after the Liberation I was their blue-eyed boy, having done much business during these five years, settled all claims and with £12,000, a lot of money in those days, waiting to be handed on.

In due course, however, I wanted a change and joined the Overseas Trading Corporation which held the export rights for Horniman and Lyons teas. I was with them for five years, travelling fairly extensively through Europe on company business. Then came the war in Korea, a downturn in trading and an invitation to join the Lyons organisation in London. I did not relish the

Born in the 1920s...

prospect of city life, and here was the catalyst for a big change in my circumstances. For some time I had pondered the thought of teaching, with consequent fulfilment, if not great material reward. I had few illusions about being able to leave the world a better place than I had found it but, without wishing to be pompous, I considered that at least the effort should be made. Thus I enrolled on a training course at St Luke's College, Exeter, and three years later returned to Jersey to teach, first at a secondary modern school and then from 1955 at Hautlieu.

By this time the Island was booming. Finance had not yet established itself, but tourism and agriculture were flourishing. Tax refugees – it was very easy to settle in Jersey in those days – also contributed with their savings and unearned income to a burgeoning economy. It was a community relatively at ease with itself and lacking the pressures on space generated later by a too large population. As for myself, I enjoyed my Hautlieu years. I joined the school soon after the Island's secondary education had been reorganised. Indeed the school's being established was bitterly opposed by many people at the time, and I recall letters to the *Evening Post* on the subject. One in particular comes to mind in which the need for 'children of the artisan class' to receive this kind of education was queried.

During the two decades since my retirement I have travelled extensively. I have always possessed a sense of curiosity: as a small boy I used to wander off and only return to my distraught parents when hunger drove me home. When I was teaching and on a miserable salary, married and with two small children, travelling had been out of the question. Now in my dotage it became possible, but money was tight and it would have to be budget travel. At first I lacked the self-assurance to go to wild places on my own and bought myself a package tour with a difference: a trans-Africa trip on a converted ex-army truck across the Sahara to Nigeria and then across central Africa to Kenya from where, on another truck of the same company, I came home via the Sudan, Egypt and the Near East. It was a good way to travel, camping wherever we happened to be at nightfall, and cheap, but I was frequently frustrated by not being able to stay longer in a place, not having the time 'to stand and stare' because it was not on the programme.

Subsequently nearly all my travel has been done on my own, footloose, moving when I was ready. Solo travel gives maximum opportunity for contact with the people of the country. I have trekked in the Himalayas of eastern Kashmir, in the Andes, in the Faeroe Islands, in Tierra del Fuego. I have met some wonderful people of all races, have travelled in midwinter from St Malo

Born in the 1920s...

to Hong Kong by train and have trekked in the Amazonian rain forest and in Borneo – but I have yet to visit either Chausey or Les Minquiers.

As to the Island today and its politics, I am not convinced that it is the governmental system that is failing us. We are rather like a Greek city state, and there are those in Jersey with the intelligence and the education to run a latter-day city state, but by and large these people are not members of the States. Why did I myself never go into politics? It was suggested! Too frequently I used to take my General Studies pupils to States' debates and, sitting in the visitors' gallery, I determined that my boredom tolerance would not have coped. It has always been so: a Member with a speech composed, no doubt rehearsed before wife and mirror; somebody speaking previously and making the identical points; and, despite that, the frustrated Deputy still delivering his now redundant speech in order to get his name in the *JEP* and to prove to his constituents that he is not a Trappist monk. It happens often and it is very dreary.

Is the Island a better place than in my youth? It is too easy for the elderly to look back to some golden age which in fact never existed. When I was a child there was desperate poverty: a lot of TB, children wearing charity shoes because their parents could not afford footwear, slums in St Helier with 12 dwellings in a yard and shared tap and lavatory. This lasted into the 1950s. And yet I worry about the other extreme today – excess materialism and the dominance of the finance industry. The chairman of the Institute of Directors recently spoke of Jersey sustaining a population of 150,000. God help us! Think of the roads and the extra hospitals. Do we want another Hong Kong or even a garden city like Singapore? I do not wish to live in a garden city with every bit of greenery manicured and trimmed. This lovely island, climatically blessed and with its varied and beautiful scenery; and we have the prospect of it all being ruined by greed.

Born in the 1920s...

Betty Brooke

Betty Brooke, whose father had previously worked in the Malayan rubber industry, was born in Aberdeen in 1922. She was educated at Aberdeen High School for Girls. Her university plans were thwarted by the outbreak of war and instead she joined the WRNS. After the war she took a permanent commission, resigning from the Service when in 1949 she married a naval chaplain. In 1957 she came to Jersey with her husband on his appointment as minister of Aquila Road Methodist Church. At this stage her career in journalism, radio and television began. Her Saturday column in the Jersey Evening Post has appeared for 40 years, and for 20 years as Hardbencher she reported on States' proceedings in her Eye on the States articles. In 1989 she was elected to the States as a Senator and served in that capacity for three years.

I had a very secure and happy childhood in Aberdeen, and from an early age and as a reaction to my parents' rabid Conservatism I became, at least for a time, a rabid Socialist. At home we had enough of everything but around us were barefooted children and women with shawls carrying their babies and coming to the back door for bread. My schooldays were particularly happy: lots of tennis, hockey and badminton and also girl guiding. My interest in journalism was sparked by my love of English. I wrote my first poem at the age of nine and used to think that I would have liked to write poetry for a living.

Then came the war and with it the end of my university and journalistic ambitions. Instead I joined the Wrens. This was a big culture shock for me: I had never gone to boarding school and I had to adapt to living in a 'wrenery' where floors were decks, rooms cabins and loos heads. I was in Liverpool for two years while the Battle of the Atlantic was waged, an exciting but stressful period with convoys crossing the Atlantic and German U-boats lying in wait for them. You danced with the sailors and officers one night and then observed the plot as a week later they were being blown up and drowned in blazing oil. Later I was stationed in London during the V1 and V2 attacks, at the same time doing a bit of journalism – ships' magazines and the like and all fairly

Born in the 1920s...

libellous and amusing.

After the war I took a permanent commission. Now at that time I was an atheist. I had been brought up in the Church of Scotland but by then I had totally lost my faith. I still went to church since as a Wren officer you were expected to set an example but it all meant nothing. Then I fell in love with the Methodist naval chaplain. It was during a service which he was conducting: I stopped dead in my tracks and realised that I had taken a wrong turning and that what I had rejected was in fact right. I was converted – like Paul on the Damascus road.

As to my relationship with the chaplain, there was a difficulty: he was in fact going to marry me to someone else, but I fell in love with the man who was to conduct the ceremony. It was a rather involved situation! And he was 20 years older than myself, and my father said to me, 'A minister is never a paying proposition, and one 20 years older is an absolute disaster.' In fact it proved to be the most lovely marriage; we only had 17 years together before he died.

On marriage I came out of the Service and became a naval wife until my husband (his Christian name was Herbert which was abbreviated to Berry) retired from the Navy. I loved the life. I was Mrs Padre and in Malta we had a Soldiers', Sailors' and Airmen's Home with 40 beds, three billiard tables and a canteen, and in that period I put more drunk sailors to bed than you would credit.

We arrived in Jersey on the mail-boat in 1957 on Berry's appointment as minister of Aquila Road Methodist Church, and by this time we had adopted a baby, our son Simon. At the time I knew nothing about the Island and we moved into the manse, a very grey and cold house; just like my Aberdeen childhood home and I loved it.

In those days Jersey was far less commercial and with a very different economic structure. It used to be described as a three-legged stool – the biggest leg agriculture, tourism creeping up as the second leg and with finance as the third. Rather an unbalanced seat! Agriculture was big in those days: potato lorries down at the Weighbridge and the farmers and growers a very significant and influential element in government. Also social security was a fairly new option and some of the Island schools were rather backward. It was a community at ease but there was also great poverty. I used to see the St Helier slums, and the appalling housing reminded me of the Aberdeen of my youth.

As to our church life we were very self-contained with no 'churches together'. We had little contact with the Anglicans and, as Methodists, even less with the Roman Catholics. Aquila Road was a well-patronised and wealthy church. I had friends, some Methodist and some not, made through playing golf and bridge. And of course I was a preacher myself, having done the requisite training, preparing and taking services every Sunday. These years were lovely; it was a rich life and I was very happily married.

In 1962 I became involved in journalism. The Saturday religious slot in the *Jersey Evening Post* had previously been written by clergy and the news editor asked me to take it on. I accepted on the condition that I could broaden its scope and move away from its being purely Christian, with the freedom to refer to other faiths as well. I have now done this for 40 years, 300 words each Saturday and just two weeks missed – one through illness and the other when I forgot. At the same time I also began some broadcasting with BBC South-West and with Channel Television. With the latter I used to do the Robin Day-style hard-hitting political interviews.

One Sunday in 1966 Berry collapsed in the pulpit and died six weeks later. Simon was just 12 and, looking back, I now know that I didn't cope with this tragedy as I should have. One did not know much about bereavement counselling in those days. I was too stoical. In fact I had to run the church for nearly a year before the new minister arrived, and I was in the pulpit preaching three weeks after my husband died. It's a different world now: people can weep, even men can weep, and we recognise that distresses should be talked through. In war it's different: there were no counsellors during the war, but in wartime there is some expectation of death. Sudden and unexpected death is awful.

It was at this time with the need to earn some money that I was asked to take over the *JEP*'s political column. In those days the paper's reporting of States business was almost verbatim, a sort of Hansard record. A more reader-friendly approach was needed, and so began my 20 years as Hardbencher writing Eye on the States. The States usually met weekly then. I used to inject some interest into my contributions by, for example, commenting on Members' ties and suits. It was said that this did much for their sartorial standards.

It is easy to look back three decades or more and conclude that the standard of States proceedings was better then than now. But I think that this is so. Senator Ralph Vibert was a great debater; Cyril Le Marquand was such a lucid speaker; that huge man physically, Senator Krichefski, with his wealth of experience, could speak at length without a full stop – it was a tour de force as he presented policies. There were also those termed Trappists who

Born in the 1920s...

never spoke, but they gave off a sense of solidity and the impression that they were listening. So for 20 years I reported on the States, did my other journalism, some of it with national papers, and my radio and television work and my preaching. I was privileged and got to know so much about the Island and how it ticked.

Then in 1989, after all those years observing the States from the gallery and reviewing it critically, I decided that I had had enough and resigned. I was looking forward to doing less; I had my golf and bridge. Within weeks Senator Jane Sandeman died halfway through her term of office. She had been a first-class Member and I went to her funeral. Now, being a Methodist, I am not given to seeing visions, but as I sat in St Thomas's church I had this image of a ploughed field with the plough resting in a half-finished furrow. I said to myself, 'No, Jane, I am not going to finish ploughing the field.' As I came out of the church Senator Cyril Le Marquand came up to me and asked me who I thought would take her place. I replied that I was going to stand. I could hardly believe what I had just uttered. Having put my hand to the plough I had to finish the ploughing, and this is how I came to be elected a Senator and complete the remaining three years of Jane Sandeman's term.

I found the whole electoral process both stimulating and a great deal of fun. I had much support from my newspaper readership and my church. We had a team of people in each parish – twelve committees working for me – and a horse and cart creating a real hustings. There were two other candidates standing against me, and there was one incident which I greatly regretted, having attacked one of them when I should have restricted myself to promoting my own policies. At any rate I won with a substantial majority.

The States in those days was very much a men's club, and women Members did not have the easiest of times. For them to get on the major committees was difficult; it never occurred to the power brokers that a woman could serve on Finance or any important committee where thinking was required. Senator Gwyneth Huelin was an exception to the rule, an imposing person who did great things for public health and education. It was harder for Deputy Corrie Stein: she was not only a woman, she was also Dutch! And I, who had never before experienced racial discrimination before becoming a Senator, was not only a woman but also a Scot. That a Scot who loved the Island dearly might know something of Jersey politics was a concept not entertained by all of my new colleagues. I encountered difficulties during my early days in the States, both in the Members' lobby and in the Chamber itself. I was not one to keep quiet, to work my way in gradually, and some thought that a

Born in the 1920s...

new Member speaking from the start was not good form

I was invited to join Deputy John Le Gallais' Public Works committee and was given the minor works responsibilities which included the public lavatories. I set to work: I made arrangements to meet the men cleaners – nobody had met them before and they were a great group – and I enquired about their work problems. They had no identification badges when they were required to enter and clean the ladies' loos. We provided them with these and also with proper protective gloves because of the hypodermic syringes which were hidden behind the lavatories. I advised them about getting immunisation against hepatitis B. We became friends because I took notice of them and their concerns.

I also went on to Senator Shenton's Defence committee and I acquired responsibility for the police. Their morale at this time was not at its highest and I would sometimes visit the night watch, go round the cells and join the night patrol cars. The chief officer of the time was a fairly blunt Yorkshireman. He and I crossed swords once or twice. We had colourful exchanges where he said what he thought and I said what I thought. But I think that it did some good. It was said that when I joined the committee it was a police force and when I left a police service.

My hardest time in the States arose over the issue of homosexual law reform. Jersey had not at the time adopted the Wolfenden recommendations. I succeeded in rectifying this and removing sexual acts, if in private, from the criminal code. But I paid a price: I encountered much personal hostility, and one Member in the lobby and in front of officials told me that I was unfit to be a member either of the church or of the States. It was all very hurtful, and only my threat of legal action – his comments were only privileged in the Chamber itself – caused him to apologise.

I was glad to have promoted the homosexual reforms (and glad too to have started Victim Support in the Island). I found, however, that I was beginning to enjoy being a Senator, beginning to enjoy the power, and this worried me. Was I liking too much being Senator Brooke rather than just Betty? The phone would ring: 'Senator Brooke here'. I found that I was subtly changing. I did not feel at ease with this and decided not to stand for re-election. The Lieutenant-Governor sent for me and questioned my decision. I attempted to explain but his comment was that he had never heard of such a thing. On reflection I should have reasoned that I was using what power I possessed for the good of the people and that, if in the process it corrupted me a little, then I should have accepted this consequence. I could have done another term, and yet I sensed that I was becoming too self-important and, with my health always having been somewhat fragile, I was getting too old. In the end I knew that I had made the right decision. I made friends from my political experience but I had also been bruised by the loss of other friends who were unable to accept my point of view, a radicalism based upon religious principles and a firm belief in caring for other people.

Undoubtedly this is currently an interesting time in the Island's history. As to the States and Jersey's system of government, looking back the civil servants in those times were not of today's quality and some of the politicians were brighter than their advisers. Nowadays the roles are reversed: the chief officers are extremely competent and some of the Members are not. In the last few years there seems to have developed this desire on the part of the States to scuttle the ship of government. They seem, for reasons I cannot fully fathom, to have lost confidence in their ability to govern. Perhaps greater exposure of States' proceedings, with Radio Jersey broadcasting debates and with comprehensive media coverage and comment, is a factor. There are of course some very good Members but they seem over-sensitive to criticism. And once you get fulltime politicians drawing a salary for what they do, you lose some of the altruism, that sense of helping the community which was such a feature of former times.

I have no sympathy with the Clothier reforms which I consider a great mistake. A cabinet of presidents would have been possible without sacrificing the committee system. The axing of Senators, with their all-Island mandate, is a wrong development. Instead we shall have government by too small a group of people. I failed to go and tell Clothier all this. I assumed that the Commission would have had more sense. I should have known better.

The greatest change in Jersey since I arrived in 1957 has been the diminution of agriculture. Tourism too is changing with the selling-off of hotels. We're left with finance and, if finance caught a cold, it would be tragic for the Island. Our whole structure – our first-class schools, our good hospital, our social security – is dependent on a healthy and vibrant economy. And it's at this point that they propose utterly to change the government. I worry.

And how have I changed over the years? I would like to think that I am a more tolerant person. I am still at heart a campaigner, but there's nothing worse than someone as old as myself pontificating about the old days. I am not an optimist about our current social problems. For example I worry about the drug culture. I am concerned too about the breakdown in family life and the difficulties of the one-parent family with no spouse. In all these respects

Born in the 1920s…

Jersey is a cameo of society elsewhere. Fortunately, however, we do not have the racial tensions experienced in other places. But we should be wary: we must not allow our wonderful Portuguese workforce to become second-class citizens in any way. It would be a great loss if the majority of them returned to Madeira. They must be made to feel an important part of our Island family.

Society here and elsewhere has been affected by the decline of religious belief. Some of the old Victorian attitudes were repressive, but compassion and love and loyalty and faithfulness are values which should still be preached from the pulpit and in the classroom. If these moral values are jettisoned, then what is left? That worries me.

Sir Peter Crill

Sir Peter Crill was born in 1925, the son of S. G. Crill, solicitor and Constable of St Clement from 1916 to 1958. He was educated at Victoria College and, after escaping to France in 1944, went up to Exeter College, Oxford, as a King Charles I Scholar. Having been called to both the English and Jersey bars in 1949, he was in private practice until 1962. He was in the States as Deputy for St Clement from 1951 to 1958 and as a Senator from 1960 to 1962. In that year he became Solicitor-General and moved up through the Crown offices, being appointed Bailiff in 1985 and holding the post until his retirement in 1995.

The Crills came to Jersey from Germany around 1780 and were originally farming stock. My grandfather was a farmer and also became a builder (Steep Hill is one of his houses). My great-uncle George decided to become a lawyer and my father joined him as a clerk, which was the usual thing for country boys to do in those days. In fact Father was somewhat dilatory in qualifying until he met my mother who told him that she was not going to marry a clerk. Hence he got on with it and became a solicitor.

Born in the 1920s...

As for myself I was born in London, my mother having previously had two still births – as well as my two older brothers. I consider myself either an Englishman by birth or a Jerseyman by extraction; it rather depends upon my mood. There is a gap of eight and ten years between me and my brothers and I grew up virtually as an only child. I was the ewe lamb for whom my mother had gone to England to ensure my birth and, as a consequence, I was spoilt somewhat rotten and confess that I may not have totally recovered from the experience.

Home was a substantial granite semi-detached house, one of two, on the St Clement main road. There was no central heating and in winter the rooms were perishingly cold. It was, though, generally pleasant and comfortable. We had a live-in maid and a woman who came and potted up geraniums and did the sewing. On Tuesdays a Breton woman came to do the family washing and returned the following day to tackle the ironing. Until the Occupation it was a very placid existence, a quiet Jersey parish life with Father as Constable close to the Rector who visited frequently with his wife. She used to drive a baby Austin and was a menace on the roads, and she had what I now understand was the height of fashion in the '20s and '30s – hair looped over the ears with a tortoiseshell decoration which was not a piece of jewellery but a hearing aid. This ordered parish life was interrupted in 1937 when St Clement experienced a molester at large who became known as the Night Prowler. Father and the other parish dignitaries decided as a deterrent to install street lights. My eldest brother, then at the Jersey bar, was furious; he had no wish for the parish to become a wretched suburb as he saw it, but the scheme went ahead and that was that.

As a small boy I wanted for nothing; I had too many sweets, too little exercise and was rather fat. I had indulgent aunts and we would go on Boxing Day to one of them and on New Year's Eve to another. Sometimes as a boy of seven or eight I would stay the night at one of the aunt's, an experience relished since, with no electricity, you had the thrill of your bedroom being lit by an oil lamp. I was instructed not to turn the wick up too high but as a keen reader did just that. The following morning's evidence of smoke on the ceiling did not please my aunt.

At around this age I used to go in a horse and van to collect moss at Rozel Valley for the church's Easter flower decorations. I have fond memories of coming back from these trips, sitting up behind the horse with the farmer, a great link with the past which perhaps developed my equestrian interests. I also remember visits to a farm belonging to the Maretts, one of the several

Born in the 1920s...

dairy farms at that time in what was then essentially a rural parish. Mrs Marett was French and gave me milk and cakes. Mr Marett was a stern but shy man who introduced me to the sight of a foal being born. Mr Vincent, the vet from Gorey, was there and I watched open-mouthed.

When I reached the age of 12 I badgered my father to get me a boat (he had done this for my second brother who was destined for the Royal Navy). He eventually acceded to my wish and I got my dinghy which I kept at Le Hocq and looked after myself. (It was to be the boat in which I made my escape from the Island in 1944.) Thus I spent summers exploring with a friend the gullies on that bit of coast and going further out to Icho. This roused one old longshoreman who had been at sea for many years: 'I've been watching you, you bloody young fool. You're going to drown yourself. I'll tell your mother.'

These then were the summers of 1937 and 1938 – sailing and learning the gutters, left to my own devices, in most respects an only child with both the advantages and the disadvantages which that can bring. Then came the summer of 1939. I was on a French exchange staying with a doctor's son in their lovely period house at Carhaix in the middle of Brittany. I have strong memories of the woodsmoke in the kitchen and the heady smell of fresh coffee and newly baked bread. The sanitary arrangements, however, were primitive: a two-holer earth closet at the back of the stables which one was supposed to share – if you were less shy than myself. Then at the beginning of September came Hitler's invasion of Poland. I was taken by train to St Malo by the daughter of the house and dumped there. The shipping agent had been phoned by my father and a hotel and money arranged while I awaited the *Brittany*. On the morning of September 3 I was in a café having a coffee and was invited by the woman proprietor to go out and listen to the radio. I came back in and said, 'Madame, c'est la guerre,' at which she had a fit of hysterics, shrieking, wailing, with brandy and smelling salts summoned. In due course I got back to Jersey. The boat anchored in St Aubin's Bay and we feared that the reason was U-boats. In fact the delay in docking was caused by a Colorado beetle scare.

For the first few months of the war our life was not greatly changed, except for a stronger emphasis at school on the activities of the Officers' Training Corps. Then came the threat of occupation and the question of evacuation. There was panic in the Island; British phlegm was little in evidence and people received insufficient guidance. The States failed to give a proper lead; they should have ordered all men of military age to go but they did not. It was left

Born in the 1920s…

to individuals to make up their own minds and there was talk from indigenous Jerseymen of rats leaving the sinking ship and so on. As for myself I was dressed ready to go: a hot day, a couple of vests on, a blue gaberdine, polished black shoes and my school cap. My mother went in to town to seek advice. She met Mr Coutanche, the Bailiff, and said, 'What shall I do with Peter?' He told her that she should keep me here since the war would be over in six months. Thus was the decision made and I stayed.

As to my schooling at this time, I was taught English and History by a retired Jerseyman, T.V. Le Breton, who had lost a leg in the First World War. His attitude – 'There's only one good German and that's a dead German' – was in the circumstances possibly understandable. When the Germans occupied the College buildings we were billeted in the premises of Halkett Place School. The trouble here was that it was an infants' school and the chairs were tiny and the lavatories only 12 inches high.

How the Occupation affected life at home is hard to assess. We were invited by the owner of a house near us (after he had left Jersey) to help ourselves to his hoarded food, and thus we had reserves of sugar, flour and tinned goods which lasted for a year or so. I kept hens and rabbits and knew how to kill, skin and clean the latter. Staple food towards the middle of the Occupation was porridge, potatoes and sugar beet syrup – quite a sustaining diet. It is true that my fairly corpulent father lost his tummy, but he had a number of country farmer clients who would sometimes give him meat in lieu of fees. I myself missed the worst privations of the Occupation when I got away, and at that time the situation was desperate until the arrival of the Red Cross ship *Vega*.

As to my escape from the Island, I had toyed with the idea for a number of weeks following D-day. With Roy Mourant and John Floyd as companions we smuggled my 12-foot dinghy to Fauvic and sailed off at 8 p.m. on 11 November 1944. We encountered a host of problems: a compass smashed and useless, spasmodic engine problems, a rope so knotted that anchoring was impossible, sea-sickness and ourselves wet through and frozen. Eventually, 17 hours after our start, we made the French coast six miles north of Coutances where we sheltered and recovered in an inn before giving ourselves up to a patrol of Americans in a jeep. In Cherbourg we were handed over to the commander of an RAF embarkation unit and, after a delay of some days, left Cherbourg for London. There we were interrogated by the War Office before separating and making our way to relatives. I went to stay with my aunts who lived in Oxford, contemplated joining up but was advised, with the war ending

Born in the 1920s...

and my eldest brother recently killed near Paris, to try for an Oxford place. I had set out with great ideas of liberating Jersey but instead went to Exeter College and in due course won a King Charles scholarship.

Immediate post-war Oxford was a strange place. You carried your ration of butter and sugar into Hall for breakfast; there was very little fuel – just one coal scuttle a week; and there was an influx of older undergraduates who had been in the Forces and disliked the rules and regulations about college hours, no women in rooms after 7 p.m. and no drinking in the town pubs. As for myself I rowed for my college first VIII, did badly academically but found the impact of my Oxford years strong. One had been shut in by the war years, part of an inward-looking island community. Nor was the tradition of going from Jersey to the university well established. Many families regarded Oxford as quite beyond their normal ideas of life. Indeed a delightful spinster lady of 85, Miss Finnie, worked my mother up into a state of some excitement and apprehension when she recounted that she had had a nephew who had gone to Oxford and become a Roman Catholic.

I went down from Oxford in 1948, read for the bar at a crammers and then came back to the Island in the following year. It was an interesting period in its political life, with the Jersey Democratic Party, some of whose members were crypto-communists, agitating against Constables and Jurats. There was also the Jersey Progressive Party, in which I was later involved to an extent and which was supported primarily by young businessmen returned from the war, whose aim was to combat what they saw as the socialist, Attlee-mirroring tendencies of the Democratic Party. Parish hall meetings, referendums and a Royal Commission meant much political activity and subsequent changes to the States, with the removal of the Jurats and Rectors and the introduction of Senators.

There was also some residual bitterness against the few who were perceived to have done well out of the Occupation through the black market. Several people as a consequence left the Island and I lost two friends whose parents had consorted with the Germans. There was one incident which shook my belief that on the whole there had been nothing but passive acceptance of German rule. I recently spotted a photo reproduced in the *Jersey Evening Post* of a football match played shortly after the start of the Occupation on College Field between the German troops and the Island team. This was a disgrace; the Jersey team used to play the British army and here they were now playing the German. It never happened again, but it should never have happened in the first place.

Born in the 1920s...

I came back home into private practice in 1949. It was a busy and profitable time for lawyers. We were a very small bar – perhaps nine or ten of us and the same number of solicitors. I myself did a lot of criminal work and also became well-known for divorce. I never endeared myself to the court, being blunt in temperament and outspoken. I fought for my clients and, if I thought that a witness was lying, then I would go for him. The bench in those days had on it so many ex-service people – a general, colonels and a commodore from the merchant navy – that it was almost as though one was appearing at a court martial. But the bar were a friendly lot; we fought one another but bore no malice; and we had splendid Law Society dinners to which one took as guests one's best clients.

I met my wife and married in 1952, became a full partner in the firm and then started to get itchy political feet. I had an uncontested election as Deputy for St Clement and entered the States at the age of 26, just a year after the passing into law of the controversial social security bill, an episode which had not shown the Island in a good light. On one occasion Deputy Venables, the only Jersey Democratic Party States Member, addressed a crowded meeting in the People's Park and, in danger of being manhandled, had to run for police protection. It was an appalling instance of virtual mob rule.

In 1960 I was elected a Senator, having done what few did at the time and issued a short pamphlet on my political beliefs and objectives. I became President of the Public Services committee and took an active interest in the protection of St Ouen's Bay from development. I recall an uncle by marriage who was Constable of St Peter saying to me, 'Why don't you want houses at St Ouen. Your aunt and I go to Worthing and there are some splendid buildings there. We could have them along the bay. It's only useless land.' That was the prevailing view then: use of land was the primary consideration whether to build or not, and if crops could not be produced economically then there would be the likelihood that a house would be sanctioned. The results of this are with us today.

I applied for the position of and became Solicitor-General in 1962 with the prospect of moving up the Crown Officers' ladder with a pension at the end and a knighthood if one kept one's nose clean. The problem with this post was not having a life of your own legally speaking. You were unable to express a legal opinion without the concurrence of the Attorney-General. In 1969 I succeeded to that office and my most interesting prosecution was of Edward Paisnel, the so-called Beast of Jersey. The case made legal history in that Paisnel opted for trial before the Bailiff and two Jurats, fearing that he would not get a fair trial from an assize jury which, it was claimed, would be prejudiced by public opinion. I appeared again for the Crown at his appeal which was dismissed. As he left the courtroom he snarled and the judges later said to me, 'You told us in court that he was a nasty piece of work, and we can now see that he is.'

As Attorney-General I had responsibility for the honorary police who refused to put their house in order (and are now belatedly trying to do so). I am not a wholehearted supporter and, if it were not for the work of the Crown Officers, the system would have collapsed a long time ago. I remember the case of a woman murdered above St Clement's church where the honorary police had tramped over the site of the crime and obliterated important clues. My belief is that they should be transformed into a special branch, trained, given a uniform and allowances and used solely for public order duties and no more. I was Attorney-General for only five years and had insufficient time in that post to effect reforms. The honorary police question has drifted and that is why, when I was Bailiff, I commissioned Sir Cecil Clothier to report on the system – a report which to date has not been fully implemented.

I then became Deputy Bailiff in 1975, a position which has all the problems of being number two. It is akin to one's educational career: rising to the top at each stage and then beginning at the bottom at the next. I had 11 years as Deputy Bailiff before becoming Bailiff in 1986. Some of my time as Bailiff was dominated by the Vernon Tomes affair, and this is a matter which I shall deal with more fully when in due course I complete my memoirs. Suffice it to say here that the dismissal of the Deputy Bailiff by the Home Secretary triggered in the Island a popular but limited uprising in his favour. It says something about Jersey. He was the first Crown Officer to reach the bench not having been an advocate. Nor had he been at university, whereas I and the Attorney-General were Oxford men. We were regarded by some as intellectual and social snobs. For a time paranoia and xenophobia held sway, with something of the same unpleasantness that had prevailed many years before over the social security bill episode. In this case there was a strong public sentiment that the Home Office was interfering, that Jersey ruled itself and that Vernon was 'a good chap'. When the Lieutenant-Governor was booed in the Royal Square this was scandalous behaviour. There were occasions at this time when I was ashamed of being a Jerseyman and it was a testing time for old friendships and loyalties.

Now some years into retirement I see the Island's most urgent problem today as inflation. This is necessarily a threat and Jersey has to demonstrate

Born in the 1920s...

both its political stability and its economic competence if it is to remain a prosperous centre for the finance industry. A weakness in recent years has been the inability of the States to make up its mind: one has seen this over inflation policy and such matters as the waterfront. A policy is determined, opposition to it is then encountered and off we go in a completely different direction.

A related problem, I believe, is the number of States Members wholly or almost wholly dependent on their States salaries. In the past the Island always had a proportion of those coming forward for political office who had either business or inherited wealth or had returned to Jersey having had careers in the army or the diplomatic service. This is now no longer the case and the States is immeasurably the poorer. Its capacity to make mistakes is the greater when almost all its Members are fulltime politicians

I am not against some change for the States in its composition and in the way it does business. Interestingly, though, the Island's attractiveness for financial services and investment is not directly related to the nature of its machinery of government. A danger is that, in order to keep ourselves squeaky-clean, we over-regulate ourselves and lose our attraction – the threat of strangulation by too much red tape. But I am optimistic about the future. Jersey has through the centuries always adapted itself to new circumstances. Currently the finance industry keeps us afloat and this has its benefits and its disadvantages; but the former far outweight the latter, and our quality of life is generally very good. Nevertheless there is some evidence in the housing market at least which shows that the gap between the 'haves' and the 'have nots' is increasing, and this is worrying. Of course there is always the danger that, if at some time in the future we could no longer pay our way, London would step in, and incorporate us into the European Union, with our ending up having some lesser offshore status. It is always a possibility but I am optimistic enough to consider the prospect remote.

Born in the 1920s...

Don Filleul O.B.E.

Don Filleul, the son of Walter Filleul, bookseller and stationer, was born in St Clement in 1926. From 1933 to 1942 he attended Victoria College Preparatory School and Victoria College and then spent three years working for Jersey Mutual Insurance Society. In 1945 he joined the family business and in 1947 was a founder member of Jersey Round Table. He became a Constable's Officer in the St Helier honorary police in 1961 and was elected a Centenier in 1968. In 1978 he entered the States as a St Helier Deputy, serving on various committees and becoming President of Public Works in 1981. He retired from the States and from business in 1987. Since then he has continued to pursue numerous public and charitable interests, most notably becoming Chairman of Jersey Heritage Trust in 1990 and Chairman of Waterfront Enterprise Board Limited in 1996 from both of which he retired in 2000. In 1999 he was awarded an O.B.E. for services to Jersey's heritage and culture.

I was born at Grève d'Azette in a house opposite the canning factory there and next to a railway station. Indeed my early memories are concerned with transport: going on the train to Gorey and to Corbière, the sad scenes of the railway tracks being taken up and travelling on the first double-decker bus and looking down into the gardens of the Harrisons and the Walkers and the other well-to-do families who lived in the vicinity of Le Hocq and Samarès.

I have a clear sense of what Jersey was like during my boyhood in the '30s. There was enormous respect for those in the professions – doctors, dentists, lawyers – and there were big social gaps between the workers of the world, the shopkeepers and the professionals. Then there were also those who had come to the Island to retire: the generals and colonels who had sufficient pensions to live permanently in hotels such as the Ommaroo. We also had what was called the visitor trade. No shop assistant had a holiday in July or August when the hordes of holidaymakers, many of them railway employees with subsidised travel, crossed on the steamers from England. This was the period when small guest houses blossomed into many-roomed hotels, the Binningtons at the Chelsea Hotel and the Seymours expanding their business

Born in the 1920s...

being examples of this process.

There was a sense of knowing one's place in life (and in going to Victoria College I was the first generation of my family to have a public school education and mix with the sons of the professional classes). It was also generally a quiet life, the era of the shopkeeper concerned for his customers. Indeed little shops abounded; there were four tobacconists in Halkett Place. Also tradesmen came to the house every week: my mother would get her paraffin from Mr Sampson's van and three grocery salesmen turned up on a regular basis. Shops were virtually centres of social activity. You bought potatoes by the measure, biscuits were always weighed out and bacon was sliced in front of you. Women did the housework and shopped every day, and then on summer afternoons my mother would sit with her friends under the sea-wall at Grève d'Azette having a gossip. The beach was my life too: Sunday afternoons, after chapel in the mornings, playing cricket on the sand with my dad in his braces. And going to the pictures was a big treat: Saturday morning cinema at The Forum for a penny admission.

In 1940 came the Occupation and its own particular memories. I was horrified to be personally machine-gunned (they missed) by a Dornier 17 doing the bombing at La Rocque. The canning factory and its tall chimney were the attraction, and Mr Binnington, who besides owning the Chelsea Hotel had the Sable d'Or in the middle of St Ouen's Bay, offered all of us neighbours accommodation as his guests there for two or three nights. My mother and father were not alone in having a dreadful fear of the Germans, and it was for many a frightening time as the troop carriers flew in at rooftop height, with the Island garrisoned rapidly and regulations immediately imposed. For myself, with many Victoria College boys evacuated to Bedford, competition in class was less stiff and I steadily began coming fourth, third, second and then first in form orders. But I left school in 1942 at the age of 16 because my father could no longer afford the fees and I joined the Jersey Mutual Insurance Society as a clerk.

I had no burning ambition to be a newsagent and stationer but it was made very clear to me when the Occupation ended that Father needed me in the family business and, after being sent away for a few months to relatives in England literally to be fattened up (hard though it is now to believe that I required this), I joined my father in the firm. In the long run it all turned out well: over the years it became a highly successful concern expanding into office equipment and the like. I have to be grateful to my Victoria College education which allowed me to meet a broader range of people and fired my ambition to do more in life than be a newsagent and bookseller.

After the war Jersey quickly recovered, and those of us in business worked hard to escape near-bankruptcy and achieve prosperity. In 1947 I became a founder member of Jersey Round Table and through its activities came into contact and gained from my acquaintance with many of those who had come back to the Island having had military service as officers and leaders of men. Their influence on me – that experience of life which during the Occupation I had missed – was significant: an ambition to get things done, to achieve, to be of some consequence in the community.

This was one of my motives in joining the honorary police. The parish of St Helier wanted to attract business people to its ranks and I became a Constable's Officer. Dare I say that there were few Old Victorians in the honorary system, and it became my ambition to effect change to it. In due course I was elected a Centenier and, as secretary of the Centeniers' Association, tried to drag the honorary police into the twentieth century. The need for change was overwhelming. For example in 1960 there was a senior Centenier of Grouville who forbade the States police to take their patrol cars into the parish without his permission. You went out on patrol in the town streets with a Mickey Mouse badge in your pocket and a red and white armband, hardly adequate protection if someone wished to start a fight. A recognisable uniform would have been an improvement. At the same time the States police was establishing itself as an increasingly effective force and encountering resentment from the honorary service which argued strongly for the retention of the power to arrest and charge (which it still has to this day).

Having reached the top of the tree as a Centenier I was persuaded to stand for election as Constable of St Helier. In fact Peter Baker succeeded in winning and made a superb Constable, bringing to the office both status, respect and authority – qualities which have not always been evident in more recent years. I decided to leave the honorary system at this point and, not lacking in ideas and vision, I was encouraged to stand for the States, being elected one of the Deputies for St Helier in 1978.

The States at that time consisted in part of what could be termed 'the Establishment': respected and unpaid politicians of whom among the most notable were Cyril and John Le Marquand, Wilfred Krichefski, Ralph Vibert, Reg Jeune and others of similar standing who were intelligent and possessed the gift of words. The public at the time saw the States as all-powerful, and as a junior politician one was wary of putting a foot wrong. I made speedy

Born in the 1920s...

progress and relatively soon became President of Public Works with responsibility for promoting the Queen's Valley reservoir and for traffic (which had been a particular interest of mine when a Centenier). I also served on a sub-committee chaired by the great Sir Robert Marett to consider reform of the States. We decided – an echo of the Clothier debate many years hence – that there should be a radical reduction in the number of States committees. Sadly Sir Robert died and our report was not acted upon. Later I lodged a proposition to split the Finance Committee, giving some of its responsibilities to an economic and industrial committee. Instead Peat Marwick were brought in to conduct a wider review of our system of government. This was perhaps an early example of an increasingly common trend: call in the consultants, not always greatly qualified, pay them a lot of money, let them talk to those engaging them and, hey presto, three years later a report is presented which contains what they have been told.

I mention two other instances of frustration, one concerning traffic and the other the airport. While president of Public Works my committee and I drew up a traffic plan, creating the St Helier ring-road and providing solutions to all the unresolved and related problems. Our plan was ready and costed, but the States turned it down. In due course it was incorporated into the Island Plan and in theory fully accepted. Sadly nothing has happened.

Concerning the airport: while I was a member of the Harbours and Airport Committee, the then airport commandant, Brian Mellor, in 1982 produced a rebuilding plan which included a long two-storey building with aircraft gates and arrivals and departures on two levels and also contained plans for moving the taxiway (which had been demanded that long ago by the Civil Aviation Authority). It would all have cost £3m. Sadly Cyril Le Marquand, then President of Finance, considered that there was nothing wrong with the airport and vetoed the expenditure. We should not have accepted his decision and should have taken the matter to the States. Instead years later we have a £23m departure building which with its wasted space fails adequately to do its job.

I retired from the States in 1987, wearied by my long (though successful) struggle over Queen's Valley and by the failure to get our comprehensive traffic plans adopted. After a short respite my public life picked up again: I became active in the Société Jersiaise and in 1990 was appointed by the States to the chairmanship of Jersey Heritage Trust.

But my main challenge in these later years was to do with the waterfront. From the start I favoured a development agency; the planning of the whole waterfront from Havre des Pas to West Park was too important an issue to be left in the hands of a States committee. The story of the Waterfront Enterprise Board, the quango set up to oversee this, is a complex one in which, to be frank, both managing director John Scally and the board itself were denied the powers which they needed; the States retained control and a host of problems stemmed from that. I became WEB's chairman in 1996. One of our first difficulties concerned Richard Falle's Les Pas Holdings and its claims to part of the waterfront; this issue was eventually resolved by compulsory purchase. A second major headache was the reluctance of the States adequately to finance developments, insisting that they should be privately funded. This requirement significantly delayed our plans for the leisure pool and the hotel. The problems were endless: our housing schemes were emasculated by the planners, and what we have got is the proverbial camel; and the hotel development, currently in abeyance and with a design of which I personally did not wholly approve, also ended up as 'a horse designed by a committee'.

There were also continuing delays and controversies over the Island Site, caused particularly by the resolve of Planning and Environment to retain not only the outer walls but also the internal structure of the old abattoir building. This resulted in the failure to implement WEB's scheme to develop this area on the Esplanade and accommodate, in a much more satisfactory way than at present, buses, coaches and taxis. After four and a half years of frustration and at the age of 74 I did not relish a further four-year term of office and resigned. (Perhaps the States would not have given me another spell: I had not made myself popular with some of the politicians. Making oneself popular is not necessarily the key to finding the way forward.)

How then ideally should the waterfront have been developed? In retrospect I consider that we needed two marinas – including the one proposed for Havre des Pas. We should have had our bus station on the Esplanade, and the leisure pool could have been part of a rejuvenation of Fort Regent, with a marvellous hotel on the site of the present swimming pool. As to west of Albert I always hankered after more space, a lung for the people of St Helier.

My own career in the States and my experiences with WEB allow me to reflect on the Island's system of government and its current problems and challenges. In the States one of the devices for delay is the ability of single members to introduce rescindment motions; this can bring a process to a grinding halt and consequently makes politicians plan objectives with undue caution. As to the committee system I regret, as mentioned earlier, the failure of proposals put forward a couple of decades ago to cut the number of

Born in the 1920s...

committees and for the presidents of the major committees to form what in essence would have been a cabinet; an opportunity sadly missed.

I also have concerns about the calibre of those who now serve in government; it was a disaster when the decision was made to pay high salaries to politicians; the quality of government was better when public service and not reward was the motivating force. There are only relatively few currently in the States who are deserving of respect; there is a real dearth of leadership, with politicians no longer having the capability or the authority to exercise control over the departments for which they are responsible, and this allows the civil servants to operate according to their own agenda. Ultimately it is not the alternative of a committee or a ministerial system that matters; it is the leadership qualities of those elected as States Members.

What then are my worries for the future of this island which I love? Take Jersey's attitude to taxation: never borrow – which flies in the face of governmental practice everywhere else. This has resulted in the deterioration of our infrastructure – roads, hospitals and so on. It has been a mistake that we have never countenanced loans and bonds to provide necessary capital. Also we are wedded to the 20% tax level; other European countries pay more in taxes for better medical services, education and transport.

There is the dominant position of the finance industry (it is only here because of a piece of fiscal luck - to allow countless thousands who do not live here to avoid tax). The problems of the cost of living and the high price of property stem from the finance industry being here. Jersey youth works in banks and finance houses and not in our hotels and restaurants and shops. As a consequence we have 10-15,000 Portuguese who keep our tourism industry and agriculture (such as it is) viable; their loyalty to Jersey and the British connection is understandably not of the strongest. As it is we are engaged in the pursuit of wealth and possessions as a result of the finance industry over which we have no control and which could disappear overnight.

And if it did we would be left with nothing other than tourism. We should surely be investing huge sums in it, not leaving the money in a 'rainy day' fund, and thus creating here a second economic line of defence. Jersey and the other Channel Islands could be a playground for the people of Europe. Think of the Island's history and exploit it: its heritage sites, its participation for 800 years as Britain's front line; its enormous range of German fortifications; its scenic beauty. In addition we need more golf courses and another marina. Our future, if it must be without finance, should lie in this direction. We shall not be able to sustain our way of life by selling Jersey

Born in the 1920s...

royals in bulk, and at the most competitive prices, to English supermarkets. We have passed the point of no return in the standards of living so much enjoyed by our people. Though many of them might resent and resist such a future, it must surely lie in the creation of "Jersey – Europe's Greatest Holiday".

Jack Worrall

Jack Worrall, the son of a schoolmaster who later became a headmaster, was born in Monmouthshire in 1928. Following his years as a pupil at Bassaleg Grammar School he did National Service first in the Royal Signals and then as a sergeant in the Royal Army Education Corps. After his army service he went to Bristol University where he completed an honours degree in French and German and a Diploma of Education. In 1952 he took up his first teaching post at Bisley Boys' School in Surrey and in 1959 went to teach in British army schools in Germany, becoming Headmaster of Windsor Boys' School, Hannon, in 1972. He came to Jersey in 1976 on his appointment as Head of Hautlieu School and retired in 1988.

Some would consider me part of that 'Taffy mafia' tradition of teachers, preachers and Rugby football, and I certainly fulfil the requirements for the first and third of these. In fact I am English-born – in Monmouthshire – and my parents were very much English in origin. Before going to my grammar school at the age of 11, starting there in the week that the second world war was declared, I was taught in the elementary school of which my father was headmaster. Despite the war I had a fulfilled and enjoyable secondary education: some good teachers, much Rugby (including Welsh schoolboy trials) and, in the latter years, church bell-ringing which has been a lifelong interest and which I took up when the ban on church bells being rung was lifted in 1943. From school I went straight into the army for my National Service (it

Born in the 1920s...

meant that with a student grant on coming out I was at least marginally better off during my university years) and, with ambitions to enter the teaching profession, transferred from the Royal Signals to the Education Corps.

After the army came Bristol University: more rugger, more bell-ringing, a course for four months at the Sorbonne, two months in Brittany where I met my future wife and teaching practice during my dip.ed. year at The Crypt Grammar School, Gloucester. My first teaching job was in Surrey, at Bisley School which was part of the Shaftesbury Homes charity. Here I taught French, played a large part in games coaching, became a housemaster and married. It was an interesting time to be there since, under an enlightened headmaster, the school was shedding its harsh, institutional atmosphere and becoming a more civilised and less austere place. These early years stood me in good stead when in 1959 I went to Germany to teach in the British army Prince Rupert School. Other German appointments followed and in 1968 I became deputy head of Windsor Boys' School and was then appointed Headmaster of it in 1972. Four years later I successfully applied for the headship of Hautlieu.

While at the time I knew little of Jersey, I had a better knowledge and experience of Guernsey where my mother, widowed in 1945 and remarried in 1957, had gone to live in 1960 and where I went to stay with her for several weeks every summer. Married to a Frenchwoman, I have often thought it advantageous for husband and wife to live and work on neutral territory. Germany had provided us with this and Jersey had a somewhat similar appeal. Hautlieu School, having opened in 1952 as a boys' grammar school and having become co-educational after amalgamation with the Rouge Bouillon girls' grammar school, was now at an interesting stage in its history. The first headteacher had been in post for 24 years, and the task now was to re-organise the school from an 11-plus to a 14-plus entry, with pupils enrolling for a four-year course to A-levels.

I look back on the Island as it was when I first came here. For me it was not a claustrophobic place; I was accustomed to small self-contained expatriate British communities in Germany, and in many ways Jersey was less restrictive than these. The Island's values reminded me in some respects of those of my childhood: less vandalism and, with the greater incidence nowadays of broken homes in mind, a more secure family life. I sensed a stability here which had already weakened in mainland Britain. An instance of this was at Hautlieu itself where many of the teaching staff were those who had been in post since the school's foundation in 1952. Soon, however, I was to register some of

Born in the 1920s...

Jersey's distinctive problems. For example, with full employment no school leaver was short of finding a job and this bred complacency and tended to take the edge off academic achievement. This I saw as a particular challenge for me, and the advent of the 14-plus entry helped here: every pupil at Hautlieu had made a conscious choice to come there; every youngster was a volunteer. I would tell my teachers that this placed a greater responsibility on the staff to repay that confidence which the boys and girls had placed in the school.

What were my biggest problems in my 12 years as Head? One of these, perhaps surprisingly, was the fact that some of the teachers remained uneasy that the school had become co-educational all those years before. Also I had to effect staff changes, as the opportunity arose or was created, so that all teachers were capable of teaching their specialist subjects up to A-level standard. And I had concerns too about some of the parents who remained unconvinced of the need for their sons and daughters (especially the latter) to pursue their education beyond O-level and were as a consequence unwilling to keep them in pocket money (hence pupils' weekend jobs) and reluctant to fund them through college or university. But besides the headaches there were also the satisfactions. The 14-plus entry became firmly established and successful, and we weathered one particular storm when a proposal to convert Hautlieu into a form of sixth form college was mooted but not adopted. Also there developed an increasingly healthy co-operation between the Island's secondary schools, and I welcomed the inclusion in our regular termly meetings of the Heads of Victoria College and Jersey College for Girls. The fact was that at Hautlieu we had managed to establish a fairly unique entry system, and the other secondary schools, if not wholly enthusiastic about it, were helping to make the arrangement work positively.

Since my retirement I have continued to pursue a number of interests. I had resumed my change-ringing when I came to Jersey and, with the bells of St Mark's restored in 1974 and a new ring of eight provided for St John's in 1979, I was active – and still am – in teaching people to ring and to ensure that this ancient and absorbing art continues to flourish in the Island (despite there being only these two churches where the bells are hung for English change-ringing). Then I have continued to follow a long interest in stamp-collecting and genealogy and, since retirement, have been an active member of the Société Jersiaise, concerned especially with genealogical matters and working two mornings a week in its library. I felt particularly honoured three years before my retirement to be appointed a *Chevalier dans l'Ordre des Palmes Académiques* given to me by the French Ministry of Education for services to

Born in the 1920s...

French culture.

I have now been a Jersey resident for well over a quarter of a century and I sense that the Island is now more subject to pressures from outside than it was when I arrived here in 1976. Television's all-pervasive influence must have, at least in part, contributed to this. Jersey is now less free to go its own way, and this is particularly so in the field of education where the changes that have led to lower standards in Britain have had to be adopted here. Drugs too are an increasing problem; it was once only cannabis and now it is the more serious hard varieties. Youngsters these days drink far too much alcohol, and mainland vandalism is mimicked here. Jersey is now just that more touched by the troubles that affect and afflict other more cosmopolitan places.

As to the Island's government, I have become increasingly disillusioned. Those leaders of the community who impressed me in my early years here now seem to be fewer in number, and those who dominated the States some years ago were more careful in not wasting public money. There is now an urgent need for some structural reform of our system: perhaps four-year terms of office or rolling elections; perhaps a greater scrutiny function for States Members. I would like to see the Bailiff remain in his presiding role over the States, but I have no enthusiasm for the all-Island mandate for Senators and would favour just one category of Member. We also have a possible danger in the finance industry turning off its computers and seeking an environment whose checks and regulations are less demanding. Tourism too seems threatened: it is not only the cost of getting here, but our hotels and eating-out are so expensive. Yes: I have concern for the future, and this division in Jersey, far greater than I have experienced elsewhere, of those who have and those who have not shows few signs of narrowing in the foreseeable future.

Chapter Three

Born in the 1930s

David Barlow
Anne Perchard
Gordon Young
Carlos Santos-Costa
Colin Powell
Anne Herrod
Mick Kavanagh
Philip Le Brocq

David Barlow

David Barlow was born in Manchester in 1931. After preparatory school he went to Dean Close School, Cheltenham, leaving in 1949. He then gained a National Service commission in the Royal Artillery and was subsequently stationed in Aden. For three years from 1951 he worked in an architect's practice and studied at night school. He then went to Liverpool University, read for a degree in Architecture and qualified in 1958. He worked for a year in London before coming to Jersey in 1959 as assistant to Nigel Biggar, going into partnership with him two years later. In 1986 he left the partnership to specialise in designing buildings for the elderly. The Limes, The Hollies Day Care Centre and Sandybrook Residential Home are his work.

The first part of my life was spent in Southport, the spacious Edwardian dormitory town north of Liverpool, famous for its elegant Lord Street and for the extent of its sandy beach which, at low tide, seems to reach the horizon (they have 30-foot tides there too).

My father came from Braintree, Essex, the home of the Crittall metal window, and it was for this firm that he moved to Manchester and then Liverpool in 1930 to open an office and extend their sales into the north-west. I attended an academically excellent, but rather Victorian, prep. school in Southport and later followed my brother to Dean Close School in Cheltenham. After the death of my mother in a car crash in 1939 my father remarried in 1941, and he and my stepmother, only six or seven years older than me, had a daughter to whom I remain very close.

In 1940-41 Southport was on the route for German planes bombing Liverpool, and occasional sticks of bombs fell on the town, including the site of the school which was straddled as we lay attempting to sleep on carpenters' benches in the basement workshop – our air raid shelter. Anti-aircraft guns blazed away only 50 yards from our home and we were fascinated by the searchlights alongside. My father took us to see the devastation in Liverpool, then an enormously bustling port receiving and despatching ships for North Atlantic convoys. The memories of the diversions on the Dock Road and the damaged, blackened, smoking buildings are still very clear to me.

Drawing skills have existed in my family for generations and I have sketch books dating back to 1930 together with many watercolours made by my mother's cousin as well as books by an uncle killed in the Great War. As a child I was visually aware and recall curtain and wallpaper patterns and the fall of light in the bedrooms as the breeze moved blinds and fabric. I could always draw and never had difficulty in making sketches or perspectives from any angle, as the shapes seemed to come out of my head.

In the 1940s at Dean Close my housemaster, the School Chaplain, was fascinated by the exquisite Cotswolds village churches, and he encouraged an interest in medieval architecture which, together with time in the art room, probably subconsciously directed me towards an architectural career.

Teaching during the war was often makeshift and delivered by ever-changing and elderly staff who regrettably never really caught my imagination and certainly disregarded artistic talent. Thus, after obtaining an excellent School Certificate, I concentrated on sport. Although I finished up Head of House my academic career was a disaster.

National Service in 1950 and 1951 was at first a bewildering sequence of artillery drill. In due course I was commissioned and sent to then peaceful Aden where I was responsible for men and equipment in three wartime forts. I was able to continue drawing and even made plans for improving barrack blocks when not playing cricket and hockey with the Command teams in Eritrea or Somaliland.

After my time in the Army I looked for employment. The Sanderson wallpaper and fabrics firm turned me down, so I then went to Liverpool, visiting firms listed in the telephone book to see if I could start as a trainee architect about which I knew nothing. In spite of the restricted amount of building taking place because of the rationing of materials, I was eventually offered a job at a very small salary.

The next three years were spent working full-time, including Saturday mornings, attending night school three evenings a week and tackling homework. I also had to prepare at weekends special drawings required by the RIBA. It was an impossible load and therefore very satisfying when my boss and night school tutor persuaded Lancashire County Council to pay for me to go to Liverpool University. The four years there as a mature student caught my imagination and gave my life an impetus which has continued ever since. How fortunate I was, for the initial practical grounding followed by a more academic approach was an excellent preparation for the architectural

Born in the 1930s...

career that I have followed.

Qualifying in 1958, I went to work in London for Nadine Beddington, an extraordinarily efficient lady who specialised in designing shoe shops for the British Shoe Corporation. In a small office of ten people I gained invaluable experience in interior design. This background has been of enormous help to me when commissioned by banks and more recently when undertaking projects at The Limes and Sandybrook where I attended to all such matters as well as selecting pictures and producing landscape drawings.

Nineteen-fifty-nine had a brilliant summer and, having moved from a comfortable Mayfair office to the first floor above a shoe shop in Oxford Street, I found looking out at the sun through an advertising grille a depressing experience. My stepmother had now remarried and was living in Jersey, so I dreamt of enjoying sandy beaches for a year or two. A job was advertised by Nigel Biggar. I applied, was accepted and joined the firm in September.

After many years in the north I found, and still find, the Island a mellow, pretty place in which to live, although it seemed sleepy after the hubbub of London. Before the growth of finance there were few young professional people – a handful of lawyers, doctors and architects. It seemed something of a backwater, mostly Jersey businesses, with the town, including our office, closing on Thursday afternoons.

Our office was then in Halkett Place, opposite the Market, in the area now swallowed up by Woolworths. We could often park outside or higher up the street by the Wesley Grove chapel. Nigel ran an overloaded practice, undertaking work for many local stores, shops, hotels, banks and doing a host of new houses and domestic alterations. It was an impossible load for a conscientious man who cared for his clients. It was ruining his health. Geoffrey Myers had come to the Island a few months before me in 1959. Two years later we both became partners, spreading the work-load and slowly reorganising the practice.

In the early '60s Jersey design and building practice were very basic. I was horrified to find waste pipes suspended outside buildings instead of being concealed. There seemed to be a rash of Ruberoid-covered flat roofs and a dedication to the use of metal windows – similar to those my father had distributed in the north. Most new buildings had little in common with traditional Jersey structures, but at that stage few people seemed to bother about this. Of course the standard of living and the amounts of money available were much lower than today, and it was not feasible to use granite and pitched slate-covered roofs which cost substantially more.

Born in the 1930s...

There was a particular emphasis on building basic bungalows for young people, costing up to £3,000. These economy houses, often covered with ginger-coloured pebbledash, frequently stood incongruously alongside splendid 18th and 19th century farm groups. Their form and character were completely out of keeping and many remain today, substantially altered and enlarged, with a price tag of between £300,000 and £400,000. As a young architect I was as appalled by these horrors as I was by the unthinking destruction of the Victorian shop fronts which had survived in Jersey longer than in other parts of the British Isles. The splendid features of St Helier were being ignored as cars squeezed their way down King Street hindered by an outbreak of new traffic lights.

In both town and country the safety net preventing inappropriate buildings should have been the Planning Office, but Jersey's was newly established and the first Planning Officer was trying to come to terms with Island ways and administer the Barrett Plan which, like its successors, was meant to provide the solution to our problems. The Plan attempted to rationalise development and to give the politicians a framework on which to base their decisions. The allocation of areas for development, agriculture and a green zone set the pattern. It was not updated and in St Helier, where the proposal to sweep away Hue Street was one of the first schemes implemented, we lost the only 17th, 18th and 19th century street in the town.

I still have the photographs and drawings of both sides of Hue Street, made as it was about to be demolished. Joan Stevens and a group of us went to see the Planning Officer in an attempt to persuade him that the facades and houses could be restored, with the back yards and gardens used for new buildings. We were ignored by him, by the Committee and by the public, who expressed little concern. Today only one small section remains, saved at the eleventh hour after much States' indecision.

Fortunately in the early 1970s the tide was turning as people began to realise that old St Helier was disappearing rapidly. In 1971 the Société Jersiaise, the National Trust and the Association of Jersey Architects mounted a campaign and persuaded the States to vote against the demolition of Dean Falle's 1737 Library, sandwiched inconveniently between the old Boutin building and the site being prepared for the shiny black building for Slater Walker that now makes the bend in the street.

At that time – the '60s and '70s – the Association of Jersey Architects was very active. A small group of us, orchestrated by Geoffrey Myers, was in regular contact with IDC (the then States planning committee) members and other

Born in the 1930s...

politicians, offering impartial advice on any public matters where we felt our technical knowledge would be helpful. I recall only a few: parking in Rozel, incineration or composting, La Rocco Tower, building controls, historic buildings, inappropriate new States projects such as the Hospital and Hue Court. Some we won; some we lost. Nevertheless it seemed to me to be the proper way for a professional body to act.

The other major contribution by the Association was the surveying of St Helier, St Aubin and Gorey in order to prepare a list of graded buildings because the IDC continually failed to act. Hundreds were photographed and the historic negatives are now in the Jersey Archive as many buildings have disappeared since then and there was a danger that the photographs would be lost at the Planning Office. Our efforts were not received with any great enthusiasm as the policy of conservation had not yet become fashionable.

In the early days we had a good working relationship with the Planning Office, being able to obtain advice and being reasonably certain that officers would put our views, even if they were unpopular, to the Committee. But the department grew and regulations and procedures proliferated and became more complex, overwhelming staff with day to day administration. By the 1980s the department had become impersonal and defensive, with officers less ready to express opinions. Today meetings are hard to arrange and one is not at all satisfied that schemes are presented with proper historic and other background information.

Despite all this, successive IDCs over the years have managed to prevent the indiscriminate sprawl that might have developed on account of a booming economy and a massive increase in population. The town is, in most respects, a more inviting place than it was, with pedestrian areas, street landscaping and, in more recent years, a more careful control of new facades – now often decorated by masses of flowers in summer, a reflection of some civic pride. St Ouen's Bay is another success, and it seems almost a miracle that in the '60s and '70s it was not overwhelmed by the type of massive hotel development that ruined so many Mediterranean resorts.

Gorey and St Aubin remain intact and steadily improve. Here and in the countryside listing has protected the older properties, although on occasions extraordinarily ordinary ugly buildings are retained for dubious reasons.

But architectural successes have been hard to come by and we could do with more buildings of the calibre of Howarth and Tompkins's sophisticated and satisfying 'hi-tech' design in La Motte Street. There are signs that architects are now being allowed more freedom by the Planning and

Born in the 1930s...

Environment Committee (the successor to the IDC), and several new housing schemes and schools have broken away from the unimaginative patterns that typified so many earlier States projects. It is good, for example, to see the bold use of colour in town and on the Waterfront flats.

What has been less commendable is the intrusion into the countryside of a rash of vast sheds which farmers have been allowed to construct, often in the most unsuitable spots alongside farm buildings which they dwarf. These wretched monsters will be with us for years and doubtless farmers will, one by one, apply for change of use as agriculture declines and their owners can see profit in using them for light industry.

The poor quality of the design and construction of earlier developments is now becoming apparent as schools and houses 30 or 40 years old have to be demolished and reconstructed, whereas so many 19th and early 20th century buildings have stood the test of time and, with alteration, are still of use.

The current Waterfront extension of St Helier was blighted from the start by the gaping wound of the road underpass which has cut painfully through the area where the town attempts to join the sea. This ill-considered route was constructed without any proper concept of what was to follow, and the situation has been made worse by the States appointment of an Enterprise Board which seems to have washed its hands of any responsibility for appearance and coherent overall design. The Waterfront was never going to be an international showpiece. It was evolved in a small provincial community with a fragmented system of government which rarely has visionary thoughts. The evolution of the scheme reflects, as most building projects do, the nature of the society that commissioned it. With luck one or two of the many buildings may show architectural flair.

In the future it is clear that the control of cars, the maintenance of unused agricultural land and the decline in tourism will produce problems that will require resolution. Whatever the changes to our system of government, the Administration will doubtless continue to muddle along, preferably without increasing the number of civil servants whose pensions are going to cripple us. Also, great care will be needed to avoid destroying the confidence of the finance industry which pays the bills.

There can be few places in the world other than Jersey where I could have completed such a fulfilling and rewarding professional career in such pleasant and peaceful surroundings. My sequence of work has included houses, private flats, conversion of farms, shops, hotels, commercial buildings, offices, banks, States flats, the Communicare Centre, day-care centres and residential homes

Born in the 1930s...

for the elderly. I have benefited from affable clients who always paid me, and I have been fortunate to work with a small local building industry which, if encouraged, produces very good results. Only those who occupy my buildings can judge whether I have been successful.

My more than 40 years in Jersey have been wonderful, and I still find it an inspiring island. I can walk the spectacular coastal paths, saunter in green lanes, run along vast beaches and amble in the clean sea. What a delight it has been to live in a law-abiding society with my family and many good friends. There is a tendency continually to find things wrong in the Island without emphasising at the same time how many things are right in comparison with the rest of the world. Our small democracy enables every individual to have a say and, occasionally, to change the course of that ponderous ship – the States of Jersey. We should be thankful for this and be ready to remind those politicians and officers who become too self-important that we are not and do not wish to be 'players on the international scene'. Long may we remain a tiny but prosperous speck on the map of the world, a world where only an infinitesimal proportion of its population has ever heard of us.

Anne Perchard M.B.E.

Anne Perchard (née Billot) was born in 1932. She attended St Martin's Elementary School and from there won a scholarship to Jersey College for Girls. She married in 1950, and she and her husband farmed in St Saviour and St Lawrence before purchasing and moving to La Ferme, St Martin, in 1957. She is the mother of six children, her eldest son dying at the age of 15. In 1980 she and three of her sons formed a company which farms on a large scale in several parishes. From 1989 to 2002 she travelled extensively as President of the World Jersey Cattle Bureau. In 1999 she was appointed a member of the Review Panel on the Machinery of Government in Jersey (the Clothier Commission).

Born in the 1930s...

I was born at Ville Bree, St Martin, just up the road from La Ferme which has been my home since 1957. My childhood was a happy one. It was a simple lifestyle, and my love of animals and the soil was there from my earliest days. I had a cow called Gyp which I used to take to the fields. Sometimes, I am told, I would be found in the shed fast asleep with my arms round Gyp. We were three girls in the family and were expected to do our bit on the farm. I became like a boy – always outside, a tough little bean, not big but strong.

In the months prior to the Occupation my father was desperately ill with pneumonia, pleurisy and empyema. This was before the days of antibiotics and for a time he had nurses day and night – all very tough financially for tenant farmers such as ourselves. In the days before the Germans came, my parents had been in Alderney, with my father convalescing. They returned quickly to face the decision to be made by so many Islanders – to leave or stay. Dad soon put an end to the discussion: he stated that if he was to die it would be in Jersey where he belonged, and that was that.

On the day that the Germans bombed the Island we were in a field close to the farmhouse digging potatoes. As a child I always hated loud bangs and, when the noise of the explosions and machine gunning started, I was the first under the lorry, with my fingers firmly in my ears. The rest of the family joined me until it all stopped. The enemy landed and in the following weeks we learnt to accept that these smart, arrogant and strange-tongued soldiers were here and that we had to do as we were bidden or else face severe punishment.

My education began at a small private school, Silk's, in one of the lanes near our parish church, and at the age of nine I moved to St Martin's School. One day my sister Ruth and I were involved in a nasty incident which made us very wary of the German forces. With several friends we were all, arm in arm and chatting and laughing, on our way for lunch to La Chasse Cottage, my grandparents' home. A smart German soldier was cycling past, threw down his bike and ran towards Ruth, giving her a mighty slap on the face. None of us knew what had prompted this and we scattered, with poor Ruth hysterical. My grandfather, then Connétable, was furious and complained bitterly to the authorities. Ruth suffered from cold sores and would lick her lips a lot. Did the soldier mistakenly think that she was putting her tongue out at him? She was so frightened by the incident that for the rest of the war she never went down that road again.

I worked hard at school to gain a scholarship to the Girls' College and, after starting, bicycled there in all weathers. The bikes were being continually patched up and by the end hosepipes and twisted ropes were substitutes for

Born in the 1930s...

tyres. Living on a farm, we were more fortunate than our town cousins, rearing chickens and rabbits as well as a few pigs. When a pig was killed on the farm – by someone who knew how to carry this out as silently as possible – the meat was shared between neighbours, and some was salted down. We had a large cold water tap in the cow stable and Dad would wash through the large intestine to make tripe. The following evening there would be a splendid tripe supper for the family and a dozen or so friends. We were sent off to bed at 8.30 p.m., and then the grown-ups would have a great game of nap, washed down by cider, and this would go on well into the night and past the curfew hour. Some slept downstairs until the morning, and others melted away along the field hedgerows back to their own beds.

As the war progressed, the Germans began visiting the farms regularly to count the animals. They also took our two farm horses for meat. Dolly, the Welsh cob, was my beloved and favourite animal. When she was taken away I was not told, my parents knowing how distressed I would be. When I realised that she was gone and, by then, dead, I ran up to the hayloft, hid among the bundles and sobbed for hours. I was inconsolable for days. Some time after, I went with Dad to see the replacement horses which we were to be given. I was surprised to witness English-speaking women riding out with some German officers. It was my first experience of collaborators and, after what had happened to my little mare, I was far from impressed; I hated these girls more than I hated the Germans.

My grandfather, as Connétable, was very troubled when the departure of British subjects to internment camps in Europe had to be arranged. When he was informed that houses and farms were to be searched for firearms, I was at the Cottage on my way back from school. Grandpa said to me, 'Anne, get back to Ville Bree quickly and tell your father to get the fire out at once. He will understand.' And so, one of my father's treasured possessions, his rifle with which he had won many trophies pre-war, was slung hastily into the liquid manure cistern. It was retrieved after the war, all rusted and eaten away with acid and, now cleaned up, is a family treasure.

After D-day in 1944 we could see from our bedroom windows the skies over France lit up with flickering red and orange glow from the intense bombing and fires. Everyone wondered how long it would be before we were freed, little realising that there would be eleven more months before Liberation. At last it happened. The Union Jack, hidden in the rafters, was brought out; the radio, kept under the floorboards and on which Dad had listened to the nine o'clock news every night, was produced and placed on the lawn for us all to hear Winston Churchill's address to the Channel Islands. We then walked to the parish church for a thanksgiving service, and emotions ran high with our deliverance from captivity. The following day our old Dodge lorry was brought out of its shed and resuscitated, and some 32 of us piled into the back of it for Town and the joyful sight of the Tommies marching through the streets and throwing sweets to the children as they passed. Liberation was for me, looking back over the years, the most important moment of my life.

After the war Jersey changed somewhat. We had an influx into the Island of rich people who wished to evade taxes in the UK. We were poor and I felt in awe of these wealthy residents. I also had a sense of inferiority at College, being a scholarship girl and having a Jersey accent.

Not many years after leaving school I married. Leslie, the youngest of 14 children, was going to be a schoolmaster and had a place waiting for him at Exeter University. On marriage he changed his plans and decided to do what we both loved – farming. We started at Maufant, St Saviour, with six cows and a few pigs and some chickens; we got onto the first rung of the ladder. It was a busy time: digging our own potatoes, having three children in three years, moving to a 34-vergee farm in St Lawrence and having some good cattle and bulls to sell. Then we found that our eldest son was mentally handicapped. In due course, as he grew older and stronger, we were unable to cope with him and he went to St Saviour's Hospital. Twice weekly we enjoyed bringing him home to be with the family. At the age of 15 he had a stroke and tragically died six months later, blind and paralysed.

In 1957 La Ferme, this wonderful big farm, came on the market. I had always hankered after it and we borrowed a fortune to purchase it. Some said that we were crazy, that we would go broke. We were confident, however, with our knowledge of farming in and out, that we would succeed. We worked hard, in the summer from 4.30 in the morning until 10 at night. We developed our herd and won a prize for milk production - and went to the Dorchester Hotel in London to receive it. Our whole life revolved around the farm and making a success of it.

Then came a crisis. In 1970 my husband's manic depression worsened and our ways parted, and I continued to farm without him. My sons were now growing up, with my eldest two at university. We steadily picked up the pieces and in 1980 three of my sons and I formed our company which, over the years, has developed into a significant player in the Island's farming scene. We did not escape criticism as we expanded; we were accused of being greedy and selfish. The facts were, of course, different and not as others saw them;

Born in the 1930s...

we were four families working together and it was the only way forward. Over the years the tune has changed. Now people say that we are lucky to be so favourably established. Our luck was when we began it all in 1980. We started modestly – second-hand tractors and the boys paying themselves the lowest of wages. We ran a very tight ship, and the result is that we believe we have a future in farming whereas many others have not. The truth is that, over the years, the States has given cheap loans to farmers, encouraging them to borrow too heavily at low interest rates. Now the market-place has become more difficult and these people are leaving agriculture because they are finding increasing difficulty in repaying their loans. Farming is now a business; you have got to have a business approach and be prepared to employ top quality staff and pay them well. Farming units are becoming bigger, and it will be the larger ones that survive. The current States emphasis in agriculture is on the environment. But we will only be effective environmentalists if we are also efficient farmers making a good living.

I have always had an interest in the Island's affairs. I come from a political family, with my father, grandfather and great-grandfather being Connétables of St Martin and with service to the parish and the Island encouraged within the family. Some years ago I stood as parish Deputy for the States and lost by 26 votes. Then in 1999 I was surprised and pleased by the invitation for me to become a member of the Clothier Commission. We were known to have started modestly with few resources and had built up a strong farming enterprise, and I believe that it was because I had been successful that I was invited to be on Clothier. I had confidence in the way I approached matters, and it was thought, therefore, that I could be of use. I already had opinions on the Island's governmental matters, being concerned that the States, with its 52 independent members, had difficulty in coming to necessary and rational decisions. For example, the Queens Valley issue – I believed strongly that it should be flooded – took ten years to resolve; the votes were close; decisions were twice rescinded; it was not the way to do business.

The Clothier recommendations emerged from concern about the way the Island was being governed. We were coming into a new century, with the finance industry large and businesslike and with its excesses requiring a control that was not in place. Then there was the committee system in the States, with Members each serving on several and with consequential split loyalties and interests. There were the civil servants and the failings of politicians in exerting adequate control over them. Above all there was a paralysis in decision-making. Clothier's proposals addressed these issues and put forward a ministerial system to remedy them, a system in which the means of proper scrutiny would play a very significant role. If, as some say, the outcome of all this is party politics, then I personally have no problem with such a development: people should stand up and be counted.

Looking into my crystal ball, I hope that a new form of government for Jersey will provide proper controls for our important finance industry. We must not tolerate any form of subterfuge, keep off international blacklists and uphold our traditional Island integrity of knowing right from wrong.

We have this most beautiful island with its heritage going back many centuries. But as the world outside changes, so must we. We must play our part in this revolution; we must be positive or we shall sink. On this hangs the future for our children and grandchildren. Through my life I have always been an optimist; I would not otherwise have coped. I remain one now.

Gordon Young

Gordon Young was born in Sutton Coldfield, Warwickshire, in 1933 and educated at Walmley Village School, St Chad's Cathedral School, Lichfield, and Repton School in Derbyshire. He started to study Medicine at Birmingham University but opted out and joined the Army as a Highlander in the Black Watch. He was then commissioned into the Royal Warwickshire Regiment. He was seconded to The King's African Rifles and had postings in Nyasaland and Northern Rhodesia prior to 18 months' jungle warfare active service in the Malayan emergency. In 1955, at the conclusion of his short service commission, he came to Jersey. He first worked in a market garden and as a hospital porter before qualifying as a building surveyor. Later he became a freelance presenter with the new Channel Television and then became a journalist with the Jersey Evening Post *where for many years his Saturday political column was a regular feature. He died in November 2002, four weeks after this contribution was written.*

Born in the 1930s...

*M*y mother died when I was on active service in Malaya and I found that living with my widowed father was difficult for both of us. Having met the sister of our next-door neighbour and learned that she was leaving England to take up a job in Jersey, I followed her for a week's holiday and never returned to the UK. Liz and I were married in 1956 at Trinity church, and we had three children, Guy, Brook and Ashley, all born and raised in the Island.

I originally found work in a market garden, Balmain Gardens and Nurseries, but the bad winter of 1955/56 caused staff to be laid off and I obtained a job at the General Hospital as a porter, having done similar work in my vacations as a student in Birmingham General Hospital.

Jersey General was a very different scene from the great Midland hospital. I worked on the Jersey Poor Law (Male), a run-down Dickensian line of buildings across the yard at the back of the hospital next to the Island mortuary. The Poor Law consisted of wards on the first floor and living and dining room on the ground. The place had not been decorated for decades and the inmates consisted of very old and incapable men and those who were either mentally ill or handicapped and/or those whom their families had abandoned. It was a sad and very depressing place.

I also doubled as a 'mental attendant' on the Observation Ward, officially entitled Marie-Louise Ward, where people admitted as 'questionably mentally ill' were housed until they could be assessed and removed to St Saviour's Hospital. There were three 'cells' in each of the two wards of the unit, male and female, of which two were padded for violent cases. Very drunken people, whom the police had managed to fob off on Casualty rather than take them back to the police station where they would be a messy nuisance, often occupied these 'pads' instead of genuinely unbalanced patients. It was through working in Marie-Louise, the Poor Law and taking patients to St Saviour's that I learned of both the high level of mental sickness and handicap in Jersey and the very primitive way in which these patients were dealt with in those days. Anyone who witnessed the electrical shock treatment could never forget it.

Two years of the General Hospital were quite enough, and I joined a firm of quantity surveyors, W.G. Nixey, where I learned the profession and became qualified as a building surveyor working for private clients and, to a large extent, for the Public Works, Architects' and Engineers' Departments. I surveyed roads, buildings, the Airport runway and taxiways and all the harbour berths (with the aid of a copper-helmeted diver). The partners and I designed

Born in the 1930s...

and drew all the plans for Sumerland Knitwear factory, the new Convent FCJ School at Grainville, including a revolutionary convent building, and many hotels, private houses and offices.

While working as a surveyor I was approached by the very new Channel Television and asked whether I would like to be a freelance presenter, and for 13 years I anchored all the current affairs programmes as well as other religious and news programmes including a special half-hour face-to-face interview with the Rt Hon Airey Neave MP, the man who should have become Conservative Prime Minister but whose career was brutally cut short by an IRA bomb in the underground car park at the Palace of Westminster.

While still a surveyor I also presented a weekly political interview programme on Radio Lions and was the anchorman for the well-produced monthly Talking Magazine for the Blind of Jersey with a team - who did all the hard work - of Phil Gurdon, Chris Clayton and Beth Lloyd. I also had the Sunday morning political interview series on Radio Jersey in its initial years.

I was 'sacked' from CTV because they were getting rid of freelancers and, while 'resting', was approached to see whether I would be interested in being 'Meridian' for the Under the Clock feature in the *Jersey Evening Post*. After a couple of years as letters editor as well as Meridian I moved on to being a full-time feature writer and then was given my Saturday political column which, although now retired, I continue to write with great enjoyment.

Over the years I have served on several committees including being president of the Jersey Debating Society and also the Jersey Rugby Football Club, of which I wrote the official history, member of the Public Sculpture Trust, lay governor of Hautlieu School, first lay chairman of Trinity School PTA and first chairman of Le Rocquier School Parents' Association.

I was a keen squash player when the body worked well, founding a club called the Pint Pots, was a founder member of the Jersey Group of Artists and am currently the bass trombone in the Jersey Big Band through which I met my second wife Mary, the band's female vocalist.

This wide variety of interests and jobs has, over nearly half a century, given me a well-rounded insight into Jersey and its society on virtually every level. My political interviews through the *JEP*, television, radio, the magazine for the blind and Radio Lions, have stood me in good stead, and I have known most of the politicians over the last 30 years from their earliest days in office – a considerable advantage for a political columnist.

Jersey was a small Garden of Eden when I came here just ten years after the Liberation. The traditional country buildings constructed in rosé granite

Born in the 1930s...

stood singly among the green fields filled with doe-eyed cattle and vergées of tomato plants growing on cords strung between wooden crosses which many visitors thought were the graves of German soldiers. People spoke to each other and smiled when they passed in the street, and in a very short time one's circle of friends and acquaintances grew and it was virtually impossible to be lonely if one became part of Jersey life rather than standing apart from it.

We lived in a tiny dower house cottage in Trinity, never bothering to lock the door, and we would come home from work to find a cauliflower, a bag of new potatoes or some flowers left on our kitchen table by a farming neighbour. We could look out of our windows and see two great horses ploughing the field across the road, and a house further up the lane was sold to a 'rich immigrant' for the colossal sum of £13,000. The buyer, an English businessman, told me that he had moved to Jersey to save his two daughters incurring death duties, which was why he had paid so much for his house.

It was an age of innocence in which Island people knew and trusted each other, when most businesses - shops, hotels, builders, farms and coach companies - were family owned and run. The name on the sign was that of a real person and not a monopoly company. Doctors and dentists became your friends; bank managers were real people – and they called you by your first name, usually after you ran up an overdraft.

Politicians were truly honorary. They took no salary nor claimed any real expenses. Certainly there were perks to serving in the States, as many of the businessmen got advantages in trade and commerce in the public sector, but the public accepted this as their just deserts for the time, energy and devotion so many gave to the Island. Many were political giants with names such as Troy, Le Marquand, Krichefski, Avarne and Huelin, and they commanded a respect rarely seen today.

But Jersey's problems were quietly beginning. Immigration was growing as more and more people like me found this island to be just what they were looking for. Many young men were coming out of National Service and, having been away from home for the first time, had got the taste, and coming to Jersey on holiday was in those days the equivalent of going abroad. Remember: going abroad meant that you could only take a very limited amount of money with you - £5 or £10 - but Jersey, being in the sterling area, had no such restriction. Hundreds of these young men, and women too, spent a week or so in Jersey and knew that this was where they wanted to live. They married local girls or other immigrants like themselves and settled here. Property prices were affordable; I paid £2,250 for my place and took out a mortgage of £4,000 to extend it, and housing qualifications were only just coming in.

The honorary police ran the law administration in the Island while the paid police, as St Helier's Finest were known, merely patrolled the town and had no powers of arrest, only of detention. Police cars were, at last, being allowed into some other parishes, but diehard parishes such as Trinity would still not allow them in without permission, a situation which actually led to police cars chasing a suspect driver through St Helier but having to stop at the parish boundary and turn back!

Tourism was booming. There were cabaret shows in every part of the Island, often with well-known national performers topping the bill. The Opera House featured summer shows which packed them in and the Battle of Flowers had real celebrities as the top draw. There was no shortage of entertainment for holidaymakers, and the many coach companies ran special tours, including the boisterous and hilarious 'Crazy Nites' which involved pub crawls around the Island with silly games, funny hats and even indoor obstacle courses at the final watering hole. Tug Wilson's coach station in The Parade had an office on the pavement which displayed photographs taken on those fun nights, and many a visiting lady blushed when she saw herself publicly portrayed struggling through a hanging car tyre in the party room at the St John's Hotel.

Jersey was very much a family holiday island with the same people coming back year after year to the same hotels or guest houses. The small boarding house thrived, with people giving up their home lives in order to let their two and a half bedrooms. One couple I knew slept behind a curtain under the stairs for 20 years of seasons as they let their bedrooms. Their guests came back year after year and were part of the family.

Agriculture was also booming, with Jersey Royals, tomatoes and other crops tended and harvested by Breton farmworkers who arrived each year by boat, more often than not carrying their own forks, and returned home at the end of the season not a lot richer but ready to come back the next year. The Jersey Royals were forked by hand with care and pride, and only those without a mark on them went into the barrels.

Jersey was not without its share of crime, and there were some notable murders of the domestic variety. But the greatest shock came with the reign of terror waged by the Beast of Jersey who silently stole into houses at night, took away children into the fields, sexually assaulted them and then returned them to their beds. He was eventually caught and turned out to be a local builder, Edward Paisnel, who had strange satanic interests. During the same period a very lovely Scandinavian au pair girl was brutally murdered in St Clement and her murderer has never been caught – a source of great frustration and anger to those of us who were involved in the investigation and the reporting of this wicked crime.

Crime is one of the indicators as to the way Jersey has changed over the last five decades. Street crime, almost unknown in the '50s, is now a major problem. The trafficking and abuse of drugs have attained horrendous proportions; but thankfully the law comes down hard on miscreants here, although the massive rewards to be gained still encourage stupid people to take the risks. Burglary, theft and vandalism have become more prevalent, while offences connected with alcohol have become endemic.

Racism is now a permanent feature of Jersey life whether the establishment wishes to recognise it or not. In those early days Jersey locals welcomed immigrants like myself who integrated into the population, particularly in the country parishes. The seasonal workers such as the Bretons worked hard and were an essential part of the Island's agricultural life; and in the main they returned at the end of the season to their Brittany homes. The seasonal staff of Italians, Swiss and other European nations likewise stayed for the season and returned home. The British were the principal immigrants both as workers and as the growing population of 'rich immigrants', the latter playing a major part in the demise of agriculture as retiring farmers, whose sons had no wish to continue farming, sold their farms as country residences. The worst outcome of this selling of granite farmhouses was the fragmentation of fields, unwanted by the house purchasers, which resulted in the remaining farmers having fields spread through all parts of the Island.

As fewer Bretons came to carry out the seasonal work, so the Madeirans took their place and were found to be good and hard workers; but they tended more to remain at the end of the season and, bit by bit, the Portuguese population has grown until now there are second and third Jersey-born generations in many families. The problem is that, whereas the Bretons only stayed for the season, the Portuguese have now built up a thriving community which has tended to become a community within a community and is now verging on the edge of a ghetto community. Advertisements, newspaper articles and other public announcements are now being issued in Portuguese, and this, I feel, is further isolating this important part of Jersey's population instead of encouraging integration.

Open racism is appearing in Jersey for the first time and it is not one-sided; and many people fear that, if the seemingly continuing widening gap between the communities is not made to close, a serious racial problem, such as that now existing in many parts of the UK, may develop, and this would be a social disaster in what has always been known as a most hospitable island.

Unlike good wine Jersey has not matured well since the Occupation. Through poor, sometimes outrageously bad, planning much of the town of St Helier and the countryside has been ruined. The greed of the immigrant developer has destroyed, and continues to destroy, much of the Island, and it is not just the immigrants who are to blame. The Jerseyman must accept that, by selling so much of his birthright and inheritance, he has contributed largely to Jersey's destruction.

Already many people who were born in or who chose to settle in Jersey because it was as near paradise as they could find have packed their bags and left, and the exodus continues today. Most of our problems are due to poor, weak and misguided government, made evident by the increasing apathy towards elections. Today, thanks to the Clothier Report, Jersey is at a crossroads but, as so often in the past, our government cannot make the brave decision to follow a straight road. Their prevarication, their indecision, their inability to control immigration and inflation and to prevent the destruction of our quality of life are echoed in their inability either to govern properly or to reform the States.

It is said that it is never too late, but I fear that in Jersey's case it is. The rot has gone too far and we do not have politicians of sufficient calibre or a government that is capable of stopping the downhill stampede. The Jersey that once attracted holidaymakers and immigrants because of its gentle way of life has gone, and in its place is an island besotted with money and greed which now depends almost exclusively on the finance industry – a case of all our eggs in what may prove to be a very fragile basket.

Born in the 1930s...

Carlos Santos-Costa

Carlos Santos-Costa was born in Sintra, Portugal, in 1935. After school he went into the hotel and tourism industry, with a break of two years from 1956 when he did his compulsory military service. He came to Jersey with his wife in 1961 to work in Island hotels and, except for a year, 1964/5, he has lived here ever since. He has held various senior hotel posts and opened a travel agency in 1976. In 1997 the Portuguese Government appointed him Honorary Consul for the Channel Islands.

*A*fter I left school I went to work as a receptionist in five-star hotels. This was a worrying time in my country's history, with the Salazar dictatorship strong and its secret police watching everywhere day and night. The future looked dark and opportunities in society went only to the privileged few. For young people such as myself life was difficult and problematic.

My army service came at a time when unrest was threatening in the Portuguese colonies of Goa, Angola and Mozambique, and military training was geared to protecting these possessions against possible attempts at seizing independence. It was a difficult period of my life as a *miliciano* (a soldier with higher education). After six months of military education and an army degree, I was one of those instructing recruits and with one's pitiable pay hardly sufficient to buy a packet of cigarettes. Then in 1957 came the darkest summer of my life when during military exercises and training I broke my neck. All my young life was thrown into confusion and my sporting activities – I had excelled at football and swimming – came to an end as, after three months in hospital, did my army service.

A career in tourism was my ambition and for a time I was involved in a travel agency until my partners' financial difficulties brought this to a close. I then sought experience abroad and, with working immigration closed in most of the big countries, considered my best option to be a seasonal position in a tourist centre. Jersey beckoned: I had contacts here through friends; 40 years ago it was a lovely place free of drugs and crime; and at least some of its people were welcoming and sympathetic.

I arrived with my wife (I had married Olivia in 1959) in the Island in

Born in the 1930s...

1961. The move was very much against her wishes. The fact was that Jersey's work permit regulations did not allow children to accompany their parents, and our son Nuno, just a year old, was left behind, cared for by my parents. This nearly broke my wife's heart. Also, the permits only allowed us to work in the hotel industry, and my first job was as a barman at La Coie, a hotel in town, and Olivia worked as a chambermaid at the Pomme d'Or. Furthermore, non-British persons needed four years of continuous residence in the Island in order to qualify for rented housing.

Things, however, improved. I remember the Immigration Department at the end of 1963 relenting and giving us permission to bring our son to Jersey. I recall my exhilaration leaving the Department and running breathless down the stairs to give my wife this marvellous news. By March 1964 we were once again a united family.

Then tragedy struck. My father died at the young age of 53 and duty called us home to sort out his business affairs and to support my mother and sister at this difficult time. We found jobs back home and thought our future life would be in Portugal, but it was not to be.

By June 1965 we had returned to Jersey, never, except for holidays, to leave it again. We loved its way of life, the relaxed attitude of its people and its fine education and health services. By the end of 1967 I was working at the Ritz Hotel (a part of the Modern Group – in due course to become the second largest hotel group in the Channel Islands) in a bars management post and with Olivia as general housekeeper. The Group was to grow fast and I grew with it, ending up 31 years later as Deputy Managing Director. During this time I was to employ hundreds of Portuguese in our various hotels; at one stage they constituted 80% of the Group's labour force.

Over the years I became involved in many other aspects of Jersey life. In 1974 I became President of the newly formed Portuguese Football Club which developed into a centre of social life for the Island's Portuguese community. I have also been closely involved in the Hotel and Guest House Association, the Variety Club, the Skal Club of Jersey and with Rotary and the Roman Catholic church. For 18 years I have organised the Day of Portugal and the Portuguese Week. In 1976, with the problems of travel to and from the Island for Portuguese working here, I opened a travel agency which operates to this day.

Our son was educated at De La Salle College and was later called to the English Bar. More recently he became a Crown Advocate at the Jersey Bar and is married to Nicola, an English solicitor. They have given us three

Born in the 1930s...

wonderful grandchildren.

In the '60s an Englishman, Mr Foster, who was an estate agent, acted as Portuguese Vice-Consul. With the 1974 revolution in Portugal and the end of dictatorship, the number of Portuguese allowed to work and live in Jersey increased, and it was thought right that there should be a Portuguese-speaking Vice-Consul. Three such were appointed between 1975 and 1996. In 1996 it was considered appropriate for Portugal to have a stronger representation here and in the following year I was appointed Honorary Consul.

So it is that Portugal is the place of my birth and Jersey for 40 years has been my home; and it has been only right for me to give some of my time to a variety of local organisations. For all these years the Island has been such a lovely place for me and my family. And yet it would be wrong for me to disguise some of the difficulties; foreigners have not always had an easy life here, and the 'system' has not always been kind to those from foreign countries coming here to work. There has been an element of xenophobia, and some locals have been too ready to mouth that well-known catchphrase, 'If you don't like it, there's always a mail-boat in the morning'.

Over the last few years as Honorary Consul I have been rather more 'up front' than my vice-consul predecessors and have been unafraid in telling the authorities that the Portuguese community had a rough deal for years, and I have been willing openly to question the logic of the Portuguese having the right to a Jersey vote after two years' residence but nonetheless not being allowed to rent or buy their own house. Such approaches by me have not always been received with broad smiles.

Some progress, however, has been made. In 1998 Jersey received, for the first time ever, a visit from a Portuguese States Minister, and this was followed shortly afterwards by the visit of the President of the Regional Government of Madeira, with him and the Bailiff signing an Agreement of Friendship. This was a significant gesture (it had been conceived some years before, but it sadly took until 1998 before it was finalised).

The world changes, and governmental systems and the way in which they treat human beings must change too. Jersey cannot remain immune from this. The electoral system here requires adaptation. Instead of, as at present, voting for an individual who vaguely promises if successful in the polls to make Jersey a better place to live in, the electorate should be able to vote for a political party which presents a programme charting a way ahead for the Island and mapping out its links with other parts of Europe and the world.

My long knowledge and experience of the Island suggests that, with the

Born in the 1930s...

right people in charge, Jersey has a great future. As to the Portuguese community, some will continue to live in the Island and be integrated into its life and culture. Some will never integrate and will return home. But if Jersey wants a better quality Portuguese labour force coming to the Island, then it must be prepared to respond to the challenges of the time and make the necessary alterations to its system of government.

Colin Powell O.B.E.

Colin Powell, born in Surrey in 1937, was educated at Wallington County Grammar School. After National Service in the Royal Air Force he went to Jesus College, Cambridge, where he gained a first class degree in Economics. After 18 months as an economist with the British Iron and Steel Federation he joined the Northern Ireland Civil Service as an economic adviser. He came to Jersey in 1969 on his appointment as Economic Adviser to the States. In 1992 this post was adapted to that of Chief Adviser to the States. He retired from this position in 1998, staying on for a further year as acting Chief Executive to the Policy and Resources Committee. In November 1999 he became Chairman of Jersey Financial Services Commission. He was a member of the Review Panel on the Machinery of Government in Jersey (the Clothier Commission), set up in March 1999.

I had a very happy suburban childhood on the borders of south London and Surrey, supported by parents who sacrificed a great deal for the benefit of my education. I attended the state primary school and the local grammar school, where I was something of an academic but played my sport and became head of my house. National Service, nearly at its end, in the RAF followed – not a very relevant stage of my life, doing clerical work. It nonetheless provided an important gap between school and university and gave those of us at Cambridge who had done our National Service an added maturity which, I

Born in the 1930s...

believe, benefited us greatly in adapting to and getting the best out of university life.

There can be little more pleasant and rewarding than three years at Cambridge. I worked hard, played football for my college, enjoyed myself and gained a first. After university I worked as an economist in London for 18 months before joining the Northern Ireland Civil Service.

These were relatively good years for the Province: much new investment and new factories, with unemployment reducing. There was no hint at the time of the 'troubles' to come from 1969 on; the discord between the two communities was considered to be a generation issue – those involved in the 'troubles' of the 1920s were considered to be of an age to have little impact, and the younger generation had grown up through the years without conflict. This was a positive period for Northern Ireland when I played some, albeit small, part in promoting the economy and advising on business development. With no anticipation of the disturbances ahead, I felt in 1968 that it was the right point in my career to test the market, and this led to my applying - successfully - for the position of Economic Adviser in Jersey.

I had never visited the Island before, seeing it for the first time when my wife and I came over for the second round of job interviews. My experience in Northern Ireland had some parallels with the Jersey position: over there I had had to be a 'Jack of all trades', a non-specialist covering all aspects of the economy, and this suited the requirements of this new post. Also I was leaving one relatively small community for another which, though much smaller still, was not so different. The Jersey job was a new one, although an economist, Dr Hugh Thurston, had previously advised the States on the issues relating to the European Common Market on a contract basis, and indeed it was he who had drawn attention to the lack of information and statistics which had hindered his assessment of what was making the Island's economy tick. My permanent position was to remedy this, and my first major task was to write an economic survey of Jersey (which was published in 1971).

Our first impressions of the Island were coloured by problems of housing. Property, said to be selling for £8000 when I came for interview, had jumped to £14000 by the time I arrived to take up my job. We could not afford to buy and were found a small rented flat. Coming off the boat on New Year's Day 1969 and driving to the apartment in Wellington Road, I unlocked and opened the door to find virtually the whole floor area occupied by the contents of the container which had been shipped from Northern Ireland with all our household possessions. This was not an auspicious start for our family which included a very young child and a pregnant wife. My political master, Senator Cyril Le Marquand, came to our aid and, a few months later, we moved to more suitable rented accommodation in Beaumont. It was not, however, until 1972 that we were able to purchase our own home.

Socially we found the Island a very friendly community and quickly made friends (and enjoyed a first February that was considerably warmer than was the following May). My job too was full of satisfaction, and all was set fair once the housing hurdle had been surmounted.

When I look back over my three decades in Jersey, one of the most – if not the most – striking aspects of the early 1970s was the small body of politicians of considerable ability who essentially led Jersey. I am thinking of Cyril Le Marquand, his cousin John, Ralph Vibert, Clarence Farley, Wilfred Krichefski, Reg Jeune and perhaps one or two others. They were a solid and capable group, and the Deputies and the Constables from the rural parishes had no problem in respecting and accepting their leadership.

In that period there was no lack of important issues to be wrestled with. In international matters there was the Island's relationship with the European Community, and the Kilbrandon Royal Commission on the Constitution was throwing up significant questions concerning the relationship with the United Kingdom. The main issue domestically was population and immigration (nothing changes!) and at the end of 1970 the States approved new Housing Regulations and in early 1974 the Regulation of Undertakings and Development Law came into effect.

Ongoing from the 1960s tremendous progress was made in health and education provision; and big steps were being taken to improve the Island's physical infrastructure. At the time the States were hardly flush with funds, nor at the end of the '60s had the finance industry yet made a real impact (in 1969 tourism accounted for over 50% of the Island's national income, with banking and agriculture each around 10%). It was, however, a period when decisions were made which helped foster the growing finance industry.

My economic survey of 1971 pointed in the direction of fostering the finance industry as a means of improving the Island's wealth, while recognising that tourism as the number one industry deserved continuing support. Agriculture, struggling against the background of the Common Market and increased competition in the UK, was identified as in need of protection.

The late 1970s and the 1980s were good years for Jersey in terms of revenue growth and, as a result, of enhancing the quality of the Island's public services and private living standards. There are doubtless some who would have preferred less economic growth, fewer new buildings and people and less pressure on the natural environment. They might regard this period not as the good years but the time when Jersey sold its soul to the god of money. I would argue, however, that overall the Island gained from this increasing affluence – of benefit both to the public sector and to individual residents. I remember that, when I came to the Island, there were politicians who would recall the pre-war times when children in bare feet ran down Hill Street, picking up coal dropped from the back of wagons as they went past.

Over the years I have had much satisfaction with this major part of my working life spent in Jersey. There is surely no better place, attractive and safe, for bringing up children, and no better place to come back to. There will always be room for improvement, but I agree with the view expressed to me by one of our eminent residents that, while Jersey may have its shortcomings, the rest of the world has many more. Along with the quality of Island life, I had a job which never bored me; every day brought new challenges and presented new issues and, as an adviser, there was reward when one's advice was listened to. I have always accepted that there may be a long gestation period between presenting ideas and their eventual fruition, and I realised that one had to adapt to a small community, not pushing too hard or too fast, and making politicians feel that the adviser's ideas were actually their own. I had a good harmonious relationship with my political masters and was never concerned when they took credit for the ideas that worked and passed the responsibility to the adviser for any that were not so successful. Looking back I do not believe that any big mistakes were made; Jersey flourished and the majority of Islanders seemed happy with the outcome.

After I retired as Chief Adviser to the States I was appointed a member of Sir Cecil Clothier's team reviewing Jersey's machinery of government. There had already through the '80s and '90s been attempts at reform: a working group proposed a reduction in the number of States committees in the early 1980s and the Peat Marwick report in 1987 proposed the formation of the Policy and Resources Committee. A motivator for the latter was increasing awareness that no one committee had an overview of States policies in any sort of co-ordinated strategic sense. There remained a need for an effective mechanism for strict public expenditure control and for committees to be required to follow strategies adopted by the States on the recommendation of Policy and Resources. My own retirement and discussion about the best way to replace me was another factor in a gradual and growing belief that a review of both the political and administrative structures was needed. Hence

Born in the 1930s...

Clothier.

On the Clothier Panel we had some very impressive wise men from outside: Sir Cecil Clothier had chaired an earlier review of the Island's police service; Professor Michael Clarke was an expert on public service issues; Sir Maurice Shock from Oxford was a highly respected academic; and Sir Keith Bloomfield was a former head of the Northern Ireland Civil Service. The States approved the members of the Panel, including its five Jersey members. It all turned out to be an intellectually stimulating exercise, and there was a strong consensus from the vast majority of those we interviewed that change was required along the lines which we eventually recommended. My initial fear that we might end up with nine separate minority reports was quickly dispelled, and our eventual unanimity was not only unusual for bodies of this kind but, in my view, gave the Panel's recommendations added force.

Since we reported in December 2000 there have unsurprisingly been some ups and downs in the implementation of the recommendations. In part this is a reflection of another difference from 1969 when I came to Jersey: pressure groups are now much more part of the stuff of government, often fostered by the media because of their potential for generating good stories.

We on the Clothier Panel recognised that one of the most sensitive issues would be the position of the Constables, with our recommendation that they should have to choose to stand for the States and not be able to claim their seats *ex officio*. We attempted to produce a report which was as inter-connected as possible, making the cherry-picking of it less easy. I believe that we put a coherent blueprint on the table. Inevitably there has been some cherry-picking, but committee restructuring, ministerial government and the machinery for scrutiny are being adopted. The real core of Clothier is being achieved and much credit for this must go to Senator Pierre Horsfall.

I have now been intimately involved in the Island's affairs for well over 30 years and I am sure that there is as much a positive role for Jersey in the future as in the past. There will always be opportunities for the Island as a niche market player. It has so many advantages: a highly attractive natural and fiscal environment, business acumen in abundance and a labour force with good levels of skill and experience. Of course Jersey will be different 30 years from now, as it was 30 years ago. The Island's strength for centuries has been its ability to change and adapt to altered economic circumstances. I have often likened Jersey to a man sitting on a river bank, having no control over the flow but always able to dip into that river and pick out what is good that is going by.

Born in the 1930s...

This is why I am pro-Clothier, why I am for ministerial government which I believe will be better able to create an environment that can encourage business initiative and entrepreneurship in a small island that will continue to be buffeted by the winds of change. We must avoid being pessimistic about the fact that tourism has reduced in size or that some firms in the finance industry may contract their work force. Instead we should work on creating the environment which allows new business to flourish and which enables new opportunities to be seized. Government structure is important; having the right policies in place is important; recognising the value of immigrants – a feature of the Island from the Huguenots to the present day – who bring in new skills and business flair is important. Looking to the future there is no reason why Jersey in 50 years' time should be any less successful than Jersey today and in the past. The so-called external 'threats' should not be over-dramatised. There will also be opportunities which present themselves. In my view the danger is more one of failure to grasp the opportunities on offer than a lack of them.

I consider myself fortunate in having been able to work, play and live in the Island since 1969. I find it difficult to understand why people criticise the Island, and I sometimes fantasise about a rolling programme whereby Islanders would be transported elsewhere for a period of six months or so. They might as a result conclude that Jersey was not such a bad place after all. For my part I can think of nowhere better.

Anne Herrod

Anne Herrod was born in 1938, the daughter of Griff Speer, for many years in the colonial service and a President of the Société Jersiaise and editor of its Bulletin, and Marguerite Speer, sister of former Bailiff Sir Robert Le Masurier. In 1946 she started at Jersey College for Girls and went in 1951 to Sydenham High School when, with her parents, she moved to England. She then read Latin at Reading University and spent two years as a secretary at The Times newspaper. Having then trained as a child care officer at Exeter University she took up a post as such in the London borough of Tower Hamlets. In 1968 she transferred to Worcestershire and from 1971 was principal social worker (children) in Dudley. Married in 1980 she moved to Nottinghamshire and undertook voluntary work. She was widowed in 1986 and subsequently moved back to Jersey as one of two senior child care officers. Since her retirement in 1998 she has been Chair of the management committees of both Citizens' Advice Bureau and Relate.

For the first 13 years of my life I lived at Les Sillettes, a house at the top of Mont Cochon which had been built in 1926 by my grandfather, W.S. Le Masurier, lawyer and for a number of years a St Helier Deputy. Clarkson House, Jersey's hospice, now occupies the site. I had a somewhat unusual childhood. My father was in Nigeria as a colonial civil servant and my mother used to accompany him there. Assuming that, in the event of hostilities, Jersey would be as safe as in the 1914-18 war, in 1939 they left me and my two brothers, both older than myself, with our grandparents and returned to Nigeria. We next saw them five years later.

It must have been a heavy burden for our grandparents with the three of us to cope with during the Occupation and its special strains and stresses. Grandfather was not the easiest of men and had the responsibilities of being a member of the Bailiff's Superior Council. But there were compensatory factors: a nanny to look after us, a farm next door providing milk and a large garden producing fruit and vegetables. I have some memories of that time: sitting in front of the fire in Grandfather's study with him reading to us such

Born in the 1930s...

books as Little Lord Fauntleroy and testing us at the start of each session on the previous evening's narrative. Then there was the filling of milk churns down at the West Park slipway and Grandmother boiling down the water for the procurement of a grey sludgy salt, and there was a contraption with potatoes going in one end and potato flour coming out at the other.

I have a faint recollection of our nanny on occasions meeting up with a German officer at the top of West Mount, and my eldest brother remembers the nannies and a bus out to St Brelade and their encounters with German soldiers on the beach. A certain amount of perhaps understandable fraternisation. My brother Peter used to walk round the Island making a study of the whole range of German vehicles and on one occasion failed to return at curfew with everyone getting frantic as to his whereabouts.

After this difficult time, when my grandmother had undoubtedly stinted herself for us children, came the Liberation. I myself was not in the Royal Square on that day but remember a short time later seeing the view across St Aubin's Bay with lines of German soldiers being marshalled out to the landing-crafts. A month later Mother came back; neither of us was particularly impressed by the other and our relationship perhaps never quite recovered. In August, and granted special leave, Father returned too. I remember being at an upstairs window with one of my brothers as a car drew up and him shrieking out, 'It must be Daddy.' For me understandably it could have been anyone!

We remained living as a family at Les Sillettes and I began going to school first at a dame school and then some months later at JCG. Jersey was an ideal place for one's childhood. In those days we had a remarkable degree of freedom: no one worried so long as you were home at a previously specified time; there was the beach and the countryside always accessible on our bikes; and the pool at Havre des Pas was a special summer favourite of mine. We would do an annual expedition across the Island to Egypt to pick wild snowdrops, and it was always an adventure to go up to Snow Hill, take the front seats of a double-decker bus, experience its being manoeuvred on the old engine turntable and do the trip out to Gorey and back again.

In 1951 all this came to an end when Father, now retired from the colonial service, secured a post at London University Institute of Education and we left Jersey for Dulwich and then Wimbledon. Not only did I shine less brightly at my new, somewhat more competitive school, Sydenham High, but also a complicating factor was my parents' attachment to the Oxford Group, Frank Buchman's Moral Rearmament. They never managed to persuade us children

Born in the 1930s...

to adopt totally the four absolutes expounded by MRA - honesty, purity, love and unselfishness. It all led to a degree of family tension, and I remember the time when the great Dr Buchman himself came and visited our house and I refused to co-operate in the way desired by my mother and father.

In one's teenage years MRA's prohibition on drink, smoking and make-up hardly eased matters, and I would go out, put on my make-up on the station platform and try and remember to remove it before I returned home. The fact was this: having been part of a large extended family in Jersey, I was now with Mother and Father (my brothers had left school by now) and their Moral Rearmament in a London suburb and at a high pressure school. It was not the best prescription for one's self-confidence.

Both my parents were Oxford graduates and I was their last hope to follow them there. I disappointed them and instead went to Reading where I studied Latin with subsidiary Greek. After happy university years I obtained a secretary's job on *The Times*, in those days historically housed in Printing House Square. The work was not particularly demanding; we had a lot of time to hone up our *Times* crossword skills, and the internal telephone system would hum with calls enquiring what a colleague on another floor had got for six down or seven across – and boredom and a realisation that I needed to do something with my life were my reasons for applying to train at Exeter University as a child care officer.

After qualifying I went to work in Tower Hamlets, a fascinating and exhausting period of my life with large families always seeming to be on the fifth floor of blocks of flats without lifts and with the experience of driving many miles and working 16-hour days to find foster accommodation for families with five, six or seven children. Two years later Worcestershire provided a less pressured routine and in due course I became a principal social worker and established Dudley's adoption service and its child protection register. On my marriage in 1980 I moved to Nottinghamshire and, after my husband's sudden death six years later, decided to come back to Jersey. I applied for a vacant post as one of the Island's two senior child care officers and, with my housing qualifications and professional experience, was appointed.

I was surprised by what I found. One of my first visits was to a family living in Clarence Court, the block of flats – now demolished – which stood in the quarry where the Jersey Archive's new building now is. This block was as insalubrious as many of those which I had known in the east end of London. I was put in mind of my experience in the 'picture postcard' village of Broadway where, behind the lovely Cotswold cottages, was the slummiest of council estates. In the late '80s Jersey was not unlike that: here were these sordid flats only hundreds of yards from the slick finance offices, and here were conditions of which the more affluent Islanders were unaware or about which they did not wish to know.

In my early days back in Jersey I also had to improve my knowledge of parish welfare, a system that possibly still functions satisfactorily in the country parishes but may not be the best arrangement for the urban areas of the Island. People, especially the elderly, are reluctant to seek parish help. Then there is no unemployment benefit; and eligibility for parish welfare requires five years' residence. Also there are associated problems: seasonal workers coming to Jersey, perhaps a girl becoming pregnant and wishing to remain in the Island but with no help for accommodation if lacking 'quallies' and unable to afford high rents or secure financial support for her child. I was torn between realising that these people should have informed themselves of the Jersey situation before getting into these difficulties and yet despairing at the lack of help available to them.

But I do emphasise some of the good things: for example the enormous amount of voluntary aid provided for families by the Variety Club and other charitable organisations; and the strength of the children's service which still retained some of the good practice which, through economic cuts, had diminished in the UK.

The biggest change during the 1990s in my field of social work was the transfer of responsibility for the children's service from Education to Health and Social Services. I had and have my reservations about this development, with the responsibility for children now becoming only a small part of a larger organisation with its own priorities tending, perhaps inevitably, to be health rather than social work – with less appreciation of the latter than the former. The Education Department had understood children and I sensed somewhat more of a gap opening up between us officers and the new committee to which we were now answerable.

The fact is that Jersey is very much a two-tier society: we have the finance industry with well-paid employees who can afford housing and have their boats and other leisure activities, and then there are the workers in the construction industry and the hotels without qualifications and who struggle to meet the cost of expensive lodging-house accommodation. This situation throws up a host of related social problems: single people in small units seeking the solace of the pub and alcohol; and children and parents sleeping in one room and lacking the facilities which family life requires.

Born in the 1930s...

The biggest problem is undoubtedly housing. The standards of the Housing Department are high and much has been done in recent years. But there is the issue of first-time buyer housing which then gets sold on the open market and as a consequence creates the demand for yet more housing in that category. Our contributory social security benefits are generous but, as I have mentioned previously, the lack of unemployment benefit and the parish welfare system are, in my view, matters of concern. It is all rather piecemeal and the plethora of States committees has stood in the way of possible reform. The whole welfare system needs more co-ordination, and this in spite of progress in recent years.

Jersey remains a wonderful and special place: its history, its physical beauty, its beaches and countryside, the growing availability of culture and entertainment. But if only the difference between the 'haves' and the 'have nots' could be reduced. Perhaps we need more emphasis on people rather than on buildings. The politicians prefer to invest in the latter rather than the former. Think of the fine new schools and the results for us all to see of the booming construction industry. Jersey is better at the glossier outward show and less good at turning its gaze onto the unglamorous and less visible elements of our Island society.

Born in the 1930s...

Mick Kavanagh

Mick Kavanagh was born in Dublin in 1938 and educated by the Christian Brothers at the City's Artane School. At the age of 17 he came to work in London, first with Brady Brothers in public houses and then with Quality Inns as a chef. He first came to Jersey in 1956 on a holiday financed by his employers. He returned to and settled in the Island a year later, working in bars and in the building trade before being employed by the States for 25 years. Throughout this time he was an active member of the Transport and General Workers' Union and became its Regional Industrial Organiser in 1988. He was elected a Centenier for the parish of St Lawrence in 2002 and retired in April the following year from his trade union position.

I was born in Dublin in 1938. My parents separated when I was very young, and my mother had a hard struggle to make ends meet. As a result I was put into a convent for my first schooling and was tutored by the Sisters of Mercy, an order of nuns renowned for its teaching. Later I went to a Christian Brothers school, a very strict and disciplined regime but known for the magnificent instruction given by the Brothers to their charges.

At school one had the opportunity to learn a trade, and I trained in the kitchens under a well-known Dublin chef. When I left school, however, I chose farming, and a cruel time lay ahead for me, leaving friends and family and living as a stranger on a farm in Tipperary. After some months there I spotted an advertisement in the local paper for Irish boys and girls to work in the UK, and this is how I came at the age of 17 to England, working in pubs in Kilburn and also at The Propeller, a huge establishment next to Croydon Airport and on the road to Brighton, where we served thousands of pints of Guinness to as many customers off the coaches which used the route.

Looking for new opportunities I joined Quality Inns, a firm that ran chic restaurants in London's west end, and I undertook a course at St Martin-in-the-Fields College to qualify as a chef. The very entrepreneurial owner of this company used to encourage his staff by giving the deserving ones cash bursaries or free holidays. And that is how I first came to Jersey – for a paid fortnight's break at the Hotel de France.

I arrived on the mail-boat, the SS St Patrick, and the memory of that crossing is stamped on my brain. Not being a sailor type I spent the night of that rough passage lying on a coil of rope on the afterdeck. What a relief to reach Guernsey – but then only to find that more was yet to come, with the rounding of Corbière. In such conditions people say that they would prefer to die, and I can appreciate the sentiment.

Of course the Hotel de France was certainly out of my league: a posh place full of the well-heeled and with the waiters and waitresses giving me and my pals little attention. But I acquired a bike and in that fortnight must have cycled down every Jersey lane. The sun shone and the people were friendly. I have fond memories of that happy time in 1956, and I can sympathise with the locals who regret that the old days in the Island are no more.

A year later I returned on another holiday, and this time I stayed. The Island's prosperity was looking up and there were good job opportunities. I worked in the Town pubs, and it was a time noted for the comradeship of the various nationalities among our customers.

At this period rock 'n' roll was all the rage and Jersey's government was rather suspicious of this fresh American import. When we went to the Ritz Hotel for some dancing there would be an intermission and a bit of rock 'n' roll was permitted during it. There was a nucleus of Jersey girls who were adept at the new craze. One night my mates dared me to approach this group and ask for a dance. I walked the length of the floor and asked one of the girls who said, 'No.' Humiliated, I made my way back up the hall and drowned my sorrows in another couple of pints of beer. But I persisted, and that girl is my wife, now married to me for well over 40 years.

I next moved into the building trade. It was a boom time and I joined CW Construction, a firm that had a big contract at Nicholson Park, and I became a painter and decorator. Later I was offered a States job as a painter and decorator but turned it down. The old adage then was that they who worked for the States of Jersey were those with disabilities, lacking skills and unable to hold down a decent job. So I stayed with the building trade until a bad downturn led to layings-off and my unemployment. My wife's parents supported us for a few months until I was offered a job at the Harbours Department. I nervously went for an interview with Captain Malcolm, the Deputy Harbourmaster of the time. He sat there covered in gold braid and smoking his pipe and asked me where I was born. I replied, 'Dublin,' and he said, 'That's good enough.' Thus started my 25-year career in the employ of the States.

These were not the easiest of times for me and my wife and young family. People today say that they cannot live on £30,000 a year. When I started working for the States my first weekly wage was £11.7s.6d, and I was fortunate to have purchased a property. I had to pay Housing £5.7s.6d and we had £6 to live on, with my wife giving priority to bringing up our children and not going out to work.

This was also a time when there were some men of considerable stature in the States. As a young trade unionist I negotiated with the likes of Senators Krichefski and Cyril Le Marquand. They were stalwarts and, unlike today, there was no awareness of things going wrong politically. They were people who possessed long-term vision and were deserving of respect. Cyril Le Marquand in particular was a compassionate man who, while appreciating the traditions of Jersey politics, had the vision to do much in creating the prosperity and good fortune which we have enjoyed since his time.

From my earliest days with the Harbour Department I was active in the Transport and General Workers' Union, becoming involved with other States employees and with the private sector. The Union has always been politically minded and we had a courageous officer in René Liron who showed me how to develop my trade union skills. We were, and still are, the largest trade union in the Island, and the politicians in the States recognised our value, since those who voted in States elections, especially in St Helier, were mainly working class and TGWU members.

For most of my career with the States as my employer I worked as a team leader at the Signal Station. But in the early days I was also a relief lighthouse keeper at Corbière - 48 hours on and 48 hours off and carrying the water over the causeway in big jerrycans. I also did split shifts at Gorey as relief harbourmaster, sometimes beginning work at 3 a.m. depending on the tides. All this time I was steadily moving up to higher levels in the Union, becoming involved in the nursing side and with other professional sectors and receiving my in-house training from René Liron. He decided to retire in 1988. I applied for his job and was the successful candidate out of a total of eight applicants.

My 15 years as Regional Industrial Organiser have given me a special opportunity to reflect on various aspects of our Island's political life. There is one matter that, sadly, has not changed: despite all our Union efforts one situation remains and that is the division between those who can afford to live in Jersey and those who cannot. I have always believed that people, given a realistic wage, will make their contribution to their own housing, to social security and to the tax system. No one exempt from taxation feels comfortable about that fact; there is a pride among Islanders and those who have lived here for many years, and their non-contribution to the Island's taxation is no bonus but a barrier.

What do I consider has gone wrong with Jersey in the last few years? Sadly it has become common practice among our politicians not to do what is in the best interests of the Island but to give priority to their own continuance as States Members. Not unrelated to this is the fact that, since we pay our States Members (and I am in favour of this), there is a greater inclination on their part to be in tune with the people - their potential supporters – when the general good of the Island might require other more pressing considerations. Change in the structure of our government has become necessary, and the recent reforms in its machinery indicate that we have to move with the times or die on the vine. At the same time we should still respect our Jersey history and culture, and I am glad that the Clothier proposals to diminish the role of the Bailiff have not been carried forward.

A related problem that worries me is the failure of our younger generation to come forward into the political arena: so many do not register to vote (and nobody is investigating why this is so) and few under the age of 35 ever attend parish and similar meetings. Our new ministerial system of government will need people with vision, and States membership should not be the sole domain of those with a business background. This island has a worthy history over the centuries of people from humble origins who have made considerable contributions to the community. Those with wealth cannot claim that they are the best. Many of them have recently been members of the States, and its record in these last years has not, to say the least, been particularly impressive (I have little need to discuss in any detail the disastrous Cavern project as just one example).

René Liron's best advice to me was this: 'When you take on this job, Michael, if you can achieve one idea on that agenda (minimum wage, unemployment rights, unfair dismissal), you'll have done a good job.' In other words, one cannot achieve everything. The minimum wage will come, but I am saddened that unfair dismissal remains an Island travesty of justice. The trade union movement will change and adapt, but it will remain a force to challenge the conscience of the politicians and continue to be a necessary pain in the neck to some of them. On the matter of unfair dismissal our government has failed to listen and hence failed to make all our citizens of

Born in the 1930s...

equal worth. The way forward is for the TGWU to work in partnership with the government and other employers so that all are able to enjoy the benefits of this island.

A year prior to my retirement from my union post I was privileged to become a Centenier in St Lawrence. I put aside any temptation to seek election for the States – my union job was in a sense a political apex – and wanted to make a contribution to the parish where, with my son and my grandchildren as residents, we have three generations of Kavanaghs. It has proved a tough assignment at times but one with considerable rewards – not least dealing with people compassionately. It can also have its lighter moments, such as the phone call at 11.45 p.m. from a lady bothered by a dustbin in the road being tossed around by the wind. I got up, dressed, drove in the police car and dealt with the problem, putting the dustbin over the lady's garden wall. In the morning she rang up again and said, 'Thank you, darling. The only problem was that you threw the dustbin into my flower-bed.'

Or there was the case of the call from an irate person living on the borders of St John and St Lawrence who rang me to report some cows loose on the road. I told the caller that from her description this was not my patch and that the cows were in St John. 'But they'll be in St Lawrence by the time you get here,' was the reply.

And where is Jersey heading? One of the Island's quirks is the criticisms we make of the system and, despite its faults, the Island's capacity to survive. We are essentially a prosperous community and I believe its prosperity will continue under a new structure of government. Despite all the gloomy forecasts, new leaders will emerge – there will always be leaders – and the public needs to go out and support them and participate more actively in the voting system. It is easy to sit back, criticise everything from the outside and make no contribution.

I have a great affinity with the people of Jersey. I love this island; it is my home and I shall die here. My sons and grandchildren will continue here. I am hopeful that its future will be in the hands of politicians who will care for the community and who will not tolerate the division of the very rich and the far less economically favoured. These two differing strands demand and deserve a more satisfactory weaving together.

Born in the 1930s...

Philip Le Brocq

Philip Le Brocq was born in 1938 and spent his early years in India. He and his family came home to Jersey in 1947 and he was educated at Victoria College Preparatory School and Victoria College, ending up as Head Boy. He read English at St Catharine's College, Cambridge, and then taught the subject from 1962 for 26 years at Eastbourne College where he was Head of English and Drama and a housemaster. Married to Sally (now Jurat Le Brocq), the daughter of Cecil Harrison, sometime Bailiff, he returned to Jersey in 1988 since when he developed his 'Learning for Leadership' business, became President of the Jersey Festival Choir in 1989, was President of the Société Jersiaise from 1998 to 2001 and elected a Centenier for St Clement in 2002.

$\mathcal{M}$y father was in the Indian police and my mother came home to have her children; hence my birth in Petersfield and my subsequent years in West Bengal with memories of mango trees, flying foxes and an American aircraft, a Lightning, crashing into the river nearby. While Father stayed on for a time after Independence, we had already returned, in due course occupying Highfield, the family home in St Saviour. Here as children we had space to explore the grounds of a rambling house with attics which yielded up such treasures as great-aunt Nellie's photographic and therapeutic equipment (she was a deaf mute) and Dr Le Brocq's wooden jar-holders which once contained his pharmaceutical supplies.

There was a marvellously chaotic workshop where Father, now back home, would teach us practical skills such as how to grind a chisel. He incidentally was a keen boxer and used to take on me and my brother in the front hall before we started to beat him. He was also a great runner and I, trying to emulate him, would go on long jogs at 6 a.m. in the morning and sleep through the first three lessons at school. Father became the first Chief of Jersey's States police and consequently had the delicate task of marrying the new paid force with the honorary police system (perhaps rather an uneasy nuptial). Mother was a splendidly active person who liked entertaining (the house was always full of friends) and was a founder of the St Saviour's Women's Institute

Born in the 1930s...

and of the St Saviour's Sunday School. She was a great organiser and thought nothing of sending me, her 13-year old son, to a Government House fancy dress party dressed as a charlady – which on my arrival confused the butler.

Two aspects of my school life dominated: sport and drama. There were the soccer, squash, cricket and athletics, and there was Ronald Youngs, who had a considerable influence on me and generations of other College boys. He had an interesting background: the son of a London metalworker, he had gained a scholarship to Haberdashers' Aske's School. His smooth accent was assumed; he was in truth a cockney. There was possibly something of a Svengali about him (and a touch of that in his appearance), and being one of his boys invited suspicion of some sort of sexual link – largely untrue but perhaps not entirely.

The most stimulating and inspiring side of Ronald was his love of Shakespeare and, while at school and under his direction, I played Juliet, Benedick, Hamlet, Macbeth and Othello. I would learn my Hamlet lines as I cycled to school and, while no doubt the acting would have been somewhat wooden, there was the occasion when the *Times Educational Supplement* came over and reviewed a performance stating that 'sometimes perhaps a 16-year old can capture the excitement of the part better than a great professional actor'.

Ronald also presided over the Gramophone Club which, in those uncomplicated distant days, we considered the high social point of our week: Saturday nights; boys and girls at different homes; the host selecting the records and introducing them; meeting and talking late into the evening. I have a vivid memory: standing with Sally at 11 p.m. outside her front door considering whether I should become a Catholic priest; her father appearing in his pyjamas; 'What do you think you're doing. How dare you keep my daughter out at this time of night'; Sally departing upstairs in floods of tears. Ah youth!

And besides the Shakespeare and the Gramophone Club there was another aspect of Ronald: his brilliant 20-minute presentations, done off the cuff in our current affairs lessons (he was an avid *Times* reader and with left-wing views and a right-wing lifestyle). He it was who saved me: after my two weeks in the sixth form on the science side, he came to my rescue and my A-levels were to be in English and History.

Another formative experience of my youth was Seymour Tower. A group of us which included Richard Falle, Mike Clapham, John de Veulle and Bernard and John Morris would go out and stay there for several days each summer on the big tides (Anthony Le Poidevin would come out for the day in his boat but not chance an overnight visit). We would build dams, go low-water and draw-net fishing and eat fish (so fresh that I have never since been able to face plaice prepared in a restaurant), supplementing this with pounds of maturing Gorgonzola, cheap white wine and delicious moist 'cabbage' loaves which we took with us. We would read Balzac and engage in other intellectual pursuits, and on Sundays Sally and other girlfriends would come out and provide tea for us appallingly smelly young men.

Perhaps my first full consciousness of Jersey and its place in the wider world came in 1959. My father as Chief of Police had arrested a man, Huchet, who was subsequently charged with murder for shooting someone for the sum of £30 and burying his body. He was found guilty and sentenced to death. Sally's father at this time was Deputy Bailiff. Both our fathers were thus intimately involved in the matter. Richard Falle and I decided to organise a petition against Huchet being hanged. I first went to see my father who said, 'If I were you I wouldn't do it. But you must be your own man.' We wanted to use the Royal Square but the Bailiff considered the venue inappropriate. Instead we set up our stall at the Pinel Monument outside the public lavatories in Broad Street, collected 140 signatures and sent the petition off to the Home Secretary who responded in due course telling us that the law would take its course. A portable gallows and two hangmen were brought over from England, and Huchet was executed in the Newgate Street prison.

University presented me with my first real reverse. Having gained a King Charles scholarship to Exeter College, Oxford, I went on to fail my Latin prelims. and had to leave at the end of my third term. Then followed a year of growing up in Italy and I was accepted by the Yeats-besotted Tom Henn at St Catharine's, Cambridge. The three years there went well: college rugby, President of the junior common room and of the literary society, even acting with Ian McKellen, and in the end gaining a good degree.

I was then offered a teaching job at Eastbourne College (and forewent the diploma in education place which I had been intending to take up). As a consequence of this appointment I received a letter from Ronald: 'How dare you go to one of those privileged public schools. You should be setting out to save the world' and so on. (There then followed a period of five or ten years of growing away from him, but by the time in the mid-'70s when I was Housemaster of School House he was coming over regularly to stay with us and continuing his lecturing and setting the rebels going.)

Sally and I were married in 1963 (at Aquila Road Methodist church by

Betty Brooke's husband, later to become Jurat 'Berry' Brooke) and our years at Eastbourne were a glorious time apart from the terrible and sudden death of John, our 16-year old elder son, on 27th November 1980. By this time I was in School House and Senior Housemaster; we were a happy busy family with our children all thriving; I was producing plays and musicals and presiding over an English department which was popular and bursting at the seams. Out of the blue came this devastating blow. The school gave us huge support in our grief, and Sally and I were able to weep about it and talk about it. We were both of like mind; Sally had her experience of working for Victim Support and my own subject was one intimately related to tragedy, death and poetry. I put a note on the staff board telling colleagues of our shock but inviting them to come and see us. (Those who say 'no flowers, no letters' are destroying their ability to grieve.) We asked John's teachers to write their end of term reports on him, and his schoolfriends wrote down their memories of him. I have these records, a wonderful re-creation of a boy of whom we only knew a part. But we were ever grateful for 16 years of his life: scholar, 'Stag' at rugger, shot-putter, actor and singer – a lovely red-headed all-rounder.

Some years later, with myself aged 50, we came back to Jersey, a change of direction after our long and intense time at Eastbourne. My first feeling after returning was that of an outsider. There was a sense of emptiness after our years of involved and active school life. Our diaries, however, quickly began to fill: Sally took over Victim Support and I became a volunteer; I set up my leadership courses which frequently took me back to English schools and into contact with old acquaintances; and there was soon involvement with a number of committees and organisations including the National Trust, the Société Jersiaise, the Arts Trust, the Samarès Players, the Sculpture Trust, the Festival Choir and acting as training officer for the Jersey branch of the Institute of Directors.

As to my impressions of the Island in the late '80s, I recognised a number of circles, each of them rather too self-contained and cut off from the others. My circle tended to be the arts one and I was uninvolved in some of the others such as the yachting, rugby or political. I concentrated on those areas of Jersey life where I could make some impact and, incidentally, resisted suggestions that I should stand for the States.

Since our return the Société has perhaps been the most challenging of my commitments. I had nine years on its executive committee before becoming President and had time to be frustrated by the nature of its complexities, its reluctance to frame any sort of vision for the future and the inability of its 17 autonomous sections to work together. I took over in 1998, forged closer links with the Jersey Heritage Trust (particularly with Mike Day, its Director) and brought to my responsibilities what skills I possess in the fields of public relations and fund-raising. I used the local press and radio to celebrate our progress and achievements, not the least of these being the near doubling of our membership to 4,500. We also acquired much-needed new facilities by the construction of an additional floor on our premises, and we moved significantly towards being more professional in our management structures. And there were also the Millennium Standing Stones, which will outlast us and countless future generations, a project involving the 12 parishes and their Connétables, plus Ronez Quarries, the Island's Territorial Army unit and Romerils.

More recently I have moved into the honorary police system by being elected a St Clement Centenier. With my father having been the first Chief of the States police and with my own experience in Victim Support, it seemed natural and fitting for me to involve myself in an organisation that has the capacity to carry out a demanding and valuable community job. There are, for example, children from deprived backgrounds who can be dealt with sensitively at parish hearings without their incurring a police record. In fact there is a whole area of social problems where the honorary police have the potential to make a positive difference, and it is this that particularly attracts me.

Currently I see two sides to Jersey. I am ever impressed as I drive or cycle round the Island by its resilience. Whatever happens to it, it bounces back; if you double or halve its population it will find its proper level and survive. The view out to sea from Sorel Point or Gros Nez; the beauty of St Peter's Valley; the Jersey lanes where, as in Venice, you can surprise yourself by getting lost in them; all this is enormously regenerative. Think too of the huge environmental strides of the last few years: the Ramsar-recognised south coast site; the late and much lamented Gerard Le Claire, an international figure; Mike Stentiford selected as leading Jerseyman for his portrait to be painted. The beauty of this island gives out so much hope and optimism by its powers of revival.

But then there are our political masters and the lack of direction, be it in our tourism or agriculture or construction industries. This sometimes fills me with frustration and despair: the heavy hand of bureaucracy, the plethora of civil servants, this stifling of initiative and resourcefulness. Take the recent Sustainability Plan, brilliantly drawn up with businessmen and politicians working together but with its recommendations already a dead letter. Take the similarly recent Cultural Strategy, with respected professionals and over 90 organisations involved, and yet the whole matter has been speedily shelved and forgotten. All this saddens me.

My final thought, however, is this: if we can still find a piece of untouched Jersey within a ten-minute drive, if there remain Islanders like myself who still want to return home after a career spent elsewhere, if there are people willing to give up considerable time for the honorary police or service to the States or charitable work, then we have nothing to fear. There will be problems and set-backs but also progress, haltingly made and bearing something of the Heath Robinson touch. Solutions will be found, moaned about by 10%, applauded by 10% and accepted without great thought by 80%. My optimism remains intact.

Chapter Four

Born in the 1940s

Roy Le Hérissier
Michael Talibard
Michael Halsey
Wade Lewis
Peter Le Rossignol
Lee Durrell

Roy Le Hérissier

Roy Le Hérissier was born in Jersey in 1943. He was educated at St Saviour Primary School and at Hautlieu and went on to the University of Leeds where he took a degree in Politics. He then did a PhD in the government of Jersey 1771-1972 at the University of Kent at Canterbury. From 1968 to 1971 he was an Assistant Governor in the UK prison service. He then spent nearly three years at the University of Ulster as a lecturer in Social Policy before emigrating to Canada and working in various positions in the Ontario Ministry of Correctional Services. In the later 1970s he spent two years teaching at the University of Malawi and then returned to his work in Toronto. From 1986 to 1990 he was Principal Lecturer in Public Administration in the City University of Hong Kong and then returned to Jersey to become Head of Business and Management at Highlands College. He continued teaching on a part-time basis after his retirement in 1996 and was elected to the States as a St Saviour Deputy in 1999.

*M*y mother's grandparents were Breton and my father was from farming stock in Trinity but spent most of his life as a baker. The parental home had been out at Les Platons until it was requisitioned by the Germans. After that we lived in the more urbanised part of Maufant but in what was still an old Jersey environment. I do not, for example, recall our being close friends with any English people.

I passed the 11-plus exam and spent happy later schooldays at Hautlieu. Here I cut my teeth as a young political activist, writing a letter to the *Jersey Evening Post* criticising the Island government and having it published under the pseudonym, 'A Humble Schoolboy'. In fact my headmaster, who was later to help me greatly with my university applications, found out that I was the anonymous correspondent and threatened me with expulsion if this happened again. I was never very good at sport but enjoyed the Sixth Form Society which forged links with Victoria College and the Girls' College, and I founded the *Hautlieu Herald* (a school newspaper recently revived for Hautlieu's 50th anniversary). As to my political activity as a sixth former this was low-key, but I found the experience of joining and participating in the Jersey Debating Society a liberating experience. We used to meet at the Pomme d'Or and Roy Mourant, who sadly died recently, and Bob Le Sueur, who was on the Hautlieu staff, were stalwarts. It was a good training ground for the testing out of arguments and the early flapping of political wings.

Home too was naturally influential in my development. Mine was a classic Jersey family, with Father almost paranoid about being stigmatised – that fear of putting one's head above the parapet. There was this residual respect for authority, a deference which allowed an element of dissent, but only if it went so far and no further. (This trait is manifested today in the likes of Senator Stuart Syvret who acts as a surrogate and is prepared to articulate what many of the population feel but fear to express.) And my parents had this notion, which I at least partially absorbed, that there was an Island 'establishment' which was sometimes more malevolent than benevolent. Father especially saw plots and conspiracies everywhere: the freemasons, the honorary police (seen then as a means of political advancement), even membership of the Methodist church. I picked all this up, intuitively, viscerally, and as a teenager began to resent what in Jersey I saw as a sometimes slavish devotion to tradition. There was, for example, the educational system, with Victoria College at the top and the assumption that senior positions within the Island establishment would inevitably be filled by those who had been educated there. I was glad to get away to university, and in those days this was still a relatively rare progression. It was certainly a novelty within my family, and my parents were sceptical, holding firmly to the Jersey view that one finished school and then found a job. All this contributed, at least in part, to the fact that I spent many subsequent years out of the Island. I was however very grateful, despite their scepticism, for the support my parents gave me, even if I proved wayward in my ambitions.

At Leeds I led a relatively subdued existence, initially somewhat overawed by the 'quality' of English ex-sixth formers, enjoying my course of study and joining the Labour Party (even campaigning in the 1964 election for Denis Healey who was the local MP). I then went on to the brand-new university at Canterbury to work for my doctorate in the development of the government of Jersey 1771-1972, with special reference to the constitutional relationship with Britain. In my studies for this I was initially struck by the paucity of writing on the subject. The constitutional links aspect was particularly difficult to unravel. For example, many assertions about Jersey's degree of independence and autonomy were made in the 19th century, not all of which

Born in the 1940s...

were upheld by the Privy Council, and the Island authorities would interpret them in the most favourable light and rely on Britain's generosity in usually being prepared to concede the case.

With the completion of the PhD my academic interest and my involvement in the Island's affairs were to be in abeyance for almost two decades as I followed my career elsewhere. My three years in the prison service satisfied my wish to find out what a uniformed organisation was like, and I then moved on to the University of Ulster as a lecturer in Social Policy. Here, as with most of my colleagues on the university staff, I kept out of the local politics at a time when the troubles there were at their peak. Despite the grim problems of the Province I did have the opportunity to appreciate some of Ulster's better attributes: the friendliness of its people, its lack of strong class divisions, its strong sense of community, its commitment to good education, and much else. I met and married my wife at this time and we decided to emigrate.

I had no thought of returning home to Jersey; for me, as a 'rebellious' young adult, it was too limiting a society where people were more likely to be judged as to who they were rather than what they were. I hankered for somewhere with more openness and where free discussion was more in evidence.

Thus we moved to Canada and I became a public servant in Toronto working in various positions such as Development and Probation Management in the Correctional Services Ministry. An innate restlessness was to take us after some years on secondment to the University of Malawi, back to Canada and then on to Hong Kong. This last posting was an interesting one – with the British connection soon to end and with my teaching as Principal Lecturer in Public Administration. Then in 1990 I was offered the post of Head of Business and Management at Highlands College and the family came to Jersey.

What were my thoughts on my return? I did not react in a hostile way to the changed environment and the buildings that had gone up in my absence; Jersey could not have been expected to stand still while the rest of the world moved on. But I was struck by the Island's parochialism: it had adopted a big international industry – finance - without, however, absorbing what the full implications of this were. And I sensed a split in the community, with the immigrants becoming very influential and the traditional Jersey way of life – with agriculture unable to survive as a major economic plank – under enormous stress. Thus there was a general discontent related to both the problems and benefits of the finance industry. I returned just as the good, cosy, comfortable years were coming to an end. Economically the Island had gone for growth and no thought had been given as to how that growth could be controlled. The powers that be were dedicated to the trickle-down theory of economics – masses of money coming in and paying for all our public services. Our policy-makers took no account of the fact that the services would have to meet the demands made by those additional people who were bringing in the money. And the trickle-down effect was blunted because cheap labour had still to be brought in for agriculture and the more menial jobs, with this labour then tending to move into the service industries.

In the late '90s, having taken early retirement but with some continuing teaching commitments, I was back into the swing of local affairs, writing letters to the press and frequently commenting as an independent constitutional 'authority' on the local radio. Forced in these ways to consider the issues, I decided to stand for the States. I failed in the 1999 senatorial elections, coming a respectable sixth and getting better known as I did the rounds of the various parish hustings. My enthusiasm was fired by all this. I then stood as a Deputy and was successful.

After taking my seat in the States I found that my previous reflections on the inadequacies of our political system were totally vindicated. I had already been involved in the planning stages of the Clothier commission, with its mandate to recommend governmental changes, even having been considered as a member of it. While it deliberated and after it reported I feared that the Jersey forces of reaction, supporting its traditional and outdated institutions, might prevail, at the same time underestimating how strong the opposition to its conclusions would turn out to be.

I am, unsurprisingly, a strong advocate of the ministerial system; and the *quid pro quo* of this is a strong scrutinising function within the States. With the right governmental structure must come the right personnel, and the worry is that those who are not ministers but scrutineers will be considered the second division. My hope is that scrutiny will develop into a vital feed-back system: analysing policy will feed in thoughts and ideas which will contribute positively to the formulation of future policy. These are exciting developments and I become more and more convinced that all this will lead to the emergence in Jersey of a party system – a process holding no terrors for me and long overdue. All this should result in a healthier and greater participation by the Island's citizens in democratic activity. As to the Clothier proposals for the removal of the Constables from the States and the termination of the Senators, I favour them but am willing, if uncomfortably, to compromise and, for the time being, go along with the status quo.

Born in the 1940s...

There is no doubt in my mind that Jersey has reached an important crossroads, and a priority is for some of the heat to be taken out of our economy. My most optimistic scenario is that the finance industry will slim down (and not vanish overnight). We shall have to manage finance differently, come to terms with the fact that we are now in a hostile international environment and realise that these problems are not going to disappear. Also it will all become yet more complex if or when Britain adopts the euro. Following such a move would be the need for us to make heavy political decisions about our own involvement with Europe, and for this we are currently unprepared.

I have now been back in the Island for well over a decade. It has been a period when my feelings have been mixed: my feet are perhaps a little less itchy than they were, and my increasing involvement in Jersey's politics both challenges and, it must be admitted, frightens me. I am both an optimist and a sceptic. We live in a very different world. The challenge is how to retain the best of our traditions and yet embrace change.

Michael Talibard

Michael Talibard was born in Yorkshire in 1943 and came with his parents to Jersey in 1945. He was educated at Val Plaisant School, Vauxhall Elementary School, Victoria College Prep. and Victoria College. Between school and university he taught in an English preparatory school and spent a gap year doing Voluntary Service Overseas in Bolivia. He read English at Jesus College, Cambridge, gaining a good honours degree. After a year's teacher training and subsequent posts at Haberdashers' Aske's School, Eastbourne College and Clifton College, he returned to Jersey in 1981 as Head of English at Victoria College. He taught at Haileybury from 1995 to 1999 and then became Head of English at Victoria once again. Subsequently he founded and became Chairman of the Jersey branch of the University of the Third Age.

It always upsets me to be asked whether I am 'Jersey-born' because I then have to confess to my Barnsley origins - and this despite having had three Jersey grandparents. However, my mother was technically English and, fearing deportation, my parents left the Island for the duration of the war, with my father working in a South Yorkshire armaments factory. We returned in 1945, at first to live at Maufant, where my grandfather was the local cobbler. I remember he had the knack of filling his mouth with nails and producing them one at a time, appropriately placed for his hammer. He also had a tobacco patch and the strange habit of urinating in a bucket, from which when full he irrigated the crop.

In about 1948 we moved into town, and my parents had a shop in New Street, with accommodation above, which became home for the rest of my childhood. Most of my early memories are of town: talkative Mrs Rabet in her grocery shop; the bakery on the corner of New Street and Union Street; the queue of potato lorries in the season stretching back to Val Plaisant and creeping slowly towards the Weighbridge. I recall the gungy black Bostik with which, after the shop closed at 9 pm, my parents would sit up, turning hundreds of little gift items into Jersey souvenirs by sticking crests on them. And there was 'Aunty' Florrie nearby who showed a kind interest in me and my sister and took us on the beach in the summer when our parents were busy in the shop. She earned her living by taking in laundry, and I recall the pungent smell of the soap and steam and the densely packed rows of washing hung up to dry. Our little piece of town had the feel of a village, and I sense this is now no more.

From beginning to end of my school days, I find I remember vividly what happened outside the classroom but little of what took place within. Thus, from early days, I recall tramping up to Vallée des Vaux – probably where Safeways now is - with a couple of friends, collecting leeches, little fish and water snails from the stream and carrying them proudly back. Then came Victoria College Prep. where I spent a year catching up on the Latin which I had not learnt at my previous schools; and so to College.

Wisely, I think, my parents had chosen Victoria, not De La Salle, despite the fact that I was Catholic: that was my father's religion; my mother is Church of England. At Victoria College, while the others on Fridays had a hymn practice, we Catholics went off for instruction in the faith from Canon Olney. Hence my early acquaintance with the history and theology of Christianity, a rather better preparation than hymn-singing for sixth form discussions of religious ideas. I have no regrets in my adult journey through agnosticism to

Born in the 1940s...

atheism about this valuable grounding and its stimulus to an interest when I was older in ethics and philosophy.

My friends at Victoria were Stan Le Cornu, with whom I first went low-water fishing and canoeing; and then Peter Ingram, Robin Godfray and Tony Biddle, a 'gang' of us who swam furiously and haunted the pool at Havre des Pas (there I remember my first hamburger – I had never previously heard of these items and thought it strange to spend one's pocket money on food, which could be had for free at home); and then Chris Guille-Marrett and Bunny Hedger, of whom more later.

Another friendship was with Bernard Krichefski, son of Senator Wilfred. He had been at College with me until 13, when he went to board at Clifton. When he came back for the holidays he would invite me to his home in St Brelade. There I first became aware of Jewish customs and their delicious food. His was a lovely family. When Wilfred, with his huge bulk, sat down to watch television, the family's little poodle, who worshipped him, would come and sit on his lap, or rather his belly, thus totally obscuring his master's view of the screen. Wilfred would brush him off, but in a few minutes the dog was back up again.

I loved Victoria College and never wanted to come home at the end of the school day. It was a place that inspired loyalty and devotion. Of course there were some poor teachers but enough good ones to provide a positive education and cultivate friendly relations between themselves and their pupils. It was to one particular member of staff that I owe so much, and I recognise it as a huge blessing that I had the good fortune to come under the considerable influence of Ronald Youngs. Nominally, he taught me English, but it was through him that I became interested in everything else, be it science, philosophy, art or music. In addition he gave us many life skills: he taught me to drive a car, how to behave in a restaurant and order a meal, how to drink without getting drunk. His idea of a school trip was not a minibus full of pupils but a Renault Dauphine with two or three boys, driving to Florence to see Michelangelo's David and the opera. At the end of a typical school day it would always cross my mind to wonder what Ronald was doing: was he busy umpiring, or would he be free to go out to tea and argue? For though we inevitably picked up many of his ideas, he did expect his pupils to argue with him and to support a contrary view.

Another advantage of being in Ronald Youngs's circle was that you formed friendships with those outside your own year group (not to mention girlfriends!). Richard Falle, a couple of years my senior, was such an acquaintance. He was in a sense a counterweight to Ronald: putting it crudely Youngs was cerebral and Falle physical; Youngs introduced us to Plato and Falle to Rabelais – plus weight-lifting, fishing and much else. Richard was also the first person I knew who truly loved Jersey and was fiercely proud of its history and culture and his own Grouville family roots. This was for me a valuable formative experience.

My friendship with Richard Falle and others of Ronald's circle such as Mike Clapham and Philip Le Brocq led to a frightening and memorable episode. A group of us would stay out at Seymour Tower for a time in the summer, sleeping there on bunk beds and fishing with draw-nets in the middle of the night on the low tide. On one occasion it was getting late in the tide and, having had only a moderate catch, we decided on a 'bass pull'. As we made for a suitable spot for this, a thick fog suddenly descended. The visibility was nil; we had no compass; and we wasted much time unsuccessfully trying to get back to the tower. We were by now completely disorientated and quickly the danger of our drowning became a reality. It was Mike Clapham's cool logic that was to save us. We had to move north-west and cross a crucial gully to gain the landward side of the rising tide. To find the main body of the tide, Mike taught us to use the seaweed, which lies down as the water falls, and having found that, we got our bearings, found the gully and crossed it with the water at chest height. We reached Seymour slip grateful to be alive, and knowing that another five minutes could have proved fatal.

Highfield, the St Saviour home of the Le Brocqs, was another haven of my school years. It had a number of attractions: my friendship with Philip, the fact that Ronald lodged there for several years, and later my romance with Joanna. It was a new world for me, going there to lie in the grass revising for O-levels with Chris Guille-Marrett, playing croquet, having tea and cake laid on by Betty Le Brocq, or more likely by Motta, her home help, and as an occasional *quid pro quo*, falling in with Henry Le Brocq's request to mow the lawn. It was thrilling to be made welcome into such a household. I was the town boy whose grandfather repaired shoes and whose parents kept a shop, and here I was, accepted by this rather more grand family out of the British Raj. I was fortunate to be living at the time when class barriers were weakening and when education was becoming more important in determining friendships.

At that period, St Helier, as a centre for young people, seemed to possess a certain style, now vanished. Led probably by Christopher or Bunny, our circle would gather in that first-floor tearoom at the front of de Gruchy's where the waitress would bring your tea or coffee in silver-looking pots on separate little trays. There we would meet the girls – Susan Fry, Suky Egglesfield and of course Jo Le Brocq. We felt rather grand, as we did also when occasionally we would eat at a Chinese restaurant, then an exotic novelty, or at the Lobster Pot at L'Etacq.

At this age, I was not particularly conscious of Jersey politics. I had little curiosity about its governmental system, and had not really noticed that it was not a democracy; but I was proud of our separateness. Among undergraduates at Cambridge, when asked about Jersey, I would say, 'We conquered you in 1066' – a joke, perhaps, but reflecting the pride of independence. Cambridge was not, at least initially, at all a happy time for me: my personal life seemed in ruins and academically I was in the doldrums. Perhaps I had been spoilt by my friendship with Ronald, but our supervisors never seemed to be at all interested in us. In the end I did little work, failed to get the first of which I was capable and came through with a good degree mainly on the strength of what I had learnt at school. By this time my parents had retired from business and gone to live abroad and, without my having an Island base, my visits to Jersey became spasmodic.

Fourteen years passed before I came back to teach at Victoria College. During this time I taught one year at Haberdashers' Aske's at Elstree, and then followed three stimulating years teaching in Philip Le Brocq's dynamic English department at Eastbourne. Clifton College was my next post, for a decade from 1971 and, just as I was contemplating a career change to law, Ronald retired and I could not resist the exciting lure of coming back and taking over from him. I wanted to carry the same torch, but also to do a few things differently: to be less elitist, to ensure good results right through the ability range, without such obvious favourites as Ronald had. Could I match his achievements? Probably not, but after a few years with very strong academic results, and when I had done a good production of *King Lear*, I began to feel worthy of the tradition.

How had Jersey changed during my years away? Physically, there was a lot more building; politically, there seemed to have been no significant change. I was irritated to discover the pseudo-Frenchification of place-names. For me, idiosyncracies of usage, such as having 'Le Poidevin's' (pronounced the French way) on one side of King Street but 'Voisin's' (anglicised) on the other, are part of the Island's character. Then there was the north coast. Previously you had to fight your way through gorse and brambles, but now cliff paths seemed to give easy access to every favoured spot – except perhaps Vicard. Jersey had become a trifle more tame, but I cannot entirely regret the change. Also the Island was becoming ever richer in cultural events, and there soon followed the establishment of the Arts Centre, and a much improved museum service. This has been a wonderful change for the better from those times in the `50s when cultural pursuits had to be sought in London or elsewhere.

It was after my return to the Island that I first really became conscious of Jersey politics, and the catalyst for this was the controversy over the flooding of Queen's Valley. It was Richard Falle who introduced me to the issue (and I believe that the passing of time has justified the stand he took – declining tourist numbers and consequently less demand for water). I now became forcibly aware of the undemocratic nature of Jersey's governmental system. A protest march was arranged, a demonstration by thousands of us walking together through the valley by candlelight, and yet our opinions were totally ignored by the politicians 'elected' by much smaller numbers. When elections came round and the question of Queen's Valley was put to candidates, the answer would come back, 'I'll make up my mind when the matter is debated in the States'. It was another way of their saying, 'You're electing *me*, not my policies. You voters are not permitted to affect decisions of the States`. This I considered profoundly undemocratic. Wherever you stood on the question of the valley - that the water was needed or not, that the place was more or less beautiful with the reservoir - no democrat could be happy. It might have been any other issue: what affected me was this huge swell of public opinion – perhaps the biggest demonstration in our history – and our government ignored it and pushed on with the scheme.

On my second (and final) return to live here, I really feel very fortunate and happy in my work for Victoria College and for the U3A. I have noticed the same physical changes continuing: much of the Island remains so beautiful, yet sadly St Helier is ugly and being allowed to get uglier. Even good new buildings can look out of place. In common with others, I am probably more politically aware than ever before. I believe that the control of population through housing has been wrong, with its consequence of producing second-class citizens. All persons permitted to live and work in the Island should have the same housing rights. The necessary control of population could come through some form of 'smart card' procedure defining residence qualifications. I would like to see a 'soft landing' contraction of the finance industry, to cool an overheated economy which inevitably stimulates population growth, and this would also ease pressure on housing.

Most of all, I would like my beloved island to become a democracy. Not

Born in the 1940s...

only do we need a ministerial system; we also need party politics, to provide some linkage between voters' wishes and subsequent policy. No wonder there is such apathy among our electors: we lack the possibility of that exciting event, a change of government, as when a Margaret Thatcher is ousted or when a Tony Blair sweeps to power. You cannot legislate a party system into being, but it might grow up naturally if the membership of the States were such that the executive remained a clear minority and a credible opposition were to emerge. To any suggested change, I detest the cliché response, 'If you don't like it, there's a boat in the morning'. To love Jersey is to want the best for Jersey, and the best is not the status quo.

Michael Halsey

Michael Halsey was born in London in 1947 and was educated as a boarder at Haileybury. He qualified as a chartered accountant in 1972, joined ED&F Man, commodity brokers, and in due course became their Group Financial Controller and Company Secretary. Later he worked for Brown Shipley and Co, merchant bankers, holding the position of Finance Director. He came to the Island in 1996 as Finance Director of Standard Bank, Jersey. He performs with the Jersey Gilbert and Sullivan Society and is a choir member and bell-ringer at St John's church.

*B*efore coming to Jersey I spent almost my whole life on the borders of north London and Hertfordshire. My father was an Anglican clergyman and my mother held senior nursing posts prior to marriage.

I enjoyed my school years at Haileybury where I sang in the chapel choir, took part in Gilbert and Sullivan productions (we actually toured Sweden in 1963 with *The Mikado*) and played rugger and cricket. After school I first found employment with Shell-Mex but switched to be articled as a chartered accountant, qualifying in 1972. I was then with ED&F Man for 11 years, seeing the firm grow from a 60-person group to one employing 600 worldwide.

I subsequently moved to Brown Shipley and Co, a firm that ran into something of a pickle when the recession of the late '80s started to bite. Cutting a somewhat long story short I left to do some consultancy work and various other bits and pieces before a former colleague, by then with Standard Bank in Jersey, invited me in 1996 to join them as Finance Director.

I had previously been to Jersey on one or two assignments, and its immediate attraction for me was the opportunity to take on as challenging a role as any within the finance industry but without the London commuting which had been my lot for the previous 30 years. For the first two years, with my elder daughter completing her A-levels, the family stayed in England, with me travelling back to them on many weekends. Despite the awkwardness of this arrangement I began to put down roots in the Island. I had always wanted to learn to ring church bells and I got my practice in at St Mark's and St John's, the only two towers in the Island with bells hung for English change-ringing. I also joined the choir at St John's and became involved with the G and S Society. There was also some golf with our ringing captain and friends from the office. This surely is one of the great bonuses of working in Jersey: do what the job requires of you, but still – sometimes at least – get off in the evening for the golf, singing and ringing. This was just not possible when in a high pressure job in London.

One of my early impressions of Jersey concerned the whole question of housing and housing qualifications. Certainly some who come to work in the Island find the inability to buy a house less than a full welcome. Is there just that hint given out by an element in Jersey of, 'This is our island; you're lucky to be here, and don't forget it'? The current situation is something of a nightmare – favourable treatment for some who come to work for the States, for doctors and for some teachers, and disappointments and difficulties for many others. Radical change to a work permit system is surely an urgent need and is fortunately already being aired and considered in governmental circles.

And what of the Island's finance industry in which I work? One of Jersey's attractions, especially for my bank which is South African-owned, is its stability as a place for overseas investors to deposit money. Along with this stability is its efficiency: the financial and legal know-how as well as good technical support (Jersey was at the forefront in bringing in a broadband service). And as with London, Jersey is time zone perfect – in the centre of the worldwide trading day. Nonetheless Jersey must not get too expensive; this is one to watch. Finance then contributes hugely to Jersey's wealth – a major provider of the wherewithal for the States to fund its budget.

As Jersey's two other key industries have declined, so finance has become all the more essential for the Island's well-being. Tourism has suffered from rising costs and the competition of sunnier climes. Also, a further championship-standard golf course is needed if Jersey wishes to attract the higher-spending holidaymakers. Farming too has diminished significantly: with a global economy, if you cannot provide the product required and at the right price, then you are out of the market. The finance industry too does not lack competition: if a back office can be run more cheaply elsewhere, then there it will go. Hopefully sufficient front office management will remain to keep the tax structure straight and the contribution to Jersey's revenue buoyant.

I am an optimist concerning the future of our finance industry, but this does not mean that we can be complacent about challenges. We now operate under a strict regulatory regime, and there is always that fear that we are being more strict than other jurisdictions and hence making ourselves less competitive. It boils down to this: if Switzerland agrees, then everybody else will. Jersey is sensible to speak out for a level playing field: we'll go along with everything that's right in the world, but we will not do it unilaterally.

Related to the future health of Jersey's finance industry are questions about the quality of our governmental system. Are we moving swiftly enough to embrace fully the Clothier proposals for ministerial government? Will there emerge an effective executive able to prioritise, to demand real accountability, to prevent itself from being overruled and sidelined? Will the States produce the determination and the ability to recognise the pitfalls ahead and plot the Island's future? Will there be sufficient people with business experience willing to stand for public office and play a part in the Island's government?

As to my crystal ball, I believe that the finance industry will remain but it will employ fewer people. IT will remain a key to the future; that must be the specialisation – niche markets must be found for doing things with the brain rather than with people. It would be good too if we could get tourism right; perhaps some steam removed from the economy would make Jersey once again a cheaper holiday destination.

And then Jersey needs to address the problem of its links with Europe. It is all very well having the trading advantages of not being in the EU, but what about the fact that some of those holding Jersey passports do not have the same employment rights as the British in France or the other member countries?

Along with my thoughts on the Island and its future remains my pleasure in having come with my family to live in Jersey. What place is more attractive; where is the air fresher or the light brighter? It was a wonderful opportunity that came my way in 1996 and, whatever the challenges which the Island faces in the future, I acknowledge my good fortune.

Wade Lewis

Born in Cheltenham in 1947, Wade Lewis spent his early life in South London and then in Crawley, Sussex. He attended Thomas Bennett School there and later gained a first class honours degree in Zoology and Oceanography at University College, Bangor, in North Wales. He then went to The Queen's College, Oxford, where he obtained a DPhil in Neurophysiology. After a year in the Ministry of Defence he joined the accounting firm, Arthur Andersen, and qualified as a chartered accountant in 1976. A year later he became UK Administration Manager for Duracell UK, rising through positions in Duracell Europe and moving in 1987 to the United States as Senior Vice-President-Finance, Chief Financial Officer of Duracell International Inc. He retired to Jersey in 1997.

I did not have the easiest of childhoods. My father left shortly after I was born and I have never seen him. We were consequently a single parent family, comprising a group of four including my uncle and my grandmother. We lived in rented rooms, first in Clapham and subsequently Brixton. For much of this time my mother worked on buses as a conductress. When I was 10 we moved again, this time to a brand new council house in Crawley New Town in Sussex. This was very exciting for me, being my first exposure to the countryside, with Ashdown Forest literally on our doorstep. I very much enjoyed the time spent during my boyhood, wandering on my own through the quiet, and at that time totally safe, leafy lanes. This contrasted with home

Born in the 1940s...

life where the television provided the sole entertainment for the family and there was little of social or intellectual interest for me.

At the age of 11 I went to the newly opened Thomas Bennett Comprehensive School (later to become the largest school in western Europe). Although I was in the top stream I did not sparkle, and this must have been a source of frustration for the range of talented and inspired teachers who had been drawn to this exciting new concept of a school, comprehensives having only been recently introduced into the UK. Fortunately, with A-levels fast approaching, I decided to apply myself with some determination at long last and obtained A grades in the key subjects.

Before this stage in my life I had already had my first taste of Jersey, and I cannot overstate its profound impact on me. Previously I had never been further afield than Ramsgate for my summer holiday and certainly never overseas. Now at the age of 11 my mother and I travelled by a steam express train to Weymouth – with the added thrill of the train going through the streets of the town to the quay – and then on by mail-boat, through a school of dolphins and via Guernsey, to St Helier. Prior to our departure my grandmother had been full of anxiety as to how my mother and I would cope in this exotic venue with everyone, as she believed, only speaking French.

For me it was a wonderful and memorable week: sunshine all the time; staying at a friendly little bed and breakfast boarding house at Gorey; walking down to the beach on my own before breakfast; exploring the rock pools and bringing the shrimps and crabs back to our lodgings in a bucket to show everyone. Our landlady and our fellow guests showed the appropriate degree of interest in what was obviously extremely important to this rather intense young boy.

I particularly remember the market in St Helier, with Breton workers, in my eyes very foreign and therefore somewhat sinister, with their blue working clothes and hanging around them the pungent smell of their Gauloises. One day we travelled by bus to Portelet Bay, and I recall the long climb up the steps from the beach and the machine at the top which for sixpence dispensed a cardboard cup of the coldest Coca Cola imaginable. This was heaven. But there was also the agony of my sunburnt back and having to sleep on my front for a couple of nights – a small price to pay for being able to enjoy fabulous beaches and a warm sea.

We ended each perfect day by walking around the harbour, with the backdrop of the magnificent floodlit Gorey Castle – a magical sight for a boy from South London council estates. This was for me the most exciting adventure imaginable, and the memories of those marvellous summer days have remained with me throughout my life. They were undoubtedly a factor in our decision many years later to make Jersey our home.

I was to return to the Island twice more on holiday. I came with my mother and grandmother during my university years. This was funded by my working to fabricate and install plastic ventilation systems in the roofs of West Midlands factories. Seven weeks of torment for one week in Jersey! I was able to hire a car, my first experience of an H-plate. As far as I can recall I made only one glaring error: starting to reverse round a blind corner, having missed the turning to Gros Nez. The second of the two visits was again with my mother and just before my marriage in 1975. During our stay we opted for a night of luxury at Longueville Manor. This strained our modest budget with the result that the gilt was well and truly taken off the gingerbread when we had to carry our suitcases down the drive and through the familiar granite arch in order to wait for the bus to take us back into St Helier.

At the age of 17 I had not the vaguest notion of what to choose for higher education and even less for my future career. I was studying Zoology and Botany, amongst others, at A-level. This fact abruptly coalesced in my mind with memories of those endless days in Gorey peering into rock pools. The result was that after school I was off to the Oceanographical Institute in Menai Bridge, North Wales, to study Marine Biology and Oceanography.

Once there I was successful in being offered a place in the University Air Squadron, and this was to prove the catalyst to a significant next step in my life. During our first summer camp at RAF Bicester, I drove the ten miles or so into Oxford with a friend of mine from the squadron. This was my first visit and I was duly impressed with the dreaming spires. The city was quiet with little traffic, and the evening sun was low in the sky, the stone of the colleges being turned into a warm golden colour with the sunlight glinting off the leaded windows. I resolved that evening to obtain the required first class honours degree in order to go to Oxford and study for a doctorate.

In due course I got my first, went to Oxford where my chosen field was Neurophysiology and obtained my DPhil. I subsequently, not wanting to pursue an academic career, joined the Civil Service through the graduate entry programme for Administration Trainees destined to be 'fast-tracked' to a Sir Humphrey position. I decided, however, to leave immediately after seeing a bright purple Lamborghini (this was the `70s after all) outside my office in Northumberland Avenue. The Civil Service was not my cup of tea – even when it was served promptly at four o'clock each afternoon.

Born in the 1940s...

I decided upon commerce and joined Arthur Andersen. Three years later in 1976 I qualified as a chartered accountant. I then left Arthur Andersen (see what has happened to them as a result) and joined Mallory Batteries (later to become Duracell Batteries) based in my home town of Crawley as UK Administration Manager. The company was undergoing radical change driven by its US parent, and all this culminated in my appointment to the United States as the Chief Financial Officer of Duracell. The company grew and went public on the New York Stock Exchange in 1991, eventually becoming a $2.6 billion turnover business with 10,000 employees worldwide. Later Duracell merged with Gillette, and all of the Duracell senior management team soon left the newly formed company. At this juncture, in 1997, I decided to retire.

We did not wish to stay in the United States and, earlier, an article on Jersey and Guernsey in the *Wall Street Journal* had caught my attention. Reference was made in it to the difficulty of securing residence in both islands. This was the sort of challenge which I have always relished and, with those strong holiday memories re-kindled, I sallied forth to prepare an application. For our meeting with Jersey officials we as a family put on our best bibs and tuckers. Our son Tristan, then aged 16, came across nicely; we looked earnest and God-fearing; and we were accepted. There was never any doubt in my mind that this was the right thing to do. My wife had never been to Jersey but immediately fell in love with the Island on her first visit.

Then followed the hunt for a suitable house. Our feeling of elation at this next stage, boosted by lovely weather and with the daffodils out in February – in stark contrast to the frozen Connecticut that we had left behind, quickly turned to a degree of despondency. We were leaving a marvellous property that we had built from scratch in a delightful New England town. It had air-conditioning, electronic dust control, piped music systems, security cameras and all the other possible features available to modern technology. Few of these were available over here in the houses which we viewed. But we were thrilled when we found our current home in St John, a quieter part of the Island with the cliffs and sea – Finisterre in fact – clearly visible to the north and west of us. We were not seeking a vibrant city atmosphere with a busy cultural agenda. Instead, we relish Jersey's climate and the sense of reversion to 1940s England, with its feeling of safety, the sense of community which a small island engenders, the civility in the shops and not least the welcome from the landlord at our local pub, the Devil's Hole.

A few years into retirement now, I reflect on the Island where we have made our home. Some aspects of Jersey today concern me and, drawing from my previous experience as a Chief Financial Officer, my first consideration would be the Island's strategic direction. What are we about?

I have been encouraged recently with the significant changes in our approach to governance. For me at least this has been a wholly welcome development. As the reforms progress, it can be seen that we are moving from the consensus-based committee structure to a more conventional system of government which in turn should prove more effective in managing the priorities of the Island. There will be a greater ability to make decisions and then translate these into action. There should be greater control with regard to the effectiveness of the actions taken as well as greater transparency and accountability of those charged with that responsibility.

On the subject of accountability I strongly believe that we should attempt to introduce a revised method of reporting and analysis on the financial position and performance of the Island. This new system would allow the facts, as far as they can be accurately expressed, to be available for review by as wide an audience as possible. We should be able to say, 'This is the definitive financial plan', and then monitor and report progress against the agreed financial targets. For a company the development of an appropriate reporting system represents an elementary step. Why can we not look at Jersey as a discrete stand-alone company, for that is surely what we are, and review the performance in an identical manner to shareholders?

This is how it could work in principle. We have three operating divisions: Finance, Agriculture and Tourism. They would each develop an operating plan that generates a certain amount of contribution to the Island. The corporate HQ (i.e. the States) would also develop an expense budget comprising all the expense areas – education, health, public services, etc., offset by whatever revenue streams are available. The results would be a clearly defined revenue budget for the next five years with a surplus or deficit generated, which would be deemed acceptable or not by the States prior to approval of 'The Plan'. In the event of a predicted deficit for any one year, this presumably would have to be funded by borrowing in the short term or use of reserves. Tough decisions would need to be made regarding what activities need to be reduced, and to what extent, until a balanced budget was achieved. From this agreed financial plan or budget would then be developed a projected balance sheet for each of the future years, including an appropriate level of capital expenditure on major projects which would need to be prioritised by the States. The results of each year's performance would then be reported to the shareholders (i.e. us) via a clearly laid out annual report. This sort of approach would go a long way to providing the facts behind some of the burning questions of the moment concerning finance, agriculture and tourism.

Concerning the finance industry, without it we are nothing – is this really true? If so, what then is our strategy for it? What is sustainable about our agricultural policy? Are larger subsidies the answer? Will agriculture ever again be a net earnings contributor to the economy, and if so what is the strategy to get there from the current position? Or do we accept that agriculture will simply be an industry whose objective is to preserve Jersey's agrarian character funded by finance?

And there are similar questions regarding tourism. How does one define the Jersey brand? The key determinants of a brand are differentiation (i.e. in what aspects is Jersey different from other tourist destinations?) and relevance (i.e. whatever these differences are must be directly relevant to the consumer – the prospective tourist). Have we defined these? Does it matter if, at the end of the day, we are no longer a major tourist destination?

What I have outlined above would provide the answers to these questions: the importance of each industry and the likely impact of changes on the total Jersey financial plan. We would also know the true position of Jersey on a stand-alone basis – are we economically viable? And will it always be thus?

I have further concerns about the Island. From my perspective there are three broad areas. The first of these is that the Island seems overcrowded – particularly so to someone who has come here from the USA. What should the optimal number of the population be and how are we going to control the total number of people on the Island to ensure that we do not exceed this total? Despite recent debate I do not believe that we have arrived at an acceptable or workable approach.

My second concern relates to demographics: emigration of the younger members of the population and the projected greying of the population (and the implication, given this trend, that there will be insufficient economic wealth to maintain future pensions and social security benefits). Consequences could be a reduction in the availability of labour and its inevitable impact on wage inflation. A good example of why the labour drain is taking place is provided by a contractor known to me who has been in Jersey for 20 years. He has three children, works hard and yet lives in the poorest accommodation and will never be able to afford a house of his own. Will he stay? Probably. But will his children? That is much less certain. Until the Island can offer the people who are the backbone of Jersey reasonable expectations of home ownership, then there is no reason for the rate of emigration of young families to slow.

The Island also faces significant social issues. The stratification of society is unhealthy. It troubles me that the Portuguese community, on whom we are so dependent, is in danger of being alienated, not integrating and to some extent segregated by their language and culture. Are we doing enough to aid the integration process, or are we allowing the creation of a minority group, many of whom will become disaffected by their apparently permanent low pay/low status future here? Is appropriate consideration being given to the longer-term implications of the immigration of other groups from overseas into the Island? What will be the impact of decisions, based initially on economic grounds, regarding the future composition of the Island's population? This issue needs to be urgently addressed by the States.

One final thought is prompted by the fact that we are a small island with just 85,000 inhabitants. Perhaps an outright and deliberate policy of plagiarism would yield considerable benefits to Jersey's management. Such an approach could apply to the whole spectrum of government activity such as transport policy, work permits, litter control, drug education, etc. Very few problems will be unique to ourselves. Does it matter to Jersey whether we take the Danish Friesian Islands approach to this problem or the New Zealand approach to that, as long as it works and has proved cost-effective in practice?

A last reflection: I want the future of my family to be in this special island which I first came to nearly half a century ago. I am committed to contributing to Jersey, and our son plans to make his career here. This is based on an expectation that the Island and its character will stay largely unchanged. If, however, there are unwelcome future changes in Jersey's financial position or unexpected ramifications in the human capital strategy, then our own future in the Island will no longer remain certain. I sincerely hope that this does not prove to be the case.

Born in the 1940s...

Peter Le Rossignol

Peter Le Rossignol was born in 1948. He was educated at Victoria College Preparatory School and Victoria College, going on from there to the Central School of Arts and then to Sir John Cass College where he specialised in jewellery and silver. He subsequently worked in London for four years with the firm of William Comyns, manufacturing goldsmiths and silversmiths. Returning to Jersey, he joined E.J. Gallichan and Co. Ltd., Jewellers and Silversmiths, leaving them in 1980 to work on his own as a valuer and antiques expert, acquiring his own premises in Halkett Place. In 1996 he completed a Southampton University Master's degree in the History of Fine Art.

Our home was in St Lawrence and my father worked in the family business, the tobacconists opposite the Market gates which my grandfather had purchased from the father of Frederick Lonsdale, the celebrated playwright. My early memories are of Jersey's friendliness, for example Christmases at my aunt's, the Le Cornus of Six Roads Farm – 14 or 15 of us, of all professions and status and getting on so well together. And there was a cheerful informality about those times. The driver, when I took the bus to Auntie's, would ask, 'Where are you going?' I would say, 'To Six Roads Farm,' and he would reply, 'Fine,' and drop me outside the door.

I am also conscious of there being great characters about in those days (or is their seeming absence now a reflection of my advancing years?). There was George Le Sueur who used to chase us down the street when we taunted him. He had a habit of kicking things, was known as Kicky George and sadly had eventually to be locked away. I also remember the woman in town who sold fish from her barrow, whelks and winkles by the pint, with the measuring jugs hanging from her cart.

The smells of town are strong in my memory: the Laurens shop in Queen Street and its hardware department with its distinctive brew of paraffin, candles and mothballs. There were cars in King Street and Queen Street, and the Fish Market was a very different place, with 30 or 40 fishmongers at their concrete slabs and the particular bustle there on Fridays. At Christmas the poultry would hang in abundance at the front of the butchers' shops, and there was a dairy on the corner of Phillips Street and Minden Place where the butter was fresh-made and homemade jams and black butter were on sale.

Also, people would come in to town from the country on Saturdays, always dressed in their best clothes – men in suits and ties and their ladies of course in hats – and take afternoon tea at Gaudin's. Town in the 1950s was so different: marzipan bars sold at Le Riche in Beresford Street for 1/9d each; hand-made crackers in the shop windows at Christmas; biscuits sold loose in bags; and those marvellous cash systems in some of the shops – aerial runways across the ceilings to the cash desk in some and the pneumatic tube arrangement at Frederick Baker's. Town was more of a community then than it is now, with all those in business knowing each other well. And the same was true in the country parishes also, with telephone operators manning the exchanges who were likely, when you gave a number, to tell you that Mrs X was off in town and there was little point in trying to get hold of her.

At school, and some will find this hard to believe, I was an exceedingly shy boy (I am still the same, and it is only putting on this front that gets me through!). I enjoyed Latin and loved History, taught at College by that wonderful master, Frank Willey. And from prep. school days I always knew what I wanted to do in adult life. I remember saying, at the age of 10 or so, to my then teacher, John Stansbridge, 'I want something to do with history, but I love objects, the decorative arts. I'm going to be a jeweller to start with and we'll see where it goes from there.' Many years later I met him and discovered that I was the only one of my group then who was actually doing what I had said I would do.

After schooldays I concentrated in my college years in London on silver and jewellery, and I then went on to work for Comyns. They had been going since 1750 and made marvellous pieces for what was termed the carriage trade. In this firm one worked on the bench for a year and then spent months in each department before being allowed to talk to clients about their specifications. I learned much, met a lot of people in the trade including J. Sherlock and F. Bingham of Garrard and the Asprey family and loved my involvement in a business which made a complete dinner service for the King of Morocco, the millionth Morris Minor (gold-plated), a Glacier mint complete with polar bear, all in silver, for the company boardroom and a scale model of a Churchill tank for the Royal Tank Regiment. I even once went to 10 Downing Street to discuss with Prime Minister Harold Wilson's

Born in the 1940s...

Private Secretary what we should produce as a gift for the President of Kenya. Then there was London's social life which included a little Greek restaurant in Soho with a three-course meal for 7/- and a monthly treat with friends when we would take afternoon tea at the Ritz, Claridge's or the Savoy for 7/-, or 10/- if we went for the *assiette à trois plateaux* flowing over with exotic pastries (no evening meal on those occasions).

In the early '70s I came back to Jersey. There were two reasons: I was offered a job with Gallichan, and London – high rents, a heavy-going tax regime, student friends going their separate ways – was changing. My affection for the Island was strong; the family had lived here for generations, and this sense of belonging drew me back. At first I found the homecoming quite strange, but there were the compensations of the intimacy which London lacked – the freedom and opportunities at weekends of the beach, the cliff paths or tennis at the recreation ground. But Jersey was changing dramatically; finance was burgeoning; people were selling off properties to banks and wealthy incomers; the old stores in town were disappearing as money was dangled in front of owners' noses by speculators anxious to buy.

My own life was changing too, with marriage and the establishment of our home and in due course the arrival of 'junior'. In 1980 I decided that it was time to set up on my own, and a year later I acquired my little shop in Halkett Place where I have sat for over 20 years observing the inordinate changes that have come upon the Island over these last two decades.

My own professional career since that time has been a satisfying one, keeping up with the art world and the auction records, and reaping the benefits of modern technology and the resultant easy access to all the relevant indices. In my business one can never know everything, and hence the research aspect is always fascinating. I have always collected from an early age and the thrill of holding something – the value is immaterial – that was, say, made 500 years ago in China is immense. Where have you been?, I wonder. If only you could speak!

After all these years I have never lost this sense of excitement, this emotion which on occasions can bring one close to tears. This was my experience in France a few years ago. We were looking through the railings of a chateau, a small one and not very grand, near Cognac. The garden was a joy and a man, perhaps in his 70s, appeared at the gate and asked whether he could be of help.

'We were just admiring your garden,' I replied.

'Come in, come in,' he said. 'Have a look round. Do you like art?'

Born in the 1940s...

'Oh yes,' I said, not adding any more (a disaster if you do).

We went into the grounds and were later taken into a little barn where there were some drawings. I looked at them and saw that they were signs of the zodiac in squares.

'I may be desperately wrong,' I said, 'but are they Dali?'

'Yes, you're absolutely right,' he replied. 'I used to know him.'

'What are the drawings for?'

'Follow me.'

We were taken to a cloister, mirrored on both ground and first floor and unique in France. It transpired that the Germans had requisitioned the chateau during the war and had sat on the balcony taking pot-shots at the ceiling and destroying it. Later, Dali had designed these squares for it, and there they were, all carved in stone. Then our host took us inside and into the drawing room which was hung with Aubusson tapestries. I turned round and saw the most wonderful collection of pottery on a Renaissance cabinet. The relief carvings on its doors portrayed troops pouring out of castles. It was a fabulous piece of work. Then he opened the cabinet doors and I wept. There revealed was a street scene of little houses carved and going backwards in perspective, a mirror at the back with tiny pillars and a marble black and white *terrazza* floor sloping forwards like a raked stage. It was an exquisite jewel cabinet where Madame could put on her finery and inspect the result in the mirror at the back. This was not an experience which happens frequently, but there are these occasions, standing in front of a picture or in front of this fabulous cabinet when the tears start and the rewards of one's vocation are immense.

Besides my professional work Jersey's politics are a continuing interest, and I keep up an involvement at parish level to a certain extent, despite the fact that the parish as a community is less so than in the '70s or the early '80s, with new people coming in and lacking the enthusiasm to participate. The Island's political scene is something we discuss at home and a continuing topic raised with friends and clients when they come into the shop. As to my own analysis of it, one must go back 20 or 30 years when everything was going desperately well and everybody had money in their pockets and life was good. It is easy to have hindsight, but we should have started to draw in the reins then and to have done more at that time to regulate the incoming workforce. Matters addressed at the time would have alleviated situations in which we find ourselves today.

We currently face horrendous problems. I am not a financial expert but it does not require the brain of an Einstein to assess some of the facts. The

Island has frequently been referred to by our political masters as Jersey plc, with States Members as the directors and us, the tax-payers, as shareholders. Now if I as an accountant came to Jersey plc and pointed out that two-thirds of its gross income was going out in wages, what should be done? We have a civil service for a population of no more than 100,000 costing £165m per annum. Of course the Island has special demands, but we have suffered a *folie de grandeur*. There appears to be no mechanism to rein in this expenditure; the employment contracts in force do not allow for slimming down. There is only one way to get out of this: a ministerial system and party politics followed by a new civil service with every civil servant re-applying for his or her job. The stark alternative is an island bankrupt in 20 years. And then what? We would be destined to become a backwater of the European Community. We have great services here for the finance industry, but we are desperately expensive and the whole boiling pot has to be cooled. If we do not tackle this, then the British government will. Talk of complete independence and a Jersey pound is a ludicrous and impracticable pipedream. We must swallow some bitter pills, and saving money means cutting staff.

Also, we have terrifying examples of bad planning and misappropriation. Take the marina: an overspend of £10m; an entrance facing the prevailing wind which in a breeze can only be taken at speed to avoid damage against the wall; and current litigation by boat-owners. Or there is the airport: the extra taxiway needed for air safety to accommodate the big jets from Heathrow, and then the Heathrow link closes. £140m is earmarked for airport expenditure over the next 20 years. Southampton airport cost £8m and has comparable traffic levels to our own.

Our tourist industry dwindles; our agriculture has all but gone. We rely on the finance industry for our income (what the locals pay is a drop in the ocean). Trust company law has been altered to such an extent that only large umbrella companies are viable, and they are currently moving much of their work out of the Island. Our income sources are thus under great threat and these issues require urgent confrontation.

Are our politicians capable of solving these problems? About them and their qualities I am pessimistic. At present we have a system in which States Members are the puppets and the senior civil servants are the puppeteers, many of the latter imported from the United Kingdom and on contracts which carry with them two-thirds pensions.

My worries are not only for the Island's children but also for its elderly (I am next on the conveyor belt). How will their nursing and other necessary facilities be funded? With all this in mind I ponder on whether to study for another university degree, perhaps put a tenant in our house and go and live elsewhere for a period and see whether or not the grass is greener on the other side.

In so many ways we are lucky. We live in a lovely island with much beauty in the northern parishes. The beaches are a 10-minute drive away. I can sit in my garden, hear the birdsong and reflect on a privileged life. But with the benefits which wealth has brought to Jersey has also come a lot of baggage. We have built these crystal palaces and marble halls, and who will have the financial resources to sustain them? It is all a far cry from the Jerseyman's prudence of my childhood: the care of money, no overspending, wholesome food on the table but with the fripperies of life expendable. As it is, we have constructed a treadmill, we are going too fast and (slightly to mix the metaphor) someone is going to stick a bar in the spokes one of these days. Who is going to apply the brakes? Will a charismatic politician, a benign dictator, emerge, someone buoyed up with the authority of party and people, able to say, 'Stop! Enough,' and guide us out of this current situation of uncontrollable expenditure for which no one seems accountable and of foolish schemes for which no heads roll?

Born in the 1940s...

Lee Durrell

Lee Durrell (née McGeorge) was born in 1949. The family home was in Memphis, Tennessee. She attended St Mary's Episcopal School for Girls in Memphis and went on from there to study Philosophy at Bryn Mawr College, Philadelphia. In 1971 she began a graduate programme in Zoology at Duke University, North Carolina, undertaking research in Madagascar and gaining a PhD. She met Gerald Durrell in 1977 when he came to lecture at Duke and they married in 1979. During the 1980s she travelled extensively with her husband from their Jersey Zoo home at Les Augrès Manor, co-presenting television programmes and working with him in conservation activities. After his death in 1995 she succeeded him as Honorary Director of the Jersey Wildlife Preservation Trust (in 1999 renamed the Durrell Wildlife Conservation Trust). She is a governor of Jersey College for Girls and Patron of Trinity Youth Club.

Ours was a typically Southern family, originally Scottish many generations back, living in the city of Memphis but with easy access to the countryside. My father was in sales for a big company but was far happier when, in retirement, he took over the management of a group of golf clubs. At an early age I demonstrated an interest in animals. One of my first memories, around the age of 3, was being given a chest of dolls' clothes. I immediately removed the doll and its clothing, found a dead squirrel in the garden and carried it around in my little doll's trunk. At 7 or 8 I used to collect things from the fields behind my school, once bringing in a spider's egg-case with the spiders then hatching out in the middle of class – with the predictable disapproval of our rather fiercesome teacher. Mine was an animal-orientated childhood: dogs, cats and guinea pigs, even caymans (the South American crocodilians).

I was brought up in a fairly conservative home but am grateful to my parents and my school, not too unlike Jersey College for Girls, for teaching me to think for myself and hold my own opinions. And there was no big deal at home when I decided to go to college up north – to Yankee-land. My father and mother believed that women should be properly educated and make their own way. I was fortunate; we had very few dramas in our household.

The late '60s when I went to Bryn Mawr was the era of flower power. I shared in the heady radicalism of the time and was strongly pro-civil rights and anti-Vietnam war. I first joined an advanced Biology class but, on the professor enquiring whether I had ever dissected the head of a dogfish (I had never even heard of a dogfish, much less dissected one's head), opted instead for Philosophy which with Sociology and the usual liberal arts components seemed compatible with the spirit of the times.

Gradually, and prompted by the first Earth Day in 1970 (an event from which the environmental movement virtually dates its birth), I worked my way back to an interest in science. It was around this time that I first heard the term 'ecology', and my interest in science and animals was to complement my philosophical studies. It was the Teillard de Chardin thing and all that, coming together nicely. Hence, on graduating in 1971, I went to Duke University to study Zoology. Duke had an extraordinary collection of lemurs from Madagascar. (The lemur is a primitive primate – most similar to the ancestors of all primates.) I earned my pennies feeding and cleaning these charming animals and became more and more interested in their behaviour as compared to the higher primates. I became hooked on the idea of going to Madagascar, and this I did after two years at Duke in order to work on my PhD research. It was when I had completed these studies, had returned, was writing them up and teaching in the Zoology department at Duke that Gerry came there to lecture.

He had become something of a hero to me, as I had begun to read his books in Madagascar borrowed from the local mission library. Now we met and he told me that he was keen for me to come to Jersey and help him set up a research programme for what was an endangered species sanctuary and unlike any other zoo. He would always claim that he had lured me to Jersey, having received from a little old lady a legacy which he could spend as he wished, allowing him to launch the research project and pay my fare (at the time I was an impoverished student). I of course fell for all this, hook, line and sinker and finally arrived in the Island on a day in January 1978.

Now for some reason I had laboured under the misconception that the whole Island of Jersey was Jersey Zoo. On landing at the airport I was surprised to find it a fairly normal place with people going about their business with not an elephant or rhino in sight. But Gerry was there, doing it in usual Gerry style: a car and driver, champagne in the back, and at the Zoo the big iron gates, only used when the Princess Royal visits, wide open to welcome

Born in the 1940s...

me. Could he have been trying to make an impression? As it was, I stayed for a few weeks and pretended to work on research matters, with it soon becoming fairly obvious what we would decide to do. The following year we were married – a garden wedding back at home in Memphis and conducted by a judge who was an old naval buddy of my father.

It would be fair to say that, in my first years of marriage, my life was so taken up with Gerry, the Zoo and the overseas conservation work that I did not reflect too closely on the island which had now become my home. Also, we were away a great deal, travelling for the TV programmes and escaping to our house in the Languedoc where Gerry had to go in order to be able to write without distraction. My early relationship with Jersey was as a consequence fairly tenuous.

I do, however, remember in the early days our shopping expeditions in town and, particularly, to the Market. Everybody there knew Gerry – they had all at one time or another contributed produce for feeding the Zoo animals – and I loved the fact that he was recognised, greeted and liked by so many. I also quickly came to learn in these years how close were the links between the Zoo and the people and States of Jersey. From the time that Gerry had established the Zoo in 1959 he had received great support. Then tourism was seen as one of the Island's growing assets, and a States low interest loan, which could be rolled over year on year, had been a major help to our work. By the 1980s the Zoo was a buoyant enterprise, a major Island attraction which the States had supported enthusiastically and the Jersey people had taken to their hearts.

Gerry's and my last expedition abroad was to Madagascar in 1990 and after that his health deteriorated. We continued to spend time in France but travelled less. We always loved returning to the Zoo; this was home, and my circle of friends here, especially those working for us or on the Trust Council, widened.

Gerry died in 1995. He had never held a salaried position at the Zoo; his was an honorary position. It was his wish that, after his death, I should succeed him as Honorary Director and I readily agreed. I have no day-to-day management role or, indeed, authority; that lies with the Council and the Executive Director. But I do have a permanent seat on the Council and a measure of influence. Certainly I continued my work for the Trust on specific projects in animal conservation. I played a major role in developing our conservation activities in Madagascar, a country which is a 'hot spot' for conservation need, with the threat of species extinctions and the destruction of forests and marshes. We started the work in the early '80s and I have only

Born in the 1940s...

recently relinquished being the co-ordinator of this.

My life now very much centres round Jersey. In 1998 I decided to fulfil a lifelong ambition and took up flying. Gerry hated flying and had not let me do this. I received my licence in 1999, bought my own second-hand aircraft and, through this new enthusiasm, have encountered a whole set of new friends. And I can say that this has given me fresh insights into the Island and its current concerns.

The economic uncertainties worry me. In the '80s tourism brought in the revenues that allowed the Trust to expand both here and overseas. But the subsequent decline in visitors has meant that we have had to tighten our belts like so many other Island enterprises. The higher cost of living in Jersey of course adds to the problem.

I remain optimistic, however, about the future of the Trust. Its heart is in Jersey at the Zoo, and Jersey's future fortunes are important to it. But we are having to tap and develop fresh resources. Outsourcing maybe is one way ahead, with research scientists, for example, based abroad and not here. We must also make a greater virtue of our international dimension, investing more in our programmes in Madagascar and the Caribbean and looking elsewhere. The Jersey Zoo will come through and survive - it is an integral part of the Trust and has an excellent staff - but it will have to adapt and do things in a somewhat different way.

And what of the broader picture, of the Island as a whole? We are surely on the brink of important decisions. The '80s were the boom time; the '90s were perhaps 'head in the sand' time; the future is hard to predict. We should have the courage to stick our heads above the parapet and see what the rest of the world is doing, at the same time observing ourselves in a wider international context. I am personally strongly in favour of the Clothier governmental reforms and for changing a system that worked well in the good times but is now proving too cumbersome, inbred and in danger of imploding. People must by necessity face up to change; there is no going back. I believe that there are many clear thinkers among our politicians wanting to make the right decisions for our future, but there are also others who are too conservative and seem to be unwilling to take account of the world in which we now have to operate. Jersey is special, as most islands are. It has good, strong values and traditions which should be cherished. It also requires a system of government which is more transparent, more representative and quicker to respond to changing circumstances. The Zoo will survive and adapt and develop. It is my hope that the Island will do likewise.

Born in the 1940s...

Chapter Five

Born in the 1950s

Julian Bernstein
Jack Minier
Francis Le Gresley
André Ferrari

Julian Bernstein

Julian Bernstein was born in London in 1950. He was educated as a boarder at St Christopher's School, Letchworth, and went on from there to the Westminster Hotel School. After completing a three-year national diploma course he gained experience in the five-star catering industry in Geneva, Paris and St Louis, Missouri. A further spell in Paris and in London hotel management followed before he came to Jersey in 1974 to take over as manager of Oaklands Lodge Hotel in Trinity. In 1990 he bought and moved to Sea Crest Hotel and Restaurant at Petit Port, St Brelade. He was elected a States Deputy in November 2002.

*B*oth sides of my family were in the entertainment business. My maternal grandfather was a former bugler in the army of the Russian tsar who deserted, came to England and became a rabbi first in Hull and then in the east end of London. My mother became the Rank Organisation's first press officer, had an office at the Odeon, Leicester Square and was much involved with royal command performances and the careers of such as Alfie Bass and other old timers. My father's forebears had come to England in the 1880s via Scandinavia. He was the youngest of nine children, with his brother Sidney (in due course Lord Bernstein) the mainstay of the family. They started by buying up old music halls and converting them into cinemas, and this was the basis of the Granada Group.

I was brought up in St John's Wood – in Abbey Road, just along from the Beatles' famous pedestrian crossing (which incidentally is still there). We were an Orthodox Jewish family, committed to Judaism as I am still, but not adhering to all the rules and regulations, particularly those concerning kosher food – too complicated for our lifestyle, and my mother had had enough of it all in her youth. It was with this background in mind that St Christopher's at Letchworth was my parents' choice of school for me: it was Quaker, vegetarian and with a tolerant ethos, and thus nicely accommodated any personal eating and religious problems.

I had made up my mind at the age of 14 that catering was the career for me. At that time my father, who had for many years through the war and later been with the Ministry of Agriculture, Fisheries and Food (ending up as its Financial Controller), was planning and building motorway service areas for Granada. I used as a boy to go round with him to these developments and to the restaurants and sweet shops of the cinemas in the group and caught the catering bug. Also at school one could opt out of carpentry and do cooking instead; it was a good way of making a little money – free raw materials for a big supply of chocolate éclairs to be sold to one's schoolmates at 3d a go. Thus catering college was a logical next step.

After completing the three-year course at Westminster I first went to work in Geneva for the Mövenpick company, with six months in the kitchens and six months in their restaurants as a waiter. I then obtained a job in America and spent some time in Paris waiting for my work permit to come through. In the mornings I had lessons at the Alliance Française to improve my French and then I went on to the Drug Store Opéra where I would do the afternoon clearing-up and polishing and work on into the late evening. All marvellous experience!

The time in St Louis, Missouri, was perhaps my most interesting period in the industry. This exceptionally dynamic caterer, Harry Pope, a man with four Rolls-Royces, ran a selection of cafeterias in the greater St Louis area and did the in-house catering for some of the biggest companies. I was technically a trainee manager, lived in style in the St Louis Athletic Club and enjoyed being taken by the boss on amazing luxury Mississippi boat trips.

After this time of hard work and fun I returned to Paris where my father was now in catering consultancy. I was brought in as Director-General's assistant for an organisation that had acquired a French company and which needed an agent provocateur to root out its unsatisfactory business practices. I lived in a small hotel near the Elysée Palace, worked something over a 100-hour week and saw at first hand something of Orwell's earlier *Down and Out in Paris and London* experiences: cockroaches in the kitchens, no refrigeration with bought-in ice blocks the size of coffins and the money fiddles which the waiters, robbers of all robbers, were up to.

Then it was back to London, working for Rank as assistant manager at the Royal Garden Hotel, with lots of celebrities, Rotten Row on one side and the Israeli and Russian embassies on the other and Lord Snowdon ringing up to complain about the noise coming from the banqueting suite. I finished up as night manager, with IRA bomb scares, the problem of guests entertaining prostitutes and the odd dead body being all in the line of duty.

Born in the 1950s...

I came to Jersey in 1974, but my links with the Island go back to 1960 when my Uncle Max retired and bought a house in Gorey just behind the castle and with a fine view over the harbour. I would come over with my parents to visit and in this way got to know a number of those living here, especially members of the Jewish community such as the Krichefskis and the Regals. A few years later my mother and father also came to live in Jersey. Through various Island contacts I was to meet the Hon. Edward Greenall who owned Randalls. I went to his office and he said to me, 'I know your Uncle Sidney; this is the job for you,' and he offered me the post of managing Oaklands Lodge. I gave up London, occupied the comfortable flat 'above the shop', was now properly in touch with my parents for the first time since going to boarding school at the age of 10 and became the youngest licensee in the Island.

At first I missed London and used to pop back fairly regularly. But I was very involved in my business here and steadily became more integrated, not only into the thriving Jewish community but also into Trinity, a particularly welcoming place with its farming people and with Oaklands providing the catering for the parish dinners and weddings. In due course I married Martha, who was at the time working for Forte at the Grosvenor House Hotel, and took over the Oaklands operating company from the brewery, running it as my own property for eight years up to 1990. I look back on my early time in Trinity and remember the 1970s when the Island was a calmer, less hurried place, where you knew your bank manager and those serving you in the shops and where you could walk up King Street and note the various Jersey-owned businesses. Nowadays it could be the main street of any town in England.

While at Oaklands Lodge I had become involved with Highlands College, first on the catering department's advisory panel and then as a governor on the college board. Now in 1990, while enjoying my connection with further education, Martha and I were seeking a fresh challenge. We had two criteria: a restaurant with rooms and a location by the sea. Sea Crest came on the market with Victor Cornaglia's retirement and we fell in love with the place, purchased it, carried out the necessary re-vamping and have had much fun, working hard and raising a family in an idyllic situation.

As the years have passed eating-out habits have been changing. The drink-drive laws have affected out-of-town establishments, and people are reluctant to travel far (even in a small island such as Jersey where a journey from St Brelade to Gorey is considered almost unimaginable). There are other factors too: to maintain high standards of food and service one has to charge accordingly; and the breweries began to realise that pubs in good locations not making any money had to start feeding their customers and feeding them well. Thus the skills required for really good food and good service are being lost; those who might be waiters go and work in banks and shops, and chefs willing to come to the Island and cook a traditional haute cuisine menu become more scarce. With the skills going, so also will the number of top restaurants diminish.

All this is of course related to the state of Jersey's tourism industry. Its decline is not solely due, in my opinion, to the cost of air travel; flight prices have not risen disproportionately over the years. The problem is that other resorts can offer facilities which we do not possess. We cannot guarantee the weather; we have too few interesting outdoor attractions when the weather is good and too few indoor attractions when the weather is bad. Also some of the less expensive operations providing cheap and cheerful accommodation have left the industry. Other hotels, taking on this business, have started discounting. The whole hotel scene here is now a discount world; businesses are taking less money than the year before while at the same time costs inexorably rise. Percentages have gone through the floor and the situation is increasingly worrying.

Some responsibility for the sad state of the industry must lie with the States tourism department. It should more strongly back those private companies wanting to invest in the Island and ensure that necessary planning permission is granted them. Tourism must promote the Island, not just with a little flyer but with the mission of informing every travel agent in Britain of the Good Food Festival or the Battle of Flowers or Liberation Day. The financing of festivals, the encouragement of the arts and music and exhibitions, the promotion of a botanical garden: these are the sorts of initiative to bring in people from Britain and elsewhere.

Of course there is also a wider problem: the nature of our Island government. Politicians, not only those in Jersey, want power and want to retain power. They never wish to make too many decisions that might go wrong; they go for the lowest common denominator; they shy away from taking chances. Here in Jersey we need a cabinet-style system. We need continuing and rising investment in public health, in education and in the structure of the Island. And I worry about our over-manned public sector and some of the fashionable and perverse decisions of our planning department.

It is unfortunate that Jersey does not make better use of those outside political and governmental circles who are nonetheless well qualified to contribute their opinions. Years ago when Fort Regent was being planned, no one consulted Billy Butlin who knew more about leisure centres than anyone else. They might have avoided what was a flop from the day it opened. Currently also, those who have considerable knowledge of the tourism industry are not approached. Perhaps our decision-makers are frightened to be told what they do not wish to hear.

Jersey is at a crossroads, and I am aware that tourism – and banking as well – is a complex industry which can easily be affected by outside factors. I have no easy prescription for the future health of either. I do, however, have a couple of thoughts as I look ahead. Firstly I believe that we should be prepared to pay somewhat more tax; 22% would not get people fleeing the Island. Secondly I sometimes wonder (how feasible would this be?) whether we should go it alone and break away from Britain. The idea of Jersey, a little mini-country, appeals. Could this be the way ahead?

Jack Minier

Jack Minier was born in 1950 on the border of St Mary and St John. He attended St John's Primary School and then Quennevais. On leaving school he trained as an electrical engineer. For some years he worked as an electrician in the winter and as a fisherman in the summer. For the last decade he has fished in the summer and travelled in the winter, in the first years to Spain and latterly to south-east Asia. Since the year 2000 he has spent the winter months in Cambodia, carrying out charitable work there.

*M*y grandfather was from St Brieuc and came with his father to Jersey at the age of 10 to do the potatoes. He stayed and married a local girl from the well-to-do Etienne family of St Clement. His son, my father, married a Morin whose own mother was a Rondel, a family that has been in

Born in the 1950s...

the Island for 600 years. They are not travelling people; my wanderlust genes must have come from the Miniers.

I had a good childhood. My father worked for British European Airways as a maintenance engineer, and he also kept a smallholding of chickens and market gardening, selling his lettuces, tomatoes and the like. We were close to the farmers, and I went low-water fishing with them and liked getting involved in the autumn threshing. From around the age of 12 I would go out in the fishing boats from Bonne Nuit and I have operated from there ever since.

I did not enjoy my time at St John's School. The headmaster was a man called Harold Le Druillenec who had ended up during the Occupation in Belsen, having given assistance to Russian workers. The experience had made him a hard man and he ran the school like a concentration camp. Transfer to Quennevais at 11 spelt freedom, and I relished the school-organised projects in Hampshire and the special week at St Aubin, learning about boats and fishing.

I left school at 16 and worked for a firm of electrical engineering contractors, but I was never happy as an electrician. Fishing was in my blood, and at 21 I bought a little boat with a Seagull engine, doing about 60 pots the first summer, all pulled in by hand – no hydraulic winches in those days. For a number of years I had this agreeable routine – fishing in the summer and working as an electrician in the winter.

What a marvellous place Jersey was in my youth, just at the end of the Swinging Sixties. It was then a flourishing holiday island with the tourists flooding in to enjoy the cheap beer and fags, going to the shows, with such places as Les Arches, Daniella's, Bal Tabarin, the Tartan Bar and the wonderful West Park Pavilion (known universally as The Pav), all booming. I not only relished all this; I also became a qualified diver, not happy only being on top of the sea but wanting to go down and see it from underneath as well. There is no doubt about it: in those days Jersey was a fun island.

The change in my lifestyle came around 1990 when a mate of mine from Rozel lost his life when fishing. It happened on a cold January day. Over the years at least 20 people whom I knew have drowned. It is tiredness and overwork, and then accidents happen. You lose your concentration; you get a rope round your leg and you go over the side, with the boat in gear. Winter is the dangerous time; no one else about and a maximum of eight or nine minutes in the cold water for survival.

As a result of his death I lost my confidence, decided to give up fishing in

Born in the 1950s...

the winter months and bought a camper van. For three winters I pottered around Spain, worked for low wages on a yacht, sailed the Med. and then got bored with it all. I decided to try south-east Asia instead, flying the Jersey-Zurich route and on from there. First I explored Thailand, Malaysia and Laos, and it was not until 2000 that I was able to enter Cambodia. I have had a fascination for the country since I saw the film *The Killing Fields*. It is a terrible story: how the whole educated class could be slaughtered and this nation under Pol Pot turned back to the Stone Age.

My involvement in Cambodia and charitable work came about like this: I was staying in a guest-house and was told of a poor fellow who had been lying at home (the place needed a new roof) with a broken leg for nearly two years. The leg had to be amputated and an artificial limb fitted, and here was this distraught man needing help. Several of us teamed up and did some fund-raising round the Sihanoukville area. Between us we collected $200, and that is how the Starfish Foundation began, with a few tourists such as myself, some ex-pats and with the help of an American Quaker charity based there.

With Sark friends I have started my own Starfish Foundation CI, raising money over here, with weekend pub nights and the like. I am hoping too for some help from the States and their overseas aid budget.

It started with the one-legged fisherman. Last year I raised money for a blind fisherman and got a boat built for him. He also needs a new well and a new roof for his house. Now there's another fisherman suffering from the after-effects of polio. The thing is this: we can rebuild their lives for $200: a new roof for $50, a boat for $100 and two nets at $10 each. These men have the knowledge but lack the equipment.

Recently we have started up the Starfish Bakery and Café; all its employees are disabled. The American Friends have helped and lent us transport, but they are pulling out. We are trying to take over and carry on their work. And I have my own fishing knowledge and experience to pass on: buy them a Tilley lamp and they can go fishing for squid at night. I am not looking for one-year or two-year projects; my eyes are set on ten years, helping to rebuild Cambodia. I enjoy the people; I go there to lose a Jersey winter; I love the climate and the fishing. During the Jersey summers I have a low-profile lifestyle and save my money. Then I book my flight and I am gone, with my charity fund in a separate account and with the prospect of the months ahead and the help we can bring these splendid people.

And what of the place of my birth which I leave behind? I am saddened by all its changes. The farming, with those supportive rural communities of the past, has all but collapsed. Tourism has gone the same way. I reflect on the good life of my boyhood when everyone was happy, with the farmers and those who ran the hotels and guest-houses true professionals. All this has gone. Those new flats at Bonne Nuit! Everyone now wants to convert hotels into luxury apartments, not for Jersey people but for rich outsiders. If we are not careful, the Island will become another Monte Carlo or a boring place like Singapore. Jersey is being taken over by the rich; the States have sold out to the finance people. The farming and the tourism: all gone.

As I land in the Island after my winter months away, I am depressed. I have left the real world and real people in Cambodia and have returned to this money-orientated place. I seek adventure; that is why I became a fisherman. Jersey has no adventure any more; it has lost it. People pay £300,000 or £400,000 for a small bungalow and get trapped here, not for the lifestyle but to pay off the mortgage. Go to south-east Asia and have a beautiful house for £20,000, with everything you want. Jersey people are governed by rules and regulations, and it's all to do with money, money all the time; in Cambodia the people there have freedom of mind.

I think of the days of my Jersey youth: the low-water fishing with the farmers; the Sunday School treats; the great day out when the threshing was done; or the October cider-making. You now have to go to museums to see all that. I think of the old days, with the Island packed for Battle of Flowers Week and the farms with their rooms rented out for the holiday-makers who returned year after year. It has all gone, and it is very sad.

The contrast is that I stay at my Cambodian guest-house for $3 a day. I am welcomed; there is a sense of community; it is a home from home for 'Ting Tong' Jack ('Ting Tong' means 'happy, crazy'). They look forward to seeing me. My landlady says, 'You, Jack, when you come back, you only come see me, go nobody else.' I have my little room, all nice and clean. She has the three rooms to let and she is so happy and cannot do enough for you. 'Place is yours, Jack.' And when I leave for Jersey, I get from them all, 'Ting Tong Jack, you come back.'

Perhaps when I reach retirement I shall be gone from this island of my birth and not be back. I am not a rich man but, as far as I am concerned, I am a rich man in Cambodia, helping its happy people.

Born in the 1950s...

Francis Le Gresley

Francis Le Gresley was born in 1951. He went to St Lawrence Primary School and then on a States scholarship to Victoria College. He left school at 17 and joined Barclay's Bank in Jersey. After three years, from 1970, with the bank in England, he returned to the Island. He remained in banking until 1990 (from 1975 with Williams and Glyn's Bank which merged with the Royal Bank of Scotland). From 1990 to 1998 he and his wife ran the St Mary's post office and shop. In 1992 he combined this with being manager (part-time) of the Jersey branch of the Citizens' Advice Bureau, becoming its full-time manager in 1995.

My first years were spent in Bellozanne Road and we moved when I was four to St Ouen where my family on both my father's and my mother's side had roots. My maternal grandfather was a farmer and my paternal grandfather was a carpenter. My dad was a schoolteacher and for my final year at St Lawrence School I was in his class.

From an early age, therefore, I was a country boy, living in an old farmhouse surrounded by fields, and with my sisters and myself enjoying considerable freedom, able to go off and play all day without Mum worrying about us. It was a wonderfully safe childhood environment. Town, full of visitors in the summer weeks, I visited infrequently, perhaps with my father on a Saturday to do some shopping. And I do remember as a young boy the Battle of Flowers and all its accompanying noise and excitement.

At 11 I gained a scholarship to Victoria College. I have to confess that I did not particularly enjoy my time there. I got off on the wrong foot: a lot of my friends were going to Hautlieu and I would have preferred it, with its co-ed intake. Also I was in the fast stream at College and, with a June birthday, at the young end of the year. I actually took three O-levels when I was still 13 and did my A-levels (not terribly well) around the time of my 17th birthday. All through my time there I was pushed and pushed in order to keep up with the academic pace. Consequently, having taken my A-levels, I had had enough of school and was glad to be out of it.

Born in the 1950s...

My life as a Jersey teenager was, in every sense of the word, insular. I had never been to England, and travel consisted of the occasional day trip to France. After schooldays and without much thought I fell into banking. It was like this: every summer I worked on Percy Le Masurier's farm, drove the tractor and helped with the cattle. I earned money for the purchase of a bicycle and, later, an old banger which took me and my friends to the beach, the pubs and the discos. My mother told me that I should get a good, steady job with a pension at the end of it; we saw an advertisement for an opening at Barclay's in the *JEP*; I applied and got it. This was 1968, with the finance industry in its infancy – just the five clearing banks and a couple or so of merchant banks in the Island.

Two years after joining I opted for a job with the bank at Gatwick as a *bureau de change* cashier. It was a great year of my life – for the first time away from home and with attractive perks such as hotel accommodation, free flights and the like. We served the transatlantic passengers and the air crews and met a lot of people. The next two years with Barclay's, this time in Southampton, was a rather different experience: back to a basic wage, sharing a house with three or four others, managing a tight personal budget and making a soup or stew that would stretch for a week's evening meals.

In 1973 I came back to Jersey. I had missed the Island and I missed the sea (Southampton Docks was not an adequate substitute). I was now working in a finance industry that was getting hectic; new banks were opening and branches were expanding; it was taking off in a big way. This was a busy time for me: sitting my banking exams in order to get the qualifications for promotion, by now married (at the age of 22), doing maintenance on our property in St Ouen and growing vegetables.

I joined Williams and Glyn's in 1975 (which was to merge with the Royal Bank of Scotland) and steadily progressed in the next 15 years, spurred on by that glance over the shoulder to ensure that we Jersey bankers were not being overtaken for the top jobs by those brought in from the UK. However, by 1990, I had become disenchanted by it all: I disliked many of the clients with whom I had to deal – people whose business we should not have touched. But there were targets to be met and credit scores to gain. Perhaps I was too moral for it all, too honest. Also the workload was huge, the staff were stretched, and the stress of keeping the 70 or 80 people under me happy became too much. I needed a change rather than a heart attack at 50, and we moved to St Mary and bought the village shop.

Here was a major change of lifestyle - lending £300,000 one day and

Born in the 1950s...

pricing chewing gum at 5p a time on the next. I was also involved at the same time in other interests: on the board of a produce marketing group and in 1992 taking over, at first on a part-time basis, as manager of the Citizens' Advice Bureau. It was not unusual for me to work 25 hours a week in the Bureau and 30 hours in the shop. The difference of the two responsibilities, the gear-change, made it bearable for a time. But in 1995 the C.A.B. commitment became full-time, and the shop went in 1998.

I came to C.A.B. in some ignorance. I had always been an avid reader of the *JEP*, knew that the Island had its social problems but was never previously interested enough to engage with them. I was quickly attracted to the Bureau's potential: a sleeping giant that, if awakened, could do great things for Jersey. I embarked on the proverbial steep learning curve.

Some of the problems dealt with by the Bureau in 1992 were different from those of today. Back then the main issue was the parish welfare system. We had a recession at the time, rising unemployment and no unemployment benefit. The attitude of the authorities to those out of work was 'get a job', and various schemes such as scraping the roads were devised to absorb the problem – hardly a satisfactory solution for an unemployed well-qualified person. One parish's welfare payments would differ from those of another, and the attitude of the Constable was sometimes critical. In the early '90s it was not the done thing to question the role of the Constable: he was on a pedestal and the whole matter was a taboo area. It was also a wider problem: the culture of the time was not to rock the boat; Jersey was booming and, if a few people fell through the net, then that was tough. I was active on the welfare issue at meetings, in the media and with the politicians; my message was that it had to be tackled and not swept under the carpet. The bloc of Constables did not like my stance and at one stage withheld their committee's grant to C.A.B. because I had upset them. They would pay up if I apologised! Here was an instance where Jersey's lack of political parties may be seen to have consequences: C.A.B. is the only effective voice of the people saying that there is something wrong and that those most in need require help.

The outcome of all this was progress: a States committee reviewing welfare; a gradual change to a system that has become more user-friendly; and the administration of welfare in St Helier moving from the Town Hall to more suitable premises. It was the Bureau that highlighted the problem in the early '90s, and there have over the last decade been radical improvements in this area.

Housing was then to become the number one issue: a new poor section of the community on low incomes, with no housing qualifications and with very high housing costs. I was appalled by the situation: poor standard accommodation at a very high rent and, sometimes, three children sharing a room with their parents. It has been a case of drip-feeding the information to our politicians, and it is getting through. Three years ago I was asked on a radio interview, 'If you could wave a magic wand, what would you change?' I replied, 'Scrap the housing qualifications. It creates a two-tier society.' Three years on, these very phrases were used by Senator Pierre Horsfall in the States debate on population.

All this relates to an argument which I have had frequently with local residents. They say to me, 'We don't need all these people. Why are they here?' The answer is that they are needed to do the work – cleaning offices, washing up in restaurants, digging the potatoes – which locals will not do. We have a fine education system in Jersey; we are all being educated to a higher standard; and we consequently aspire to having fulfilling jobs. The abolition of housing qualifications is now on the Island agenda. It is another instance of the move away from the paternalistic political attitudes of the 1980s. Politicians now have to listen more to the public; radio phone-ins, the talk-back programmes and the letters to the press are making our elected representatives more responsive. Government is steadily and healthily becoming more open.

The other big problem coming C.A.B.'s way is relationship breakdown. We must have the highest divorce rate in Europe. There are many pressures operating here: the need to work long hours to keep up with one's peers, buying their new cars and taking their expensive holidays, and the consequent neglect of partnerships; social heavy drinking leading to some straying is another factor, as is the fact that we are a small island with everybody knowing everyone else. Hence the Bureau finds itself dealing with a host of related problems: housing, children, division of assets, social security and bank accounts are some of them.

A matter soon to be addressed, and not before time, is the problem of employment rights. In this area we are way behind the UK, having had virtually full employment for years. Thus we have got away in the past with our not having the concept of unfair dismissal. Up till now C.A.B. has been unable to help in these cases. We are able to say little else than, 'Just forget it. It is not worth trying to do anything about it. Look for another job.'

If I look into the crystal ball I have to say that I see the Jersey good life about to come to an end. We cannot expect the finance industry to continue

Born in the 1950s...

contributing the scale of tax revenue which we have recently been receiving. The threat to offshore centres from the E.U. – and the British government – is real. We have tried hard since the Edwards report of a few years back to clean up our act, but we have had a good run. We tapped a source of money which we thought limitless and the industry will now almost certainly contract. A lot of the back-office operations will go. And we are a too expensive location for the finance houses and their staff costs – housing and salaries – and office rents.

Concerning tourism, if only we were 1000 miles nearer the Equator! As it is we lack good indoor facilities, we fail to co-operate jointly with our neighbours in promoting the Channel Islands and we would have to tap that rainy day fund if we really wanted to build a new tourist infrastructure. Why not a new inland 18-hole golf course and a luxury resort hotel on land no longer profitable for agriculture? This sort of development could be achieved without great environmental damage.

Politically I am pro-Clothier, hook, line and sinker (including the removal of the Bailiff from the States, where a Speaker and Deputy Speaker should be appointed for the good conduct of its proceedings). The Clothier report also included the appointment of an ombudsman, and I feel passionate on this issue. The Bureau can only go so far in negotiating the settlement of disputes between individuals and our government. We need the scrutinising powers of an ombudsman, able to call for evidence and to impose an adjudication. I have recently seen the system work very well in Gibraltar with its 30,000 population. We need it here in Jersey – an independent arbiter to protect the interests of the citizen.

I worry too about the calibre of some of our States Members. We have paid the price of a disillusioned electorate and low turn-outs at the polls. Will we have the politicians of sufficient standing and substance to provide for the office of Chief Minister, Ministers and their deputies? The answer may lie in the emergence of political parties in order to stimulate electoral interest and to improve the quality of those elected. Currently someone enters politics with his or her own manifesto and has no means of delivering it. A candidate only needs to state a belief in the importance of the parish system and the desirability of stemming immigration to gain the necessary votes. At present those seeking election dare not be too brave in proposing alternative policies, whereas a group of people with a manifesto, in other words a party, would have its policies either endorsed by the electorate or its attempt at power turned down. This would be a healthier system and lessen, if not end, the current attacking of personalities which has brought so much recent discredit to the workings of our legislature.

My hope for the Island's future is that, with the finance industry contracting, we shall become somewhat less materialistic and use more of our energies in caring for each other than in making money. On that recent visit to Gibraltar I sensed a community friendliness which has gone from Jersey. We have the flickering of such a spirit on those occasions when the Battle of Flowers and Liberation Day make their annual appearances, but much of this over the years has been lost. Perhaps with less tax coming in and less money in our pockets, something of the old rallying around and support for each other will return. Let us hope that, with some pain, there will also be some gain.

André Ferrari

André Ferrari, son of a Jersey mother and Italian father, was born in St Helier in 1954. His primary education was at First Tower School and his secondary at Hautlieu. He then did an art foundation course at Leicester and went on to Loughborough College of Art for his degree studies. He returned to the Island in 1979 as a painter and since then has also been active as a campaigner for conservation issues and tenants' rights. Under the auspices of Save Jersey's Heritage he has published two books: Jersey's Lost Heritage *(in 1996) and* Jersey's Disappearing Heritage *(in 1998). He continues to work as a painter.*

*M*y father came to Jersey from Italy after the war as a waiter and then became a barman, for many years employed at the Grand Hotel. My mother, Jersey-born, started work at Swanson's as a chambermaid and in due course was promoted to housekeeper. Tourism in the Jersey of the 1950s was booming and my mother found her work exciting, enjoying the company

Born in the 1950s...

of her cosmopolitan colleagues. In those days the Island had a particular feel and attraction as a tourist resort, a time when the Battle of Flowers, especially for us youngsters who lived close to the Battle arena, was a greatly anticipated annual event. Living at First Tower we were well placed for the beach and for the countryside which 40 years ago seemed to start not far from our doorstep. There was a kind of seasonal rhythm as the holidaymakers came to visit our special island, when on summer evenings West Park and the Esplanade would be thronged with tourists taking the air after their guest-house evening meals.

Even as a young boy I had a fascination for the quirky corners of town. Standing with my mother and looking up at the Woolworths counter I would register the intricacy of its ornate plaster ceiling; there were the strange backstreets, one never being quite sure where they led; and I used to notice the gas lamps on the corners. St Helier possessed a sleepy small-town feel and, even when the summer visitors were around, it was only the so-called Golden Mile of shops from Cheapside, up King Street and along to Colomberie where the quietness was displaced by bustle.

Am I seeing all this through rose-tinted spectacles bequeathed by the passage of time? I suggest not. As I did research for my books that came out in the 1990s, there in the old photographs was that special character and atmosphere of St Helier which has been irretrievably lost. As a boy I had a point of reference with which I could compare and test my reactions: my grandparents lived in a quaint and pretty village on Lake Como and we visited them almost every year. Jersey I preferred. (As a family we made two disastrous attempts to settle permanently in Italy when my father bought into a restaurant business in a small industrial town near Milan. The ache for Jersey was too strong, and the relief on our return was overwhelming.)

I attended the primary school at First Tower where the redoubtable Miss Hacquoil crammed us (was this ethical?) for the 11-plus exam. I was not particularly academic and I recall that I had trouble doing fractions. After I had asked my teacher twice to explain the method, I was too frightened to admit that the penny had not yet dropped. In the end my mother, who had herself years before been taught by Miss Hacquoil, was summoned. She too received her former teacher's tuition concerning fractions on my behalf and admitted to me afterwards that, like me, she could not understand it either. It was typical of Mum then to go to the Lexicon bookshop, purchase a 'teach yourself' maths textbook, learn how to do the fractions (in a roundabout way) and to pass on the instruction (equally roundabout) to me.

I enjoyed my years at Hautlieu, a school somewhat different from Victoria

College and with a rather more liberal ethos. I particularly valued the liberating effect of my Religious Studies A-level course which was taught by a member of staff willing to discuss all sorts of related social issues, a rather good introduction to those later all-night instant coffee sessions with one's fellows at art college – Loughborough, where painting was my specialism and the empty interiors of buildings a subject frequently tackled.

During my art college years I came back to a Jersey that was subtly changing. Each time I returned I would find that yet another pub had been knocked down and rebuilt. My favourite hostelries were those that paid no concession to prettification and whose character derived from their customers. The Farmers Inn at St Ouen was one such. But they were becoming a rarity as other pubs' interiors were redesigned like hotel lounges with ersatz milk churns as bar stools and farm implements incongruously suspended from the walls.

At this period, the late '70s, the finance industry was burgeoning and while England endured its various recessions, fuel crises, unemployment and rampant inflation, there was in Jersey a smugness, a self-satisfaction that we had no problem here because we did things better. This was a time when, having finished my degree and come back, I felt rather isolated and alone, with old school friends now dispersed. Occasionally I would put pen to paper and send angry letters to the *JEP* on various of the issues about which I was becoming increasingly exercised.

There were, for example, plans to widen the ring road and to build a monstrous raised underpass at West Park. At the time no one seemed to address the notion of traffic restraint; all the talk was of dual carriageways and more multi-storey car parks. Reclamation was another live topic and decisions were made about the area to the west of the Albert Pier without any regard for aesthetic considerations and with a carefree attitude to destroying the traditional seafront with a dreary angular block of infill. (Some are pressing today for more reclamation at St Aubin as though they are unaware of the results at the other end of the bay.)

At this time too I started painting from life corners of St Helier, and an exhibition of my work was given publicity on Channel TV. This brought me in touch with Alastair Layzell, then still in television and not yet a politician. Christopher Scholefield, who had contacted me after reading some of my letters in the press, and Alastair were instrumental in setting up Save Jersey's Heritage, and the States planners, then the IDC, brought a number of us together, including Alastair and Chris, several architects and others as an urban design panel, charged with giving our opinions on controversial schemes and projects.

One horror which we studied was the underpass and we also considered the plans to demolish Government House and Colomberie House. Our influence, as the outcomes showed, was questionable. We pushed for an initial list of protected buildings; Government House, Colomberie House and the Hue cottages were on it. The first and third were saved; the second was lost. One branch of Planning wanted to preserve while another was giving permission for valued buildings to be knocked down.

Along with others in Save Jersey's Heritage I was active in my criticisms of intrusive new buildings that paid no respect to their neighbours. I pressed too for the preservation of traditional details: railings, mouldings on façades and the like. What sadly began to happen was the emergence of pastiche: old buildings knocked down and replaced by dull copies – a solution that pleased neither the modernists nor the conservationists. And the listing process has dragged on for ever, with the politicians fearful of stirring up too many hornets' nests and lacking the will to face up to commercial and special interests. The fact is that it takes more courage and application to save and adapt a building than to flatten it.

The early '90s were a time of recession and the pressures for building temporarily lessened. For myself it was an upsetting period with my rented flat in a building destined for redevelopment and me facing eviction. This followed on the Troy Court affair when 98 families were taken through the eviction court. These were Jersey residents with qualifications, but the housing authority was willing to help only those who were pensioners, with medical problems or with children. There was tremendous outrage and hurt, and this led to my cousin, myself and others forming an association for tenants to represent and help those who were being so ill-used. My own eviction experience, with landlord threats and harassment, was painful in the extreme. I was shattered by the episode and resolved that, if I failed in finding myself suitable alternative accommodation, I would leave the Island for good. Fortunately I obtained my flat and was able to channel my anger into the work of the association, conscious of building destruction and redevelopment being done in the interest of others at the expense of those who actually lived here.

Did we manage to effect noticeable change? Sadly the situation now seems worse than ever, with the States having encouraged another boom, no doubt in the process keeping the construction industry happy. Currently we are

Born in the 1950s...

seeing yet more development, and the scale of what is going up in the Esplanade area is truly shocking: the three or four storeys of a decade ago are now six or seven. This is building on a city scale, further destroying yet more of what remains of St Helier's character and 'feel'.

I have now been back in Jersey for over 20 years since my student days, at first concerned with the urban environment and then with tenants' rights, and I ponder what went wrong with the place of my happy childhood. I believe that the Island has been a victim of its own success; Jersey has chased after wealth, and the down side of this prosperity has been its increasing population and the pressures on its infrastructure. It has lost its sense of ease and peace.

I go back to my grandparents' Italian village and my blood pressure falls as I arrive: a different pace of life, in harmony with the rhythm of the seasons and a palpable sense of its roots and culture. Years ago visitors' letters to the *JEP* would commend our quieter lifestyle. The Jersey of my youth retained that element of tranquillity. Go across the water to France and you will find it there today. Instead we are running ever faster in order to stand still, and we have become a divided society: the gap between the 'haves' and the 'have nots' has widened; great wealth on the one hand and cramped and inadequate housing on the other. And the arguments of 30 years ago are being stridently repeated: demolish the old parts of the town because we need the housing. It is hard nowadays to relax, to enjoy a sense of security: if it is not fighting to save a corner of St Helier, then it is a battle to prevent a housing estate on the Plémont headland or to abort yet another reclamation scheme. We always seem under threat whereas I can go to my aunts on Lake Como and find the village and its mountainside untouchable; you can look at it, enjoy it and there is no need to get up a petition to save it.

The truth is that campaigners can suffer from burn-out; exhaustion and resignation threaten. Our problems stem in large measure from finance. As to our previous industries, farming depended on having a countryside to cultivate; tourism was dependent on having an environment that was special enough for people to make the choice to visit. Finance does not depend on such factors. Jersey could be the ugliest place in the world and the finance industry could still thrive here, and this is a thought that haunts me.

Born in the 1950s...

Chapter Six

Born in the 1960s

John Asbury
Charles Alluto
Christina Price
Andrew Syvret
Sarah Williams

John Asbury

John Asbury was born in Jersey in 1964. He attended St Peter's Primary School and Les Quennevais School and then went on to do a two-year Highlands College catering course (followed by a two-year day release advanced course). He worked as a chef in Jersey and abroad, living for some time both in Australia and New Zealand. He came back to the Island in 1989 and in the early 1990s changed his occupation from catering to gardening.

*M*y home life as a child was always fun. I recall no family traumas, and I owe this contentment to my Italian blood, my mother's parents having come to Jersey in the late 1930s to do hotel work. The Asbury side of the family was originally from Birmingham, my father's father being a coach builder, and my father was a weather man at the Airport met. office. Indeed 30 or more years ago we kids seemed to have a free run there, with few restrictions and the ability to climb the control tower and virtually invade the runway.

An early memory was our Italian Club Christmas dinners, held in local hotels, with us children running amok and the men sitting there in their suits as though at a meeting of the local Mafia. The beach was also a big feature in our lives – when you live in St Peter's there is a proverbial playground down the road.

Our headmaster at St Peter's School was big cuddly Wally Challinor who was a member of the St Aubin Yacht Club. He used to take some of us out in his boat round the bay on activities days. It may only have been 30 years ago but it seemed a simpler life with fewer distractions and with TV still something of a novelty – black and white, only one channel and something you watched sometimes on Saturday or Sunday mornings, being otherwise outside most of the time.

Les Quennevais meant that life was getting a little more serious – uniform, catching the school bus, more regimentation. At the age of 16 – perhaps it was my Italian blood again – I decided that cooking was my way ahead, a means to travel the world and work and surf, and went to Highlands College

Born in the 1960s...

for its two-year course.

At this stage in my late teens I was already aware of my island as a marvellous place and have always been astounded by its beauty. What a wonderful childhood location, with its freedom and safety! At the time I unsurprisingly thought little of Jersey's government, but we used to go into Town for any pageantry, and my mother would have us up at the Airport for the arrival of any visiting Royals. We learnt little at school about current local politics; history lessons and the like were more about kings and queens and wars, and I had to do a project about Mont Orgueil and Mum came along and helped me with the writing. Thus I knew little of what really was going on (and perhaps it remains a bit like that now, still being kept somewhat in the dark).

After Highlands I had several years travelling: working in London and the English counties for a time and then going off to Australia. The pull of Jersey was always strong, and copies of the *JEP* sent by Mum or a photo of a friend surfing at St Ouen's would make me nostalgic for home. I came back in 1987, worked for a time at the St Brelade Bay Hotel and then, this time with my girlfriend, went off to New Zealand. We came back two years later and I continued as a chef until I tired of the split shifts and the general stress of the job. I turned instead to gardening, took a cut in my earnings but was now working in a more relaxed and – in many ways other than financial – more rewarding occupation.

One of the things that struck me on returning permanently to the Island was the housing question. Now with a partner and no longer living at home, the big issue was accommodation and paying the rent. It brought home to me awareness of the big social divisions here – the case of those who have and those who have not. I began to wonder how the person with a very large mortgage could also afford to run two brand-new cars. And work as a jobbing gardener gave me a more intimate insight into the homes and lifestyles of the very wealthy.

All this fails to make me angry; I don't get hung up on such issues. I neither own a house nor am ever likely to. I don't allow problems to bother me if they are not in my province. But it does make me more conscious of Jersey and its social structure. In other words, if wealth floats your boat, just don't make me pay for it.

I am now also more aware of the Island and the way it is governed with, as it seems to me, the constant ability of the States and persons in the States to mess things up. There never seems to be good news in the paper; it is always

Born in the 1960s...

doom and gloom. Also, everyone in Jersey has this huge capacity to moan. Moaning seems to have taken over from conversation and debate. I heard someone in the pub recently ask his chum, 'Why are you moaning?' The friend replied, 'Because it's my turn.'

Besides the moaning Jersey's big problem concerns money. The constant theme is, 'We've got to get rich'. Take an ordinary fellow (certainly not me): his parents die and he inherits the house; instantly he does it up, sells it and makes £200,000. So many get caught up in this money trap, ensnared by the wish to get rich and stay rich. And Jersey has fuelled all this by constant development and inflation. It's a concept of greed, and the Island suffers from it.

As to Jersey's future, we seem to lack anyone in government with sufficient charisma. Might party politics help? People ganging together make more powerful lobbies than can individuals, and this could bring improvement and greater openness to our government system.

Overall I am content with Jersey as my home. I pay a high price to live here, and so be it. I love my job - whatever the weather. I am a positive person and that is my outlook on life. If you're down about everything, you'll remain down. I let the difficulties ride, or I'd go mad and be forever angry. I always bear this in mind: you can't always have what you want!

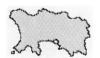

Charles Alluto

Charles Alluto was born in Jersey in 1966 and was educated at De La Salle College where he was latterly Head Boy. He then went to Durham University and read English. During the 1990s he worked for the Burton Group in London and for estate agents Strutt and Parker in Canterbury; he gained a masters' degree in property valuation and law and a diploma in historic building conservation; he also renovated a London Georgian house. In 1998 he took up a position with the Heritage Lottery Fund and in 1999 was appointed Secretary (now termed Chief Executive) of the National Trust for Jersey.

My father has an Italian great-grandparent (hence my surname) and my mother is a Le Cornu. We lived in various parts of the Island as my father moved from being a hotelier into property, renovating houses and then selling them on. For five years during my early childhood our home was along the Route Orange at Red Houses, and my early memories of St Brelade's Bay, Ouaisné, the Railway Walk and the dunes are strong.

At a fairly young age I came to appreciate that Jersey was different: for example I noticed that the recession and unemployment in the UK reported on television and in the papers had no significant impact on our lives over here. Also I was conscious at De La Salle, a fairly strict school with its Catholic traditions from which I as a non-Catholic benefited, that there was no differentiation between the pupils – a tolerance of a wide variety of backgrounds without any awareness of class distinctions. All in all mine was a safe, easy-going childhood in which I had a nascent interest in the natural environment: walking the cliff paths, bird-watching, collecting birds' eggs (now of course forbidden) and butterflies and even having a precocious interest in gardening. I was conscious too, with my father's building interests, of housing development and the threat posed by it to Jersey's precious country lanes, fields and hedgerows. As to political awareness I possessed little, and taking part in an Amnesty International march was the extent of my schoolboy involvement and interest in such matters.

For a young person, growing up in Jersey can be a restricting experience.

Born in the 1960s...

This was one of my reasons for choosing Durham, almost as far away as possible, for my university years. It is also a beautiful city, possibly rather too small, with a stunning cathedral. I read English there, with some philosophy in my first year, studied wine-tasting, joined a scheme to do gardening for the elderly and helped man the university's nightline 'Samaritan' service.

After finishing my degree in 1989 I spent time searching for a career path: a period in the Burton Group's London head office, a spell with Strutt and Parker, upmarket estate agents, at their Canterbury branch; a year or more back in Jersey working for a trust company and studying for chartered surveyors' qualifications. Then in 1995 I bought a derelict Georgian house in the Spitalfields area of London and spent two and a half years restoring it and then selling it on. It had an interesting history: originally a domestic dwelling, and then a silk weaver's house with the Huguenots coming in, followed by the Jewish community and latterly Bengalis (who used it as a sweat shop). Its value increased fivefold as the work on it was completed, and my practical knowledge of properties of its period similarly progressed during this time, together with a growing determination to be involved in safeguarding historic buildings.

My final job before returning to the Island was with the Heritage Lottery Fund, monitoring the progress of projects which had received grants. I had responsibility in my portfolio for 230 of these – too many for adequate scrutiny – and it would be a visit one day to inspect renovations at the Royal Albert Hall and quickly on the next to a new visitor centre at the Tower of London or to a wildlife trust seeking to acquire new areas of land.

Then I spotted the National Trust for Jersey's advertisement for its paid executive in charge of office, staff and operations. Much of my recent experience was relevant and I relished the prospect of a post where I could be fully involved and have the potential to make a difference. The job description perhaps suggested a relatively relaxed regime of visiting sites and gently cantering through the working week. It has turned out to be slightly more intense! The Trust, I quickly discovered, had considerable scope which was not being fully tapped. As the biggest landowner in Jersey, except for the States, and with ten or so large properties and much land to manage, it has the very laudable objective of being an organisation for the benefit of the whole Island. Everyone in Jersey should know of the Trust and its purpose, but this is clearly not so. Steadily its profile is improving, but we still have some way to go. One problem is the need for more expertise among our staff, but staff are expensive and our resources not limitless. Also the Trust has in

Born in the 1960s...

the past been cautious when reacting to matters which it deemed 'political'. Have we at times been unduly hesitant? If our mission is to preserve the Island's areas of natural beauty and its historic buildings, then perhaps we should be prepared to fight and campaign more enthusiastically in the future. Things are moving in the right direction and, for example, success in reclaiming Plémont as a natural headland would be a marvellous and encouraging achievement.

I have returned to Jersey after a decade or more away. My big concern is the Island's lack of a long-term objective, the absence of a sense of direction. With an island such as Sark there appear to be no problems: an easy-going, less pressured way of life and just one function – tourism. Instead Jersey has taken the finance industry route and has not fully caught up with the consequences of this step. How large should the finance sector be? What are its benefits? How does it impact on the quality of Islanders' lives? The finance industry, rather than our government, seems to lead the way. We appear to be supporting it in the fear of what might lie ahead if we fail to do so. I question the wisdom of this current approach. And what have been the consequences? We have a booming, over-heated economy which has a detrimental effect on our environment and a housing shortage, all this in an island with a finite land base. With an absence of party politics, no one seems to ask these questions or formulate strategies. Take, for instance, the issue of sustainability – leaving the environment in the same or a better state for future generations. The States adopted a statement on sustainability several years ago, but no one asks whether its provisions are being implemented and, if not, why not. Not only a ministerial system of government but also political parties might enthuse electors and create a machinery of government which is more accountable.

The National Trust for Jersey has at least a partial relationship with the Island's tourist industry. I feel that Tourism are heading in the right direction: the demise of the 'bucket and spade' holidaymakers, the encouragement of higher-spending visitors, the emphasis on our natural environment and our history and heritage. The answer does not lie in an island of many golf courses or Centerparc-style developments. Jersey's charm should be cherished and utilised as its main attraction.

I have a particular concern for agriculture and the lack of vision here. Our current strategies do not look far enough ahead. Everywhere else there is talk of the removal of subsidies and direct aid, probably inevitable in the long run. Here in Jersey we should be reviewing this now. Is the Island benefiting

Born in the 1960s...

from the present system? What about the issue of nitrates? Maize crops are planted, the stubble remains exposed after harvesting resulting in large-scale soil erosion. Rye grass gets planted throughout and there are no wild grass mixes. Fields are ploughed right up to hedgerows which are cut inappropriately with little room for growth and maturity. Our farmers argue that the subsidies enable them to manage the countryside. But the question remains: do we want it managed as it is now? There may be better ways of achieving a decent and satisfying landscape, where production is no longer the sole aim of the farming industry.

I am not convinced that Jersey has the capacity to come to grips with the problems which it has been instrumental in creating. Undoubtedly there is a price to pay for everything: if we want a more natural environment, then we may need a smaller population, and this would have implications in terms of our current standards of living. Jersey needs to start addressing the issue of where it wants to go, and there needs to be a governmental system that can reflect the choices and aspirations of its inhabitants. My own future lies here so long as I see these issues being tackled. I would, however, not wish to remain in an environment steadily deteriorating and with only Jersey's north coast remaining as a token of the Island's once beautiful countryside.

Born in the 1960s...

Christina Price

The Reverend Christina Price (née Riss) was born in West Germany in 1966. Her school education, with a year in England at the age of 16, was in Germany. In 1990, having studied Chemistry at the University of Maintz, she returned to England and gained a University of Leicester degree in Law and Philosophy. She then joined BBC Radio Northampton and worked there as a journalist for seven years. In 1998 she was selected for training in the Anglican ministry. She was ordained Deacon in 2001 and Priest in 2002. She is Curate of All Saints' and St Simon's churches in St Helier. She married in 1992 and her husband, Matthew, is Assistant Editor of BBC Radio Jersey.

I was born and grew up in the Rhineland. We were a Protestant family living in a Catholic part of Germany. My father, an army officer, was originally from East Germany, having come to the west in the early '50s before the barriers went up.

My parents had been very much involved with 'twinning', and we had frequent holidays in England before I came at the age of 16 for a year to Kettering in Northamptonshire in order to improve my English. As a family we were strongly anglophile and I was to return to England in 1990 to study at the University of Leicester.

My call to the Christian ministry, with a few diversions along the way, pre-dated my English university years. But Matthew and I wanted to marry in church. He put himself forward for confirmation and I, not previously confirmed by a bishop, joined him. At the same time I began training in the Church of England as a Reader.

After seven years with BBC Radio Northampton I was accepted for ordination training and became a part-time student on the Cambridge Theological Federation's stimulating and satisfying course.

Then came the year 2001, the completion of my studies and my ordination as a Deacon. I went to my college office and sifted through the profiles of parishes offering curacies. All Saints', Jersey, had its attractions: its work with the homeless and with the Hospice, and its place as a town centre parish with these social responsibilities and a strong sense of community. Not only that, Matthew had a number of Jersey connections and contacts and we had holidayed here several times. We loved the Island. It all added up, and I rejoiced

Born in the 1960s...

at coming to Jersey. In 1999 we had been sunning ourselves on our holiday balcony at the Mountview Hotel in St John's Road, admiring the newly-built houses just below us. Two years later we were happily living in one of them.

I already knew Jersey as a beautiful and special island, but I was less aware of its sense of community. This came over strongly once I arrived and started on my parish work. An initial question for me had been about my German roots. But this has subsequently never been an issue and never raised. The fact is that the Occupation was a very dark phase in the Island's history. This was forcibly brought home to me when I visited two of our parishioners who had been isolated on their farm during this terrible period. With great pride they showed me the Red Cross box which they had received in the final months before the war ended. The parcel had arrived and at last they had had some food to eat. They knew my own background, but they shared this experience with me, and that for me was a great privilege. Those traumatic years had a huge impact on many lives: people isolated, relationships broken and unformed, loved ones lost, family against family. I am able to empathise strongly with them.

A special part of our work at All Saints' is Outreach, set up by the Vicar, Geoff Houghton, and others a few years ago. This provides care for those who live out in the streets and in the car parks, and I go out regularly bringing comfort in the form of blankets and hot drink and food. Among these unfortunates is a community spirit with its own rules of fairness and morality. They all have their own personal stories; they come from varied backgrounds; and their various situations throw up a host of related issues – mental health problems, relationship breakdown, alcoholism, drug abuse and so on. It is an aspect of Jersey life of which many in the Island are unaware.

And then there is our work at the Jersey Hospice where I am one of the four chaplains – two Anglicans, a Roman Catholic nun and a Methodist minister. There is of course stress in this commitment, but there is also great reward. You journey with people; you share their fears, their joys, their concerns, their ups and downs, their disappointments, their little successes. Simply you love them as people. Not everybody dies at the Hospice; there is respite care and a broad range of treatments. We do lose some patients; and then there is sadness – you have lost a friend.

I am conscious of a problem which is perhaps special to Jersey, and that is distance and isolation. People come here, possibly on a short-term basis, and are cut off from their family networks. And there are those at times in the Hospice who may be far from family, and relations have to fly over to visit them. Others have to go to Southampton or London for essential treatment and are separated in these circumstances, seriously ill and yet away from home and friends.

Born in the 1960s...

My work brings me into touch with a range of social issues. There is the housing question, with Jersey a third the size of, say, Derby but with the same numbers of homeless. The whole housing debate – for example people in the Portuguese community living with families in cramped accommodation and relatively ghettoised – is hugely complex and resistant to easy answers. Then there is alcohol abuse, with cirrhosis of the liver twice as prevalent as in the UK. Divorce rates too are very high and said to be twice the British figure.

Some may wonder whether I as one of the few women priests in the Island have encountered prejudice on this score. 'Not so' is my response: no one to my knowledge has left All Saints' because of my coming there. Indeed our church numbers have been on the increase, and I believe that, with our special work at the Hospice and with the homeless, we play a very positive and productive role within our community. It is not a numbers game concerning church attendance. There is a job to be done, and I love my ministry. I believe that God is out there, and the excitement is in going out to discover more about him.

In my short time in the Island I have become very conscious how passionately people care about the Island and the community. Here we are, a few miles off the French coast and somewhat further from that of Britain, and an island with its special status. Whatever the particular Jersey issues are, they are always going to be incredibly complex. And whatever our thoughts about letters in the paper, whether we agree or disagree with them, or whether we are for or against certain politicians, here are people who are passionate about making decisions and really caring for the community. God is at work and works through them. We shall inevitably always be right on the edge of having to make really hard decisions within the world context. The world is getting smaller; Jersey is a small island, and it is important that its community issues are being addressed. It is necessarily an evolving process, and God is in that process.

Jersey I love. I love its people and love the challenging work that has come my way. Here is this small community with people genuinely caring about others. Shelter, Outreach, the Women's Refuge, the Council for Alcoholism: these are issues being tackled, often with individuals on a one-to-one basis. God willing, I and my family will be part of this Jersey community in the years ahead. God knows, and I trust in that.

Born in the 1960s...

Andrew Syvret

Andrew Syvret was born in 1968 and lives in St Ouen. He attended Les Landes Primary School and Victoria College and then spent four years working in the Island's finance industry. From 1988 to 1992 he was employed by various States Departments and other employers, doing a variety of jobs mostly related to the Island's coastal waters. He then went to the University of Plymouth where he gained a degree in Fisheries Science. He returned to Jersey in 1996 and was appointed Coastal Officer with the States Planning and Environment Department. His contract there ended in 2001. He is now self-employed, doing work associated with his marine and environmental interests.

I was born into a well-known St Ouen family which has its base at Léoville, at the top of Grève de Lecq Hill. My father is a graphic artist and my mother is the executive officer of the Société Jersiaise. I had a wonderfully rural and idyllic childhood: summers on the beach at Grève de Lecq and by Barge Aground on St Ouen's Bay, visiting my lighthouse keeper uncle at Corbière, cycling the quiet country lanes in the holidays and to school, exploring German bunkers, avoiding the Battle of Flowers and grockles in general, scrumping apples and tomatoes, pottering in rock pools, and I remember getting my first real fishing hooks, having moved on from bent pins. We were given a lot of freedom in those days: no parents fussing as I climbed down a cliff to collect seagulls' eggs or when I went over to Sark or Alderney for a week's camping with my pals. It was all good training for independence and worldliness.

From my primary school, Les Landes, I went on to Victoria College. It was something of a culture shock: Vic. was town and not my territory. I did not greatly enjoy my time there. Its education then was rather too prescriptive and there was not a great deal of opportunity to expand the mind within the confines of both the syllabus and the culture. One or two of my teachers encouraged the development of individuality, but it was above all a traditional establishment. For example, I did not relish the emphasis on team games - my mind was on nature and other things. Consequently on Friday afternoons, instead of undergoing sport or joining the cadet force, I took the option to spend time at the Le Geyt Centre with less able people. I started on my A-levels but was soon told by my headmaster, Martyn Devenport, 'It is probably time you offered yourself to the employment market, Mr Syvret.' And so I did. I left school on a Friday afternoon and was with the Hong Kong and Shanghai Bank on the following Monday morning. It was not what I had dreamed of - a degree in English and teaching - but I was pleased to be away from school and somewhat more independent.

Now at 16 I was surrounded by a host of people who judged their success not in school ties but in balance sheet terms. They would leave work on a Friday evening for a drink; I would be out of the office, checking the wind direction and deciding where to go fishing. Fishing is what drives me; I can't help it. It is a family standing joke that I have sea water and not blood in my veins and that one day I shall wake up and find that I have gills. It was ever a cause for surprise to those at the next desk that I would be spending the coming weekend not joining in their indulgences but marooned somewhere in the Channel Islands, fishing rod in hand.

I had four years in all with the Hong Kong and Shanghai Bank and then with James Capel, the stockbroking firm which the bank had acquired. I do not deny that I enjoyed parts of my time within the Island's finance industry, but I rapidly realised that for me it was all a chess game with money, essentially unproductive and lacking any true fulfilment. I never did like chess, so I was thus not greatly upset by the redundancy which caught up with me, and I exchanged sitting in front of a bank of computer screens with phones going left, right and centre for work at the harbour. Walking the marina pontoons to collect dues from visiting yachtsmen was like a breath of fresh air.

Between the years 1988 and 1992 I did a range of jobs, principally for the States but also for a number of other employers. Some of the things I enjoyed most were hoisting flags as Signalman at Fort Regent Signal Station where I took observations for the Met. Office, replacing harbour moorings, working as a lackey on a dredging barge, cleaning the Island's beaches and public toilets, a season on the potatoes, researching our local lobster fishery and vehicle traffic, and so on. All the while I was fishing every spare moment. This period was very instructive, giving me a valuable view of many facets of Jersey life.

Within weeks of my starting work for the States for the first time, friends informed me that I had a job for life. Initially I found this statement quite puzzling, but over the years I have come not only to understand where they

Born in the 1960s...

were coming from but also to realise just how far things go in that direction. Given the Island's incredible affluence and the relative scarcity of labour and resources, our government in many areas was and continues to be a very 'charitable' employer and 'provider'. It has been said too often, but I have to agree, that if private businesses were managed as many functions of the States are, then they would likely fold in a very short time.

What I have always been particularly shocked by is the enormous influence one individual and his or her empire can wield on a whole sector of Island life, and wider. At the same time I acknowledge that there were and are extremely capable and diligent individuals within States service whom I have come to admire for their tenacity as much as anything else. Back then, even from my position at the very bottom of the 'management structure', for the first time I was able to see very clearly the disproportionate impact that a single domineering or incompetent politician or public sector employee could have in our nine-by-five mile democracy. The years working for the States, both then and later, opened my eyes, not least to the intimate relationship between local politics and business.

Then came a life-changing experience: with help from Jersey's generous mature student funding programme, I went to university in Plymouth and did its Fisheries Science degree course. Above all this taught me how to challenge my intellectual boundaries, how to question, how to research and how to express myself more confidently. Naturally I also made some wonderful friends and, in common with many of them, I hoped to use my new qualification to travel and work in the fisheries field. On my return to the Island, however, I learned that a new environmental team at Planning and Environment required someone to help develop and implement a coastal zone management strategy. I spoke to them, liked those I met and what I saw and heard. They offered me an initial three-month contract there and then, and so I did what I had once said I would never do again and resumed working for the States of Jersey the next day.

In all I spent about five years with Planning and Environment as a consultant, and on the whole I was pleased with what we achieved on the marine front while I was there. The process of designating our south-east coast as a Ramsar site was a major undertaking, with, thankfully, a successful outcome. A great number of people were involved and, considering that our inter-tidal habitats are globally unique, I was in truth more relieved than elated when the need to conserve them in an international context was finally acknowledged.

Born in the 1960s...

Another debate I feel I influenced in a positive way was the discussion leading to the development of future options for the sea defences in St Ouen's Bay. Perhaps, though, the most rewarding experiences I had during this period were those I had with children, eager to learn and connect with their environment, nature and the elements, in the same way as when I was a child - and still am.

My contract at Planning and Environment came to its natural end in 2001. After much reflection I concluded that, regardless of established States policies and the outcome of any review of government, too many of our local politicians do not see environmental work as a valid priority. Given this fact, I decided it was time to make my own way. I had also tired of my status as a pseudo-States employee. I value my integrity and my independence; silence does not come easily to me when I feel further information will better inform a discussion. Too often I found myself having to bite my tongue. I realised the extent of my disenchantment when I began to feel embarrassed when I told people that I was employed by the States.

Sadly I feel the whole States administration is something of a rudderless ship. How then does the ship acquire a rudder? Perhaps Jersey lacks a politician of real vision at the helm. Certainly there has been no such person during my lifetime. Also, I have a hunch that Jersey's lack of direction, its fairly random laissez-faire course, is not entirely accidental. I often think that this drifting ship actually suits the interests of the pro-economic development lobby. The loyalty of the finance industry as a whole depends upon the outside world's perception of our stable government and regulatory performance while, on the other hand, local corporate society clearly benefits from the absence of control afforded by our fragmented, conflict-based political process and perpetual lack of effective opposition. A curious juxtaposition?

Until the late '60s we had a fairly balanced economy. Then the finance industry started to thrive and, like a cuckoo, started throwing everything else out of the nest. Most traditional industries have been squeezed into a corner as a consequence. Some visionary planning action could have afforded them a better chance of survival, justly recognising their cultural place in the Island alongside an undeniably desirable offshore finance sector. Instead, much of what I love about this place has simply been sold to the highest bidder and the quality of life for many has been eroded beyond their tolerance.

This island is an incredible capsule, only an hour away from London. Sir Walter Raleigh described it as the most beautiful place he had ever visited and Karl Marx used to decry its decadence and decay when holidaying here.

Born in the 1960s...

We have so many assets which our government, in its singular quest for economic growth, has failed to recognise or respect. Consequently many people, with whom I have been forced to share my native island, have no genuine emotional investment in its future, only a short-term financial interest. This cannot be good for the health of our community.

One of the principal mistakes has been allowing uncontrolled population growth, a virtual open door policy despite States protestations to the contrary. I would not be so foolish as to suggest that we should build a wall around our island, but by bulk immigration is Jersey's identity most greatly threatened.

Nor has the States committee system helped our democracy: it has proved cumbersome and inefficient. I have worked within it and witnessed its operation - committee meetings with unread agendas and papers on the table in front of sleeping politicians. And with elections every three years, who will take unpopular decisions, who will ever administer unpleasant but necessary medicine if re-election is jeopardised as a consequence? Clothier and a ministerial system is perhaps the answer but it is not a debate which has interested me deeply, since I have viewed its arrival as something of a *fait accompli*. In common with so many in our population I feel disfranchised by the nature of our government and am never surprised by election apathy. Perhaps, as we can now vote for pop idols with our television remote controls, we should use the same device for referendums - securing direct electoral involvement. Or why not a bar code on electoral papers, with eligibility in a lottery draw as a reward for those who vote – surely guaranteed to encourage folks to play their part in the democratic process? It is hard to be negative all day when you live in St Ouen!

As to the future, I offer a few suggestions. Why not control more strictly and equitably exactly who does come to live on our rock? Why not have a finance industry slimmed down, with only high-earning 'blue chip', 'ethical' finance houses which we pick and choose? Why not make local agriculture and horticulture entirely organic and further develop our marine industries? Why not have good public transport or only electric cars that stick to speed limits? Why not use imagination to promote our identity as a truly unique tourist destination? An opulent retreat an hour or so from most European capitals. I guess it doesn't do any harm to dream.

At the heart of it all Jersey still has a core identity that will remain intact. I may have a love/hate relationship with the Island and I do suffer from cabin fever at times when the confines of the place get to me. But Jersey is a virus and I have it. I am content here right now and, whatever the current problems and discontents, I have the confidence that the nature of this sacred place will, against any odds, prevail. St Ouen will forever be my spiritual home.

Sarah Williams

Doctor Sarah Williams, daughter of Anthony (medical practitioner and Anglican priest) and Louise Williams, was born in Jersey in 1968. She went to school at Moorestown College and then Jersey College for Girls. From 1987 to 1991 she studied Medicine at the University of St Andrews, subsequently doing her clinical training at Cambridge. She took further qualifications and undertook general practitioner training in Poole where she met Cliff McClelland, a corporate event manager. They married in November 1998. A year later they came to live permanently in Jersey where she is a family doctor. She and her husband are active members of St Paul's church.

I had a very happy Jersey childhood and I have strong early memories of our big farmhouse home, Sunday lunches with family and grandparents (Frank and Marian Perrée) and boating holidays on the French coast. I was an avid reader as a child, and my one frustration then was Jersey's lack of rivers - rivers always seemed to be exciting features of children's stories. That was my only grumble. Otherwise it was a charmed existence of beaches, swimming and sailing. And only on my return to the Island as a doctor just a few years ago have I realised how fortunate I was, especially when I was aged 11 and my mother inherited Beau Vallon, a marvellous farmhouse property in St Saviour, from her godmother. It has been my home since then.

During my early years at school, enjoyment was diminished by the fact that, as I was bright, I was often bored in class and frequently told that I was no good at sport – at least those sports which were on offer. Similar frustrations continued in my first years at JCG: too little art and music and too much maths and science, and one's potential, with restricted options, never fully

Born in the 1960s...

exercised. But the sixth form was different: I studied my A-levels with the Victoria College boys. This was far more fun socially and academically and suited me much better.

It was at this stage - as a sixth former - that I began fully to know Jersey and appreciate it. There was the sailing and the social life of the yacht clubs at St Aubin and St Helier, and there were also the means, with the driving test passed, of exploring the Island. Several of us at school chose photography as an activities option, and this was a nice excuse to visit the beauty spots, especially those with refreshments available. There were the cliff paths to discover, and my grandfather told me about Crabbé where the ladder was still in place and the caves invited exploration. There is no doubting that my love affair with the place of my birth deepened during these teenage years.

As to Jersey's political and economic situation I had at the time few strong views. There was, of course, discussion at home, and I realised that the finance industry gave us considerable wealth. I sensed that, if for example a new hospital was required, then there was the money to provide it. I found this too as a student - never any problem getting grants for education and travel. As to politics, I remember how shocked I and some of my classmates were when, at the time of the 1984 British general election, we asked our teacher how she would have voted, and she said, 'Labour'. How, we thought, could anyone vote Labour? Surely, our youthful prejudices seemed to tell us, it would be the downfall of the Channel Islands if a Labour government were returned to power.

On leaving school medicine was not my initial ambition. I went off to St Andrews to study Biochemistry, and quickly realised that this would not fulfil me and provide a lifelong career. The university authorities agreed to take me on the medical course the following year and I thus had a 'gap'. For part of this I travelled on my own through India and worked for a time at Mother Teresa's children's home, actually meeting the great woman on one occasion. It was all very formative for an 18-year old, not the least experience being witness to the extreme poverty on the streets of Calcutta. It acted as a big boost to the development of my social conscience and Christian faith.

Then it was back to St Andrews and the speedy confirmation that I had made the right career choice. In my first year I also did some moral philosophy. Nobody at school had ever asked me to think, and I had always been able to sponge up new material very adequately; the moral philosophy was a valuable corrective to this. After St Andrews came three very satisfying clinical years in Cambridge (I was a member of Queens' College). The truth is that I loved

Born in the 1960s...

my student years and took every opportunity to travel: three trips to South America, building houses and churches under the auspices of a Christian mission called Latin Link and a Jersey overseas aid project in Zambia. I also did my medical elective in Papua New Guinea as a member of a team bringing medicine by hovercraft to remote areas of the country.

Then after all this came the shock of finding out that one isn't really trained for the practicalities of being a junior doctor. There was that first day, trying to prescribe paracetamol and not even knowing how to write it up on a drug chart, and the experience of encountering patients who were in fact dying and with me being the first person called to treat them. It was a case of being thrown in at the deep end and learning very quickly how to swim. Nevertheless I enjoyed the challenge and camaraderie of hospital life.

In September 1997 I went for six months as a medical officer in a mission hospital in Nepal. I had a two-week crash course in Nepali and discovered that amongst other duties I had responsibility for covering obstetrics of which I had done little. Without CT scans and other sophisticated testing available it was clinical medicine in the raw, and I loved it. Also the Nepal experience was a determinant in my decision to return to and carry on my career in Jersey. Fuelled by my Christian beliefs and practice I believe in sharing what we have with the developing world, materially or in skills and time. Much as I loved my work in Nepal, I felt that what skills I have in communication, essential for good general medical practice, could best be exercised in my own country and culture. I wished to use the professional gifts I possess to the fullest potential, and it became clear to me that coming back to Jersey was the right course.

By this time I had a husband who favoured the move. Cliff and I had met through our church in Poole. In some ways he was an improbable partner - a divorcee with two children (one of whom was bridesmaid at our wedding) and a former army physical training instructor. His immortal chat-line to me - at a church lunch - had been this: 'I bet you're the sort of girl who leaves her clothes all over the bedroom floor, aren't you?' He had me summed up in one (and has failed to cure me of the habit). It is a huge testimony to his and my Christian faith that we are so compatible, with similar views on what we want out of life. And that is why we are married.

General practice in Jersey has its advantages: patients pay for the service, and they have respect for our time as we do for theirs; the standard of patient care is good, and to some extent the system of competition between practices keeps the GP up to the mark. Compared with the UK, however, I find a

Born in the 1960s...

certain lack of academic stimulation. For example, many practices have been slow to adopt computers, and this makes audit very difficult. Doctors lack incentives to attend training sessions since this means seeing fewer patients and a loss of income. Also the payment system conspires against having practice nurses carrying out basic procedures which in Jersey are performed by doctors, and this is an inefficiency for which ultimately the patient pays. Discussion to remedy some of this is proceeding; general practice here cannot remain unchanged, and perhaps some sort of European insurance scheme could be the way ahead.

There is possibly a greater Island problem in secondary care - hospitals and long-term nursing. Waiting lists are burgeoning and Jersey has a public spending crisis at the same time as the medical services are suffering from chronic under-funding. All this is exacerbated by the greater demands now being made by an ageing population on a health service with the potential, as medical science advances, of offering more comprehensive and expensive treatments. Crisis point has been reached within secondary care; in primary care we can probably continue for the time being, but the situation is not tenable for ever, and we must be pro-active in order to avoid difficult problems in the future.

How then did I find Jersey, returning here as a professional woman? Sitting in my GP surgery I quickly began to discover aspects not evident to me in the surfing, sun-bathing island of my youth. Many of my patients were presenting problems which derived ultimately from the housing situation. There was, early on, the Jersey-born girl - the same age as myself - who, instead of growing up in a lovely farmhouse with its big garden and handsome yard, had lived with her family in what was nothing more than a garage with an outside loo. This shortage of housing throws up a host of problems: children's behavioural difficulties; high rents causing debt; meeting accommodation costs with long work hours and consequent stress to marriages and relationships. Changes of lifestyle rather than anti-depressants would be the answer, but this is seldom a possible remedy.

I also quickly became aware of a serious Island racism problem. Jersey has over the generations relied on immigrant workers, and it seems extraordinary to me that there is so much xenophobia. I hear criticism of the Portuguese - unfair complaints that they are given housing at the expense of Jersey people. One is aware of it on the streets and in the shops, and this is a racism not necessarily aimed at others not of Jersey descent who also come here in large numbers to gain work. I believe that there is an urgent need for some form of racial equality commission to address this sad element within our Island society.

As well as racism, I sense a somewhat old-fashioned attitude to women within the Island. I am not a feminist and celebrate the diversity of men and women. But what about those income tax and social security forms, with the man cited as head of the household? And what about the sort of maternity rights which women in Britain and other European countries now rightly possess? Not to mention paternity leave!

A danger in Jersey is that all-pervasive culture solely concerned with the acquisition of wealth. Here is the big divide - between the very rich and the very poor. Such divisions inevitably lead to inequalities particularly in health, with recent evidence from the UK (published in the British Medical Journal) showing a life expectancy gap between professional and unskilled workers of 9.5 years for men and 6.4 years for women. We must work to close this so-called poverty gap. Our wealth-oriented community throws up so many related problems: the fear of scaring off the richest by taxing them too much; the labour required to service the needs of the wealthy; dissatisfaction among the younger people of the Island, unable to afford a house; increased drug usage as a means of obliterating hardship, and dealing in drugs as a way of making some money.

All this, in one way or another, stems from the finance industry's grip. It has made the Island rich and has also produced a disadvantaged workforce to service it. I am not an economist, but it seems that Jersey has become something of a slave to Finance, our one remaining big industry. Along with this is our current situation: the need for taxes to go up to pay for the budget deficit and improved social services; a civil service which needs to be made more efficient; a large public sector which requires pruning; a shortage of labour and the consequent grip of the unions. In addition to all this I have a deep concern for our environment: new Island plans erode and re-define greenfield sites, and little is done in the way of sustainable development. I believe that it would not be the end of the world if the finance industry contracted, but I wonder whether we have the political machinery effectively to manage its decline.

I am not an expert in these matters, but I see many of those in the Island's government who are well-intentioned but not always well qualified. We have individuals elected to the States, making policy promises and yet lacking the means of implementing them. The answer to this is surely party politics, with the electorate presented with genuine choice and with a coherent opposition

Born in the 1960s...

within the States to challenge and scrutinise what the elected majority propose. I believe this would allow us to move forward constructively.

In the final analysis I am committed to Jersey. I see patients of mine leaving for Australia and elsewhere in search of a good job, cheaper housing and a better quality of life. But I am staying here. I am not one to sit inactive; but professional considerations make my standing for the States not a current possibility. Perhaps this may be a future option, but in the meantime an initial dipping of the toe into the more restricted waters of medical politics is a more practicable course. I do, however, believe that it is those such as myself, willing to express their views on Island problems, who also have a responsibility to do something about finding the solutions.

The answer does not lie in looking back and reflecting on, even wishing for a return to, a Jersey that has passed. That does not facilitate moving forward. We should instead enjoy the very positive aspects of life here. We must not be afraid to make the changes that are surely necessary to maintain and improve our quality of life in this beautiful, if slightly quirky, island that I am privileged and proud to call home.

Chapter Seven

Born in the 1970s

Louise Read
Maria da Silva

Louise Read

Louise Read (née Hodsoll) was born in 1976. Her childhood home was in Battle, East Sussex, where she attended the local primary school. From there she went on to Tunbridge Wells Girls' Grammar School and then to Southampton University where she read Business Economics and Accountancy. In 1997 she came to Jersey as an audit assistant with Cooper and Lybrand, married in 1998 and qualified as a chartered accountant in 2000. The following year she became the Financial Accountant at Jersey Post. She is a bell-ringer and a choir member at St Mark's church.

*M*y mother was a teacher of P.E. and then of Special Needs who left the profession and now works alongside my father who has his own joinery company. With my brother and sister I had a conventional family life and, after primary school, passed the 11-plus examination for Tunbridge Wells Girls' Grammar School. I was particularly pleased about this: it meant that I would not be taught by my mother (an early attempt at her teaching me to swim ended in us both vowing 'never again') and also, not having been allowed to watch *Grange Hill* when I was younger, I had the sneaking suspicion that many co-ed schools were just as anarchic. Despite the long train and bus journey each way I enjoyed my grammar school years, did not miss out by its being single-sex and obtained good GCSEs and A-levels (in Geography and Economics with A/S levels in Statistics and French). I managed to have a full social life outside school which included cricket scoring (I once actually scored for the MCC).

I achieved my first choice university, Southampton, attracted by the fact that it was not a big city establishment, that it was quite 'green' and, most importantly, that it was not too far from home. Having done work experience during school holidays with a local Sussex firm of chartered accountants, I went to university clear in my career ambitions, and the course – Business Economics and Accountancy – was the right one for me. These years were not all work; I was a great ballroom dancing enthusiast and keen, much more so than now, on circuit training. One particularly bizarre episode at this time remains in my memory. One of our professors took 20 of us to a disused army base where we were put through a range of management skills-related exercises: climbing down sewers, checking houses for booby traps and the like. Unknown to us at the time, the composition of the various teams had been 'fixed' according to our personality types. One team, for example, consisted of quiet, reserved personalities and was consequently ineffectual. My own team had been 'packed' with budding leaders and proved so useless that we were threatening to go home after the first hour.

My links with Jersey had begun during my sixth form years. I had taken up church bell-ringing at the age of 16 and there was a connection through our local tower with the Jersey ringers. Thus I first came to the Island as a schoolgirl on a ringing weekend.

Between my second and third year at university I decided to take advantage of the long summer break and came to Jersey for some work experience, doing a fortnight or so with Ernst and Young, Price Waterhouse and Coopers and Lybrand. Both my favourites, Price Waterhouse and Coopers and Lybrand, offered me jobs and I decided to accept a position with the latter. I had no wish to work in a bustling city but recognised the importance of having a 'big name' on my c.v. Thus Jersey, fulfilling both these conditions, suited me well. I liked the Island's size; it was a community not too unlike my own home town. I relish the freedom of walking to work or to the beach and of driving for ten minutes and being in the middle of nowhere. In addition, I had the bell-ringing links and, by the end of the summer, through a fortuitous meeting in a fish and chip shop, I made the acquaintance of my future husband, both bell-ringer and banker. I acknowledge my good fortune.

In fact my first Jersey summer was made the more brilliant by having a temporary job with Flying Flowers before starting with Coopers. I worked in the visitors' centre cafeteria there, serving thousands of Jersey cream teas to old age pensioners. The OAPs would get themselves into all sorts of bother from picking up the wrong walking stick to leaving their teeth or glasses lying around. I even once had to promise an elderly gentleman that I would stand guard over his rather battered hat. But I did fulfil a long-held ambition: I learnt how to use a Mr Whippy ice cream machine.

After months of navigating my way around via the airport I began to familiarise myself with the Island. My accountancy work, where I had opted for commercial auditing, got me into a variety of local businesses from tourist attractions to the big local groups. There were also contacts with the finance industry and growing social links with my Jersey and Guernsey work

Born in the 1970s...

colleagues.

I also became aware of the Island's problems, especially that of the 'haves' and 'have nots'. There is a bigger divide here than in the UK – more of a 'keeping up with the Joneses'. Compare King Street with an English high street; note what designer-labelled bags people are carrying and the level of income such purchases demand. Then consider the other people and the temptation to some to them of living beyond their means.

Related to all this is the accommodation problem. My husband's employer houses us, but I think of those less fortunate local people (not just immigrants to the Island) coping in inadequate yet expensive bed-sits.

After qualifying as a chartered accountant in September 2000 I made a career move. By this time Coopers and Lybrand had amalgamated with Price Waterhouse and I was finding the pressurised work and overtime too much. I decided to seek more balance and control in my professional life. I visited a recruitment agency who suggested work in trust companies and banks, but what I really wanted was to be involved in a business that did something tangible. I was interviewed by Jersey Post and was offered the position of Assistant Management Accountant. On the day I started (although not, I was assured, as a direct result) the Financial Accountant gave in her notice and I was invited to step into her shoes.

My predecessor had done much for Jersey Post, having introduced an up-to-date finance package into an organisation where there was not so much as a PC seven years before. I now took up the baton and began with the task of preparing Jersey Post's first 'commercial' accounts. Few realise that the States of Jersey do not follow all the standard accounting rules and regulations and that the States accounts are not audited. My first task was therefore to create a 'commercial' set of accounts from the information available, thus helping to bring Jersey Post, moving towards incorporation, from a States to a commercial standard. (It was only in mid-2000 that Jersey Post was given its own bank account.) I had the good fortune for all this experience to come my way by the age of 24. I just happened to be in the right place at the right time; it was an opportunity taken on with some misgivings but not to be missed.

My job gives me at least some insight into the way Jersey and its government function. I am partially within the system and thus experience something of the frustrations of decision-taking. Although many powers are delegated down to Jersey Post's directors, certain decisions have to be made by the States of Jersey Postal Committee which only meets once a month. This can cause delays. Then, coming from a commercial background, I often encounter decisions that would be justifiable on commercial grounds but which do not sit with the political climate of the day. It is a challenging adjustment to make.

Although we are a States entity rather than a commercial body, things are changing: incorporation will remove some red tape (but will introduce more in some areas), and in these financially leaner times, where we are for the first time controlling our own money, we are acquiring a new mind set and are beginning to embrace concepts such as cash flow planning and strict budgeting.

With huge surpluses in the past the need for stringent financial management throughout the States has perhaps been overlooked. The Island's full employment situation has meant that, throughout Jersey and not just in the public service, people can be over-promoted. Consider the overspends on various big capital projects or recent proposals such as the Jubilee obelisk and the new waterfront bridge. Jersey's money, however, is becoming tighter; such matters are being subjected to even closer scrutiny. The case for a system of government with a better central planning function becomes stronger, and a ministerial structure with proper accountability is surely the way ahead. Also we require well-qualified and properly rewarded people in charge of these ministries, a beefed-up civil service staffed at the top by those who have had experience as leaders of businesses or as heads of banks or as former partners in law firms.

Another area of Jersey's government that causes many newcomers to the Island (myself included) to raise an eyebrow is the parish system. So much efficiency, co-ordination and economy would be achieved if it were to be scrapped. It is surely rather weird that in an island of this size we have different bases for rates, and with welfare benefits seeming to depend on differing discretionary decisions. If defenders of the parish system argue for it on grounds of history and tradition, then surely the stage has been reached when the price of sentiment should be assessed.

Our taxation system is currently being reviewed and, I believe, cries out for reform. We need to guard against Guernsey and the Isle of Man stealing a march on us. The people of Jersey have had it easy for far too long. The taxation of benefits in kind should be considered, and the introduction of PAYE is long overdue. PAYE would collect more tax, catching up with those who come for a few months and then disappear in a puff of smoke. It would also have a one-off cash flow benefit. At present the States is forced to pay out before it received the revenues it is due.

Born in the 1970s...

The future of the finance industry is a topical issue. I am certain that it will continue in one form or another, but Jersey's time for complacency is past. My husband and I are not able to buy property here but, if the option were available to us, would not be confident enough about the Island's future to do so. A decline in the finance industry and a consequent fall in property values could leave us with considerable negative equity. We are happy to be Island residents; its lifestyle for us is congenial. But, besides concern for the future of the finance industry (which would threaten our own employment), there are developments which slightly tarnish our Jersey experience. A particular sadness is the reclaimed waterfront area. Instead of the equivalent of a Sydney Opera House or a Bilbao Guggenheim we have a mess: a massive and unattractive housing development and a cinema complex which will require the attendance of most of the population twice a week year round in order to make it viable.

I would love to think that someone somewhere, in an influential position, will have the courage very soon to stand up and say 'stop'. Stop the obliteration of 'old' Jersey and the building of brightly coloured blocks of luxury flats and chain stores; stop the decline in the tourist industry and in agriculture (Jersey needs something other than Finance); and, finally, stop looking backwards to 'the good old days'. With careful planning and changes now, the future can be just as rosy as was the past.

Maria da Silva

Maria da Silva was born in Jersey in 1979. She attended Les Landes Primary School and went on from there at the age of 11 to Les Quennevais. She then studied at Highlands College, gaining a GNVQ in Tourism. At various times she has done translation work for the police and joined the States Tourism Department in 1999 as a Visitor Services Information Officer. She was chosen as Miss Battle in 2002, the centenary year of the Battle of Flowers.

My father came to Jersey from Madeira in 1976 and my mother followed a few months later. They worked on various farms, in due course spending 15 years at Grantez Farm, where my father was foreman, before returning permanently to Madeira in 1999. My brother David was ten months younger than me and my parents, unable to cope with both their work and their young family, sent us both back to our Madeiran grandparents. At the time I was just 14 months old. Almost a year later my heartbroken mother came and brought us back to Jersey.

It was at this time, on our return, that my childhood memories start. Our first day at primary school I remember vividly: my brother and myself sitting in the corner and unable to speak a word of English, and Mum, knowing only a bit more, staying with us all that afternoon to keep us company.

But we quickly found our feet, despite there being only one other Portuguese child in the class. Our teachers I can only describe as brilliant (I am still in touch with some of them), and several mothers used to come in to school to help us with our English and our reading. We both made swift progress and found it all very exciting. It was really quite simple: we wanted to be with Mum and Dad, and this therefore meant Jersey and school here.

David and I encountered next to no discrimination or unpleasantness at Les Landes. The school had sensible policies and disciplined any boy or girl who caused any problems of this sort. And my love of Jersey grew. We would go back to Madeira every year, excited to be on the plane and thrilled by the prospect of seeing family, but at the same time I was dying to come back. We both made a pact at this young age that we would always live in Jersey, and there has been no weakening of my resolve in the intervening years. The attraction at the time was powerful: school, with its educational trips and its computers; our marvellous landlady and the trips to the beaches with her and her own children; our friends from school – Jersey boys and girls – living along the road. This was home and where we would remain.

At the age of 11 and with good school reports for both of us, we followed the well-trodden route from Les Landes to Les Quennevais School. Here a number of us, and not only Portuguese, encountered difficulties. Those of us from St Ouen had received such a good grounding at Les Landes and were picked on for that, and, into our second and third years at secondary school, we began to experience particular anti-Portuguese jibes: the usual comments such as 'Go back home' and 'What are you doing here?' I suppose one just learned to take it. If we had been, say, French we would not have attracted such remarks. Also the irony was that we were actually Jersey-born and our mum and dad had lived here long enough to have housing qualifications. It was upsetting but we took it. The school had its disciplinary procedures, but there was our natural reluctance to go and seek teachers' help and then be accused of telling tales.

This sort of discrimination was also encountered outside, but it was worse in school. Speaking with other Portuguese students I know that others had bigger problems than myself. As a young teenager, however, I was not at all a confident girl, and this was the result of being called names and the sort of isolation which that causes.

What saved me and got me out of my shell was El Tico, the café down on St Ouen's Bay. I worked there at weekends and in the holidays, starting at the age of 13 doing some of the cooking and progressing to the till, front of house, being pushed to do it and then never wishing to relinquish the position. My bosses there, Pat and Richard, were so good to me, so down to earth, and it was they who gave me my self-confidence, having been put down so much at school. The whole work experience there gave me that love of communicating with people and pointed me in the direction of Highlands College and a career in Tourism.

My time at Highlands on the Tourism course was a marvellous experience. Our teachers were great; I was relaxed and happy; we had lots of careers advice as well as some relevant experience – trips to both Spain and Italy to observe the tourist industries there. At the same time my social life was expanding. When in 1999 Mum and Dad went back to Madeira, that was fine but, in line with my early pledge, I took the big step to stay, knowing that Jersey was for me.

After I had left school and before starting work at Tourism I did some translation work for the police. It was an interesting and illuminating experience, sitting in interview rooms at the police station and witnessing a particular and significant aspect of the Jersey-Portuguese interface. I saw the difficulties that some Portuguese have in adapting not only to Jersey's language and culture but also to its laws. Law in Madeira is perhaps somewhat more flexible, with petty crime not regarded as too serious and with what might be acceptable in Madeira not being acceptable here. It is understandable, if not excusable, how a Portuguese person cannot always make the required adjustment to a stricter code. All this gave me some insight into the whole area of community relations. I recognise and favour the 'when in Rome, do as the Romans' instruction. But it is difficult for some Portuguese to understand and respond to it.

Is it the fault of the Portuguese in not being better integrated? Perhaps it is six of one and half a dozen of the other. Portuguese can be blamed for not making greater efforts to learn English and to adapt to the Jersey lifestyle. On the Jersey side, however, there are some Islanders who want Jersey to be for Jersey people and are unwilling to see things changing. Jersey needs to be just a bit more pro-active in encouraging and welcoming those from Portugal and elsewhere who come to the Island to fill the employment gaps and do the jobs which Jersey people will not do. At the same time, those coming to the Island should make an effort to adapt to Jersey life if they wish to prosper. I myself (Jersey-born, it is true) and many in my situation have done just that.

I have now been with Jersey Tourism since 1999, on the front desk and dealing with the public. It is a fairly demanding job but so satisfying, trying to make the experience of visitors to the Island just that bit better and more enjoyable. I have great faith that Jersey will continue to be a fine holiday destination. It has so much to offer, and the amount of repeat business is an indication of this. I believe that there has to be a fine balance concerning States investment in tourism: too much development in providing tourist attractions threatens the Island's natural beauty, while many people come to Jersey because they love Jersey as it is. Tourism will have its ups and downs, but I am an optimist about its future.

One of Jersey's problems today is that people take the Island for granted, grumble about what they consider to be wrong with it and fail to realise what are its advantages. They should hear the comments I receive frequently from visitors – the positive feedback such as, 'You are so lucky to be living in Jersey'. We all tend to complain too much and overlook all the marvellous good things about the Island.

I had the wonderful opportunity of being Miss Battle in the year 2002. It was undoubtedly the experience of a lifetime and I had such a marvellous response from everybody, both Jersey people and the Portuguese community. What a privilege to act as an ambassador for the Island and to be welcomed everywhere with open arms!

There is perhaps a general lesson here for all of us: being ready to seize every opportunity to do something for the Island. I am fortunate in having the knowledge and experience of two islands. Jersey is my true home; Madeira, where my parents are, is also a home of sorts. Both islands are, in their different ways, stunning. Madeira has the better weather and is an up and coming place, but Jersey has that special ingredient which draws me to it and holds me here. If we who live in Jersey are prepared to do more than just talk about our island but also be active for its good, then surely its bright future will be assured.

Chapter Eight

Born in the 1980s

Christopher Le Quesne
Robert Michel

Christopher Le Quesne

Born in Jersey in 1984, Christopher Le Quesne was educated first at La Pouquelaye Primary School and subsequently at Victoria College Preparatory School and Victoria College where in his final year he was Head Prefect. In 2002 he went to the University of Leeds to read English. His family home is in St Mary.

*M*y mother, a Perchard, is a primary school supply teacher and my father is a sales manager at Abbey Garage. We are also related to de Gruchys, and I seem to be at least a distant cousin of anybody I meet. It may be a strange way to express it, but I have quite a lot of family behind me.

One of my strongest early memories is of Sunday afternoon family walks in different areas of the Island and, living then near the top of New St John's Road, we were close to the sea along Victoria Avenue. Also, we could get easily to the west of the Island, with barbecues for family and friends on the beaches and up in the sand dunes.

I had a marvellous time at Victoria College Prep., a wonderful school which I attended from 1991 in John Hibbs's final years. I have nothing but good memories of it and ended up as Head Boy. Moving up to College at 11 was something of a shock: back to being the most junior, and ever-hungry as I burned off a lot of energy lugging my school bag, weighed down with text-books, round the campus all day.

It was around this time that I became aware of my being Jersey rather than British, that Jersey was nicely unique in the great scheme of things. Victoria College played its part in this, presenting itself powerfully in comparison with similar schools on the mainland. My school years have confirmed for me all the opportunities which the Island has to offer. Before becoming Head Prefect in my final year I was sent on a leadership course in Nottinghamshire (my first time away from home on my own). The other students on it displayed much ignorance about this little island in the Channel and were both surprised, and perhaps somewhat jealous, to learn of the full life on offer over here – the

Born in the 1980s...

beaches, the surfing, the social activities, the diversity of the cultural scene. Of course many of the Island's young people would not admit to this; there is something of a false consensus of there being too little to do here. But if there is this apathy, there is also huge fulfilment for those who wish to exploit all the Island's many opportunities.

Jersey has yet more. This small population, with diverse backgrounds and differing goals and aspirations, has its own special and unique traditions, be it the Battle of Flowers or the continuing historic parish system. It is when one goes away and talks about the Island to others that one's sense of good fortune is reinforced. My Nottingham leadership course brought all this home to me. Here I was with public school boarders, some of them unashamedly snobbish, from prosperous backgrounds and with their expensive holidays in California and elsewhere. I was able to reflect on our own bustling town of St Helier and our marvellous bays and beaches. I was able to say with a touch of pride, 'Yes, I'm from Jersey'.

I am developing an interest in the Island and its political affairs, and in this respect I am probably not typical of the average person of my age. I have had the advantage of studying a Political Philosophy module for my A-levels; I keep up to date with the *Jersey Evening Post*; and there are the times when family are round for lunch and my father and uncle get chatting about this and that. Some of my contemporaries may be interested in these matters: interested – yes; bothered – no. The majority of them are on their way to university, unlikely – at least for a time – to return to the Island and are indifferent to the issues of Jersey's governmental system. Those of my acquaintances who are able to have an intelligent conversation on these matters and put forward a rounded view are definitely in a minority.

At the present time there is much moaning about Jersey's current state. It cannot be as bad as made out by some of the merchants of gloom. And yet there are flaws. Are we truly a democracy? Does the system sufficiently encourage people to have and express a viewpoint? Are electors too inclined to vote for personalities rather than for issues? In all this I favour the thrust of the Clothier reforms but I want to see change which at the same time respects our special culture and history. I believe, too, that we are fortunate in not having party politics, with parties inclined to apply their energies in fighting against each other rather than promoting what they believe to be true.

I increasingly recognise Jersey's great strengths; these are not only its geography and heritage but also its people. Those teachers at school, over here on five-year contracts, could never get over their surprise at the locals' politeness – people letting you out in traffic or giving directions in town. Then there is the relatively high standard of living, the restaurants, the rich quality of social life where, as I have said previously, we are spoilt for choice.

What then is the down side? There is, unsurprisingly, an insularity. I look, for example, at a *JEP* headline and ask myself, 'Is this really news?' Then there are recent developments in architecture. Take the waterfront constructions. Seen by a visitor coming in by sea, do they adequately reflect the true character of the Island? I am also saddened by the decline of tourism (my father used to be a hotel manager) and Jersey's loss of this particular niche.

Another concern is the attitude shown by some to the Portuguese. There is, most unfortunately, a measure of ill-feeling towards them. What are they doing here? Why can't they get work in their own country? Such sentiments I strongly deprecate, and they are held by comfortable Jersey youths who would not themselves dream of doing the jobs which our Portuguese undertake. It is true that in some cases the Portuguese do not help themselves, at times unwilling to learn English and hence integrate more easily. But this whole issue is one of the biggest criticisms that can be levelled against us. It would be good to have members of the Portuguese community active in our politics and for us to be positive and avoid treating them as a kind of sub-society.

Now at university, I shall definitely, after a period of travel, return in due course to Jersey. Not all my contemporaries share this aspiration; they want to see the world, spread their wings and would regard coming back as being a dead end, with only well-paid jobs as advocates or in the finance industry likely to make them think otherwise.

We may grumble about Jersey's politics and its current difficulties but, as somewhere to live and to be happy with a family, it is surely the most wonderful, safe and secure place in the world. My generation will not appreciate this until they are older. It is then that they will recall those marvellous summers and look back and say, 'Wasn't it great when we could go down to Grève de Lecq and sit on the rocks, jump in the sea and do whatever!'

I have pride in being part of this island's culture and history. It marks me out as being a little different and I will carry this with me when it is my turn to go out and see the world and meet new people. I will return, and of that I have no doubt. Jersey is my home and always will be.

Born in the 1980s...

Robert Michel

Robert Michel was born in 1987 and lives in St John. He attended the parish primary school and then progressed to Haute Vallée in 1998. Judo and the Air Training Corps are two of his out-of-school interests.

*B*oth of my parents work in the banking industry. My mother is English and came to the Island from Bath and my father, born and brought up in Trinity, is Jersey through and through. I have a sister three years younger than myself, and one of my first memories is of going to see her in hospital just after she was born.

From an early age I was in the habit of leaving the Island and, with the family, visiting our relations in Bath. Initially I felt somewhat envious of them. There they were living in that big place, and in contrast Jersey, on our return, felt just that bit closed in. But then when they came to us I had a change of opinion: they marvelled at our beaches and with everything on hand and no more than a 15-minute drive away.

Going to secondary school came as something of a shock to me. Here we were from quiet St John and quite well-behaved, brushing against the tougher town lot. I really did not like my first terms there and was not the only one to come in for a bit of bullying. Those of us from this northern parish were targeted as being less rough and rather posh, and it took time for us to find our feet, grow in confidence and cope.

Now in my mid-teens I consider Jersey a great place to live: not much crime and, certainly in St John, a fairly peaceful environment without loads of people vandalising everything. It is a great island, definitely home for me, and I shall miss it when I go away. And, despite the many who moan, there is much to do if you seek it out. I have my judo twice a week and all that goes on at the Air Training Corps (there's only one drawback: being in Jersey, there is

Born in the 1980s...

too little flying experience). Go to England and see a city like Bath; there is less to do for young people than here. Of course, if you don't look for it and aim for it, then you won't get it.

I have a growing interest in what goes on in the Island. There is the chat and discussion at home round the table, and, for instance, driving past the waterfront building developments will spark off a big family discussion about the States and what they are about.

The waterfront in particular concerns me. People will arrive in the Island, come off the boat and see a building site. If flats have to be built, it should be somewhere other than a pretty shoreline. As to the leisure centre and the multi-screen cinema, they're a fine idea but in the wrong place. It's not quite the Sydney Opera House, and I can just hear those first-time visitors saying, 'Wow! See that Odeon there!' The whole site should have been kept quiet, a nice open space.

I think that one of Jersey's strong points is its community feel, with people friendly to each other. Walk round town and you see loads of people you know. The down side is that we are cut off from the mainland and that the cost of air fares to get off is high. There is the feeling sometimes of being stuck on this ten by four island for months and not being able to leave. Others of its problems do not trouble me. At present I am more worried about the future of the school bus service than the finance industry. And as to traffic – which others say is appalling – think of sitting in a traffic jam on the M25 for a few hours and consider how lucky we are.

In due course, with my ambition to join the RAF and become a flier, I shall leave the Island for a while anyway. That is the problem: you grow up here, but with most careers you have to go away. Eventually I shall come back – because it's home.

Thinking about Jersey's future, my main worries are the amount of development and over-population. Will all this ruin the tranquillity of the Island? Will it become just a mini-city? But there is also the problem of those who criticise it a bit too much. People should step back and see what they have before they judge it. We should think of our nice open fields and our beaches down the road, be thankful and not take what we've got for granted.

Chapter Nine

Born in the 1990s

Daniel Tardivel
Josephine Cabot
Madeline Jouanny

Daniel Tardivel

Daniel Tardivel was born in 1991. He has lived all his life in the parish of St Peter and attends its primary school.

Dad is the local postman, doing our village round, and Mum is a nursing sister at the General Hospital. I have a brother, two years younger than me, and a cat called Gilly. I usually prefer the cat which is less annoying and doesn't shout loud and call me names.

The sea round Jersey has been a big part of my life: not only the beaches but also going out in Dad's boat from Grève de Lecq. I must have been only two or three when I first went fishing with him. He has lobster pots but I don't much like lobster. Other fish are all right. When I was young Mum used to come too, keeping an eye on me as Dad pulled in his pots.

I have travelled quite a lot – not to America but to France, Guernsey, Sark and England. I liked London. As to hobbies, besides fishing I like playing football and going on the computer.

I give Jersey almost full marks as a place to live. I definitely like the sandy beaches and all the entertainment, including the trampolines and skate-park on the waterfront near the upside-down café. And what can be better than the views from the cliffs – of France and the other Channel Islands. England might provide more variety and sights to see, but for me Jersey wins by a big margin.

At present I don't know what I shall do in adult life. Perhaps living in Jersey and with lengthy holidays away from the Island will be what I would like to choose.

I like Jersey and its views and its beaches. Its people are nice too, but there are the odd one or two who don't quite come up to scratch.

Born in the 1990s...

Josephine Cabot

Josephine (known as Jo) Cabot was born in 1992. She lives in St Brelade and attends St Peter Primary School.

*M*y dad is a builder and my mum works in an office. I have a younger sister and we live in a house on Mont à la Brune, with nice views of St Ouen's Bay and the good sunsets.

I have a membership card for the Zoo and we go there a lot. One of my first memories is of a monkey jumping on my sister in her pram. They used to let out the tamarin monkeys.

I have hardly ever been to England and never to London, but we go skiing every year in the French Alps. In the summer my dad takes me and my sister boogie-boarding at St Ouen's, and sometimes we cycle round the lanes.

What I really like about Jersey is the load of things to do: not only the beach but amusements like The Living Legend. What I dislike is litter on the beach. This is not nice.

When I grow up I might like to be a vet. Shall I live in England or Jersey? I shall have to think about that one – perhaps stay here and have a house near the ski slopes.

Jersey has got everything. It's fun and I am very happy about it. Marking it, I give the Island 9 out of 10.

Born in the 1990s...

Madeline Jouanny

Madeline Jouanny was born in 1996 and lives in St Saviour. She attends Beaulieu Convent School.

*M*y mum is a physiotherapist and my dad is a sports teacher. I have a brother at De La Salle. I like art but music lessons bore me.

Jersey is a good place to live because there are lots of beaches. I wish Jersey was colder in the winter so that it snows. I've never seen any proper snow. It would be good to be closer to fun parks and water parks, like there are in France.

I am lucky living in Jersey because we have a big house with a big garden and room for a paddling pool and two tortoises. Another nice thing is that it is an island, and that means we have to go on a boat or plane when we go away on holiday. I like the plane best. At some time I would like to go to Spain because it's hot.

When I am older, I think I will go away, but I'd like to come back to Jersey because my family all live here.

I would like to be an artist and paint pictures of Jersey beaches....or I might be a vet.

tattered

LARK COVE SERIES

USA TODAY BESTSELLING AUTHOR

DEVNEY PERRY

Editing & Proofreading:
Elizabeth Nover, Razor Sharp Editing
www.razorsharpediting.com
Ellie McLove, Gray Ink
www.grayinkonline.com
Julie Deaton, Deaton Author Services
www.facebook.com/jdproofs
Kaitlyn Moodie
www.facebook.com/KaitlynMoodieEditing

Cover:
Sarah Hansen © Okay Creations
www.okaycreations.com

Formatting:
Champagne Book Design
www.champagnebookdesign.com

dedication

To Jenn, Karen and Ana.
This surprise baby is for you.

prologue

"WHAT CAN I GET FOR YOU?" I ASKED THE MAN across the bar.

He flashed me a straight, white smile. "Macallan 18, if you've got it. Double. Neat."

I nodded and turned to the shelves at my back, glad for the task. I needed a distraction from the heat. He'd turned the hotel bar where I worked into a sauna.

For the last three years, I would have argued that this room was always cold, even at the peak of summer. Even with the heat blasting through the vents, like it was now. But here I stood, sweating like I'd just run to catch the late train.

From the moment this handsome stranger had walked through the door, my heartrate had spiked. Not because of the way his dark hair fell in a soft wave around a part above his left eyebrow. Not because of the expensive suit that hugged his broad shoulders and draped down his long legs.

My heart was thundering because of the air.

He charged the atmosphere with his confident stride. His deep-brown eyes had taken me in with no more than a blink. He exuded class and power and *heat*.

He'd walked into my bar and claimed it as his.

And I was drawn to him, like shivering bones to a warm blanket.

I guess that was natural. People always wanted what was

out of their reach. And this man was so far out of my reach, he might as well be standing on the moon.

He drank whisky that cost twice my hourly wage, while I splurged on cab rides every Saturday night instead of walking home at two in the morning. If my tip jar allowed it, I ate lunch on Wednesdays at the corner diner instead of nuking ramen noodles in my cramped apartment. I was just a bartender, surviving life one lick at a time.

He was probably a corporate raider with the world at his feet.

Still, I couldn't resist pulling in a deep breath of his Armani cologne as I reached for his whisky on the top shelf.

Even in my mandated heels, it was a stretch to grab the bottle that I'd just cleaned yesterday. It wasn't uncommon for rich men to stroll in and order our most expensive whisky, but it didn't happen often enough to avoid a weekly dusting.

"Quiet night?" he asked as I came back to the bar with the bottle.

"Mondays are always slow." I set out a glass on a black square napkin, then poured him two jiggers.

"Lucky me." He took the glass. "I get your undivided attention."

"Yes, you do." I set the bottle aside, doing my best not to blush. Hopefully I wasn't sweating through my cheap shirt.

Everything about this man was smooth. Sexy. Even his voice. Definitely the way he licked his lips after taking a sip.

But despite him being my only customer, I stayed quiet as he swirled the amber liquid in its glass. I'd been bartending since I turned twenty-one, and I'd learned these last three years to let the patrons do the talking. No one wanted a bartender who couldn't shut her mouth—especially in a classy hotel like this. Especially when I was as far from classy as you could get.

My black slacks and white button-up shirt didn't have a stitch of natural fiber—just a synthetic blend that was uncomfortably affordable. My tattered heels had gotten a new scuff tonight, one I'd have to cover with a Sharpie later.

He swirled his whisky a few more times, his gold cufflink peeking out from underneath his suit jacket. "I'm sure you get this question a lot in your line of work. What's your drink of choice?"

I smiled. "I do get that question a lot. Normally, I answer with whatever was the first drink I served that day."

The corner of his mouth curved up. "And today's?"

"A local IPA."

His mouth split into a full-blown grin. "What's the real answer?"

That smile made my heart beat wildly again, sending my temperature up another notch.

"It depends." I pushed off the bar and walked down to my gun, filling a glass with mostly ice, then water. "I've always believed in pairing drinks with the occasion."

"I'm intrigued."

I took a sip of my water. "Weddings, obviously champagne."

"Obviously." He nodded. "What else?"

"Bachelorette parties require anything fruity. Beer always goes with pizza—it's one of my drinking laws. Margaritas on Tuesday nights because I don't work on Wednesdays. And tequila shots if anyone says, 'We need to talk.' "

He chuckled. "What about whisky?"

"I don't drink whisky."

"Hmm." He took a long, slow sip from his glass, then set it down. "That's a shame. A beautiful woman drinking whisky is my weakness."

The water glass in my hand bobbled and I nearly spilled it

on my apron. I'd heard a lot of pickup lines standing behind this bar, and I'd mastered the art of turning down a man without bruising his ego—or losing his tip. But I'd be a fool to dodge that line.

"Then maybe I'll give it another try."

"I'd like that." He smiled wider as he reached across the bar, his long fingers leading the way. "I'm Logan."

I placed my hand in his, already lost in the fairy tale. "Thea."

one

LOGAN

Six years later . . .

"I HATE MONTANA."

Nolan rolled his eyes. "How can you say that when you're standing in front of that view?"

I gazed past the tree trunks to the lake on the other side of the forest. I hated to admit it, but the view was rather stunning. The deep blue water had a glassy sheen. The summer sunlight bounced off its gentle, rolling waves. In the distance, the mountains still had white snowcaps. There was even a bald eagle circling the shoreline across the bay.

But I wouldn't give Nolan the satisfaction of admitting the truth.

"What is that smell?" My nostrils flared as I sucked in a long breath.

Nolan chuckled. "That would be *earth*. Dirt. Trees. Wind. Also known as clean air. It's what air is supposed to smell like without all the carbon emissions."

"Always with the sarcasm."

"I save it all for you." Nolan Fennessy, my friend and the CEO of my family's charitable foundation, loved to give me shit.

"Lucky me," I deadpanned, turning away from Flathead

Lake so he wouldn't see my grin. Then I scanned the camp, giving it a more thorough inspection than the cursory glance I'd taken when we'd arrived ten minutes ago.

Beneath the evergreens, six small log cabins were scattered throughout the forest. Next to them was a building marked SHOWERS with a separate wing for boys and girls. The main lodge sat at the back, closest to the road and the gravel parking area. And as it was the hub for most camp activities, the lodge was as big as the six cabins combined.

It was a child's paradise.

In Nowhere, Montana.

Personal experience had tainted the state for me, but I couldn't deny this camp had a certain appeal. And it would be a perfect addition to the Kendrick Foundation.

"Five million?" I asked Nolan, confirming the purchase price.

"Yes." He turned away from the lake, stepping to my side. "The price includes everything. Buildings. Furniture. Appliances. Though the bulk of the value is in the land."

"Okay." I nodded. "I've seen enough. Let's go."

"Logan, we can't go until we meet with the director and hear her pitch."

At the mention of the director, a flash of long, blond hair caught my eye. She came scurrying out of the lodge with a handful of pamphlets and a manila folder tucked under her arm. I knew without seeing that it contained the proposal she'd sent into the foundation three months ago.

"I don't need to hear her pitch. I'll approve the purchase and kick in another fifty thousand for improvements." I glanced at my Bulgari watch. "It's only two. Let's say our hellos, give her the good news and head back to the airport." We'd be back in New York tonight.

Nolan chuckled. "As much as I'd like to sleep in my own bed tonight, we can't leave."

"Why?"

He stepped past me—hand extended—ready to greet the director, then smirked over his shoulder. "It's rude."

Damn. "Well played, Fennessy," I muttered.

Nolan knew I'd never let my personal hang-up about being in Montana impede my reputation as a philanthropist. As my father had taught me years ago, just as his father had taught him, the Kendricks—above all else—took the utmost care to preserve our appearance.

Which meant I was in Montana for the night.

I sloughed off my mood and gave the camp director, Willa Doon, a pleasant smile.

"Mr. Fennessy." Willa's smile widened as she shook Nolan's hand. "Thank you so, *so* much for coming out here. I couldn't believe it when you called. I'm just . . . it's so awesome you even read my proposal in the first place."

"The pleasure was mine. Your proposal was one of the best I've read in months." Nolan released her hand and gestured toward me. "Let me introduce you to the chairman of the board for the Kendrick Foundation. This is Logan Kendrick."

"Ms. Doon." I extended my hand. "Nice to meet you."

She blushed scarlet as our hands connected. "Mr. Kendrick."

"Please, call me Logan. We're looking forward to learning more about your camp."

"Thank you." Her smile was confident but her fingers were trembling with nerves. "I'm not sure, um . . . should I just go through the proposal again?" She fumbled the brochures in one hand as she went for the file folder. "I don't know if you've had a chance to read it or have questions. I, um—shoot." A pamphlet dropped to the dirt.

"How about a tour?" Nolan bent to retrieve the paper for her. "We've both read your proposal, so if it's all right with you, we'll keep this informal and just ask you any questions as we walk."

Willa nodded. "That sounds great."

Five minutes into the tour, the nerves began to leave her voice. Once she began telling us stories from past camps and the children who'd spent countless summers here, her confidence rallied.

While Willa's stories were endearing, they didn't keep my mind from wandering back to my last visit to Montana. The visit where I'd come to surprise my then girlfriend—the one I'd proposed to twice without a *yes* in return.

I'd come to Montana to surprise Emmeline for a Thanksgiving weekend. The ring I'd bought for her had been in my coat pocket. My plan had been to propose and convince her to move home after she finished a year teaching kindergarten. Instead, I ended a five-year relationship when I learned she was still in love with a man from her past.

Her husband.

After our breakup, I'd gotten the hell out of Montana, flying back to New York without delay. The second the plane's wheels had touched down, I'd ordered a courier to return Emmeline's ring to the jewelry store.

It had been over six months since we'd broken up, and I'd spent that time working my ass off. Not only was I more involved than ever in the Kendrick Foundation, but I was also overseeing a large clientele as a managing partner at my law firm, Stone, Richards and Abergel.

I didn't think of Emmeline much these days—there just wasn't time. But being back in Montana dredged up a slew of unwelcome memories. Memories of what I'd lost.

And I hated losing.

"Have you ever been to a camp like this?" Willa asked me as we stood outside one of the smaller cabins.

"No, I haven't." I peered through the cabin door, taking in the wooden bunks inside. "Where are all the kids?" Sleeping bags were laid out neatly on the beds, backpacks on the floors, but no campers.

"Oh, they're all on a hike today. We bussed them out early this morning. They'll have a picnic lunch and then be back before the dinner bell."

"I see." I stepped away from the cabin and gestured toward the lodge. "Can we see the main building next?"

"Of course."

I took a step to follow Willa just as a streak of dark hair and skinny limbs went flying past the cabin.

The young girl didn't slow down a bit as she sprinted for the lodge. She looked over her shoulder, giving Willa a huge smile, but kept on running.

Willa waved. "Hey, Charlie!"

"Did she miss the bus?" Nolan teased.

"No, that's Charlie." Willa laughed. "Her grandmother volunteers in the kitchen so she spends her mornings and afternoons here."

Charlie's long hair streamed behind her as she ran, only trapped by the backward baseball cap on her head. Her sneakers were covered in dirt, just like the seat of her shorts. "Cute kid."

"She's adorable." Willa smiled. "Should we continue the tour?"

"Actually," I said, "I think I've seen enough."

Willa's feet stilled and her shoulders fell. "Oh. I see."

"From what I've seen and read in your proposal, this camp would make a wonderful addition to the Kendrick Foundation."

Willa blinked twice before her entire face lit up. "Really?"

I nodded. "Really."

"Gosh." Her hands flew to her cheeks. Pamphlets and her manila envelope dropped to the ground. "I can't believe it. I just—oh my goodness."

Nolan grinned at me as we gave Willa a moment to let it all sink in.

She was young, likely in her midtwenties, with a delicate face. Her wavy blond hair fell nearly to her waist. Her hands were constantly fiddling with something—the tie on her simple navy sundress or her papers. But despite her timid demeanor, it was clear that Willa loved this camp.

A camp we'd just saved from closure.

The local church that currently owned the camp was letting it go due to increased overhead and maintenance costs. Luckily for us, the church wasn't looking to make a payday on the property; otherwise they'd be selling it off for private development. Instead, they just wanted to recoup their investment and find new owners who would continue it as a children's summer camp. The only problem was, they hadn't had any offers in a year and were looking at closing it down permanently.

Now it would be part of the Kendrick Foundation.

We'd keep the original charter intact but come in with fresh eyes and a bigger wallet. The foundation would make a few overdue improvements and teach Willa how to better manage expenses while increasing attendance. We'd ensure this children's paradise would be around for many more years to come.

"Thank you," Willa whispered as tears filled her eyes. "Thank you so much."

"You're welcome." I looked to Nolan. "Anything you want to add?"

"I think you covered it all," the corners of his mouth turned up, "boss."

Smug bastard. As CEO, he had just as much authority to approve this purchase as I did. He just liked to toss that word around to remind me who was really in charge here.

"I'll have the attorneys contact the church and start drafting a contract," he said. "We'll get everything transferred over to the foundation as soon as possible. And Ms. Doon, we'll expect you to stay on as director."

Willa gasped. "You don't have to do that. I mean, I'm grateful, but it wasn't about keeping my job."

Nolan smiled. "We know. That's why you're the best choice for our camp director. And as long as things are going well, the job is yours."

"I just—I can't believe this is happening. It was a long shot, sending that proposal. I never . . ." She pressed her hands to her cheeks again. "Thank you."

"Congratulations. Let's celebrate." Nolan clapped me on the shoulder. "Willa, now that we've got business out of the way, would you mind giving us the rest of the tour?"

She nodded, composing herself once again. "I'd love to."

"And afterward, would you mind showing us around town a bit?" I asked. "We'd love a recommendation for dinner and drinks."

Willa nodded again, her face beaming. "I know just the place."

"Then lead the way." Nolan waved her on, then leaned close as we followed. "Now aren't you glad we stayed?"

Days like today were the reason I stayed so in tune with the foundation's activities. Outside of the countless hours I put in at the firm, I didn't have hobbies like my friends did. I didn't golf or own a yacht.

I worked.

Hard.

Nolan didn't need me along for these foundation trips, but the truth was, I didn't want to miss out. I didn't want to miss the chance to make someone's dream come true. Or the opportunity to put my family's fortune to a better use than buying my mother diamonds or my sister divorces.

"Fine. I'll admit, this place isn't so bad. Once you get past the smell."

An hour later—after we'd finished touring the camp and Willa had driven us around town—Nolan and I followed her through the steel door of the Lark Cove Bar.

"This is . . . quaint," I muttered. Were those peanut shells all over the floor?

"They have the best drinks in the area and their pizzas are amazing." Willa smiled over her shoulder but it fell when she took in my grimace. "But there's a fancier place up the road in Kalispell. It's about forty-five minutes, but we can go there. I'm sorry, I didn't—"

"This place is perfect." Nolan placed his hand on my shoulder, his dark skin a stark contrast to my white shirt. "We don't need fancy."

"Okay. Good." Willa relaxed and walked over to a table.

"We *don't* need fancy," I whispered to Nolan. "Just sanitary."

"Shut up."

"You're fired."

He chuckled and looked at his Rolex. "That's the first time you've fired me today, and it's past four. Usually you fire me before noon on these trips. Maybe the Montana air agrees with you."

I huffed. "I can't wait to say 'I told you so' after we get food poisoning."

"Let's get you a drink."

"Finally, he says something intelligent."

We were both grinning as we joined Willa at a tall, square table in the middle of the bar.

"Is this okay?" she asked.

"Great." I smiled as the wooden stool creaked under my weight. With my back to the door, I studied the room.

The ceiling was high, with exposed iron beams running from one side to the other. Much like the floors, the walls were paneled with battered wood. Though instead of being covered in peanut shells, they were filled with signs and pictures. It reminded me of those chain restaurants—the ones all ending in an apostrophe *s*. Applebee's. Chili's. Bennigan's. Except this decor hadn't been staged but pieced together naturally over the years.

The L-shaped bar was long, running across both of the back walls. There had to be at least twenty stools along its path, and judging by the wear and tear on the foot rail, it was the place most people chose to sit.

Including the five patrons seated near the bartender.

"Welcome, folks. Be right there."

Willa looked over her shoulder, giving the guy a shy wave. As she spun back to the table, her fingers tugged at her hair in an attempt to hide her red cheeks.

Nolan and I shared a grin, then each continued silently scrutinizing the bar as we waited to place our order.

Neon signs advertising various beers and liquors littered the windows facing the parking lot. Next to a large flat-screen on one wall, a set of antlers was adorned with a bunch of hats. *Wait. Is that a bra?*

The Fourth of July was over a week ago, but the decorations

were still up. A red, white and blue banner hung above the juke-box, and a handful of tiny flags sat in a cup on the bar.

This place was as far removed from my favorite bar in the city as you could get, but at least they had alcohol. Though, I doubted the Lark Cove Bar carried my preference.

"Gentlemen. Willow." The bartender appeared at our table, depositing three cardboard coasters and a paper boat of peanuts.

"It's Willa. Actually." She tucked her hair behind an ear, sitting taller. "With an *a*."

"Damn. Sorry." He shrugged off his mistake—one I had a feeling he'd make again. "What can I get for you?"

"I don't suppose you have Macallan 18," I said.

It had been a long day, flying out early this morning and then being assaulted with reminders of Emmeline once my feet had touched the Montana soil. Today called for whisky.

The bartender grinned, then ran a hand over his blond buzz-cut hair. "As a matter of fact, I do."

"Nice." The Lark Cove Bar might not be pretty, but whoever stocked their shelves had good taste. "I'll have a double. Neat."

"I'll have the same," Nolan said.

"You got it." The bartender smiled at Willa. "And for you?"

"Just, um, a beer. Anything is fine," she stuttered, blushing again as she stared at the stubble on his jaw. "Thanks, Jackson."

"Be back." He tapped his knuckles on the table, then ambled back behind the bar.

"How long do you think that bottle has been up there?" Nolan leaned over and asked as Jackson stretched to pull down the Macallan from the highest shelf.

I opened my mouth to comment on the cobwebs in the upper corner, but stopped when a swish of dark hair caught my eye.

From out of a back room, a woman emerged and smiled at

Jackson, then at one of the regulars as she set down a pizza pan.

Her simple black tank molded to her breasts and flat stomach, leaving her tanned arms bare. Her jeans sat low on her hips, cinched tight with a black leather belt that was just a shade darker than her long, thick hair. Her white smile was full of straight teeth, except for one in the middle of the bottom row that sat slightly off-center.

It had been over six years—nearly seven—since I'd spent the night with my hands wrapped up in that hair. Since I'd memorized that smile while I'd held Thea in my arms.

Years, and she looked exactly the same.

"Logan, do you want pizza?"

I shook my head, sliding off my creaking stool. "Excuse me for a moment."

At my movement, Thea's dark eyes—nearly black, like her hair—swept the room. She smiled at me for a second, but the expression fell away and the color in her face drained as recognition dawned.

She remembers me. Thank god, she remembered me. I was man enough to admit that it would have crushed my ego if she hadn't remembered me. Remembered that night.

I still thought about it now and then—whenever I was in the neighborhood of that hotel. Did she ever think about it? About me?

I'd gone back to her hotel bar once, months after we'd hooked up. But she hadn't been there. The staff had told me that Thea had quit and moved out of the city. I'd been disappointed and pissed at myself for waiting too long—I'd been busy with work. Then life had moved on. Not long after I'd tried to find Thea again, I'd met Emmeline.

Still, I'd never forgotten Thea, even after all these years.

I'd never forgotten how those dark eyes had lulled me under

her spell. How her amazing body—the perfect balance of toned, lean muscle to soft, feminine curves—had felt beneath mine.

As I crossed the room, I held her wide, unblinking stare. "Thea."

Her body jolted at my voice. "Lo-Logan."

"It's been a long time. How are you?"

She opened her mouth, then closed it without a word.

"Hey, Thea," Jackson called. "We're finally cracking that bottle of Macallan you insisted on buying."

I grinned. That was why the Lark Cove Bar carried Macallan. She'd bought my favorite whisky for her bar, even if it had never been served.

"I . . ." Thea took a long breath, shaking her head and closing her eyes. When she opened them, the shock of seeing my face was gone.

But instead of the confident, sexy woman I'd expected to see once the surprise had faded, I saw fear.

Why would Thea be afraid of me? I'd treated her with nothing but respect during the night we'd shared. Hadn't I?

Before I could say anything else, she sprang into action, grabbing a shot glass and slamming it on the bar. Then she reached behind her, swiping a bottle of tequila from a middle shelf. With a flick of her wrist, she poured the shot, not spilling a drop.

"Drink that," she ordered. "We need to talk."

two

THEA

MY HEART WAS BOUNCING LIKE A PING-PONG BALL BETWEEN my sternum and spine. I couldn't believe Logan was standing right in front of me.

Logan.

How many hours had I spent looking for him in New York? How many times had I searched for his face in the crowds? How many nights had I laid in bed, replaying our night together, hoping I'd be able to recall something—anything—that might lead me to this moment?

Eventually, I'd given up hope that I'd ever see him again. I'd made peace with my situation.

Logan Whatever-His-Name-Is was the best, and only, one-night stand of my life.

He was just another person I'd left behind in New York. He was a memory, one of the few good ones from back then.

Yet here he was, standing in my dingy, happy bar, staring at the tequila shot I'd poured him.

A shot he really needed to drink before I took it myself.

"Please," I whispered. "Take it."

His gaze snapped back to mine and my heart pounded even faster. Confidence radiated off his tall body in waves. He was just as intimidating now as he had been years ago, except instead of being alluring and charming, today it was terrifying. His frame was locked tight and his brown eyes were narrowed, silently demanding me to speak.

Did he know what I was going to tell him? Did he know that I was about to change his life?

I swallowed the lump in the back of my throat and sucked in some oxygen so I didn't topple over. Then I gripped the edge of the bar to keep myself upright.

Do it. Say it, Thea. Tell him.

If I didn't tell him today, I might not ever have the chance. And for her sake, he needed to know.

"I had a . . ." God, I was dizzy. Why couldn't I find the words? "You, I mean we, have a—"

"Mommy, look." A little hand tugged on my jeans.

I jumped, clutching a hand to my thundering heart. So shocked by Logan's presence, I hadn't heard Charlie come into the bar. Maybe it would be easier with her here. Maybe he'd take one look at her and know what I'd been trying to say.

"Charlie." I turned and bent at the waist, ready to ask her to wait in the office for a minute. But instead of looking into my daughter's brown eyes, I stared at two slimy eyeballs.

"Ah!" I screamed as she thrust the thing right at me.

"I found a frog."

"Eww!" Its slippery nose touched mine and I jerked away, swatting the frog away from my face. Except in my hurry to put some distance between me and the creature, I hit Charlie's hands. The contact was just enough that her grip faltered and the frog slipped loose. It springboarded off her palm into my chest, leaving a wet spot, then landed on the floor with a thud.

"No!" Charlie screeched, scrambling around me to capture the frog. But its legs were a blur of motion, propelling it farther and farther out of her reach.

"Damn," I hissed and sprang into action, dropping to the floor beside Charlie. My hands and knees thumped on the hard floor as I tried to keep up, but the frog was leaping too fast.

"Get that frog!"

Chaos erupted at my back. Stools scraped as a couple of the regulars abandoned their seats. Someone knocked over a glass because I heard the unmistakable sound of beer splattering on the floor in between a slur of curse words. And Jackson started howling with laughter.

"Jackson, help," I barked over my shoulder, only to make him roar louder.

"What is happening?" Hazel's voice floated above all the other noise. "Oh, no. Charlie, what did I tell you about that frog?"

"But Gran, I had to show Mommy," she said, abandoning her pursuit to defend herself.

"You can't bring frogs inside," Hazel said.

"But—"

"Could I get some help here?" I shouted, bringing the frog back to focus.

"Jackson Page," Hazel scolded. "Stop laughing and catch that frog."

"Yes, ma'am." He chuckled as the thud of his boots echoed on the floor.

I kept chasing the frog, right to the corner of the bar. It had stopped by the edge, so I swiped fast, gripping one of the frog's back legs. "Gotcha!"

Relief washed over my shoulders, but as I tried to pick the frog up, the damn thing squirmed hard and got free.

"Shit!" I yelled as it landed on the floor and bounded away.

"That's a bad word," Charlie chastised.

"Shoot!"

Still on my hands and knees, I rounded the corner of the

bar, hustling to catch the frog before it could disappear into a nook or cranny. I stretched to reach for it again but lost my balance when one of my palms skidded on a peanut shell.

Damn it! This wasn't happening.

My daughter hadn't just brought a frog into my bar, violating every health code in the book. I wasn't on my hands and knees, chasing an amphibian through peanut shells in front of the classiest man I'd ever met. I wasn't about to make the most difficult confession of my life with frog slime on my shirt.

This could not be happening.

I regained my balance and looked up, but instead of seeing a frog, I saw a pair of camel wingtips.

My eyes ran up the shoes, over their laces, to the crisp denim that covered long, powerful legs. As I stood, my gaze continued up past the leather belt that wrapped around hipbones I'd once tasted on my tongue. Then up a starched, white polo that covered Logan's washboard abs.

Steady on my feet, I avoided looking at his face in favor of his muscled arm. Veins snaked over his bicep and down to his tanned forearm. His wristwatch cost more than my car. And his fingers . . . held a squirming frog.

"You got him." Charlie appeared at my side, smiling up at Logan as she reached for her latest captive. But before they could make the transfer, her hands froze and her head cocked to the side. Under the backward band of her baseball cap, her eyebrows were furrowed.

Oh, god. Did she recognize Logan? Charlie had asked me a couple of years ago about her dad, and since I hadn't been able to tell her much, I'd drawn her a picture of him. Did she see the resemblance to my sketch? This was going to turn into a cluster—well, more of a cluster—if she started asking questions before I had a chance to tell Logan about her.

My head was swirling and my breaths came in hard pants as I tore my eyes from Charlie's puzzled face to look up at Logan.

But he wasn't paying me any mind. His attention was entirely on Charlie.

"Your pinky has the same bend as mine." Charlie touched his finger, then lifted her hand, wriggling her fifth finger.

The chaos and noise from moments ago was gone. The bar was deathly silent as Charlie's words rang in the air. I could feel everyone's eyes on me. Jackson. Hazel. Wayne and Ronny, a couple of our regulars. All I could do was stand frozen, waiting for Logan's response.

"Um, Charlie." Hazel's voice broke the quiet. "Let's get that thing outside."

"Okay, Gran." My daughter reached up to collect her latest pet from Logan's hands, just as Hazel came around the bar to shuffle her away.

"Thea, we'll see you at home."

"Bye, Mommy."

I nodded but didn't glance away from Logan's clenched jaw.

I waited until Hazel's and Charlie's footsteps disappeared and the back door closed. I waited until the silence returned. I waited for Logan because I didn't have the courage to speak first.

"How old is she?" In front of my nose, his broad chest was heaving.

I blinked and cleared my impossibly dry throat before meeting his dark glare. "She turns six in a month."

It didn't take long for Logan to do the math. He'd come into the hotel bar at the end of October, not quite six years and nine months ago.

"I'm sorry," I whispered, hoping to calm the angry waves rolling off his body. "I tried to—"

He didn't let me finish. Spinning on the heel of his fancy

shoes, he stormed out of my bar.

I didn't follow.

Instead, I took a deep breath, squared my shoulders and walked over to the table where Logan's friend sat stunned next to an equally shocked Willa.

Then, six years and many months too late, I asked for Logan's last name and phone number.

"Is she asleep?" Hazel asked.

"Yeah. Chasing frogs all day wore her out." I collapsed into a padded wicker loveseat across from where Hazel sat on the white railing of our back porch.

"That girl. She's not happy unless there's dirt under her fingernails." Hazel smiled and took a long drag of her menthol cigarette. Her wrinkled hands shook a bit as she lifted it to her lips.

She wasn't as steady as she used to be, though I guess that was to be expected after you reached sixty-five. But I kept my observations quiet. Reminding Hazel Rhodes that she was not as young as she pretended to be was just asking for an ass chewing.

"Is she still mad that you made her set the frog loose?"

I nodded. "She told me she'd just find another one tomorrow."

Hazel laughed and shook her head. "Oh, Charlie."

Her laugh was more of a cackle these days. Her voice held a permanent rasp from all those Virginia Slims. But as rough as it was, that sound had soothed my worries more times than I could count.

And tonight, I could use some soothing.

With thoughts of Logan running through my mind, I

propped my head into my hand and stared blankly across the yard.

The house where Hazel, Charlie and I lived wasn't much, just a cramped three-bedroom cottage that barely fit us all. But it was home, and the backyard was a sliver of heaven.

The lawn was wide with thick green grass that spread between two groves of evergreens. The trees stood as tall posts on both sides of our gravel shoreline. And in the center of our rocky beach, was a long, battered dock that stretched out twenty feet into the lake's rippled water.

It was no wonder that Hazel's little cottage with the sage-green siding and aqua door was worth millions.

Land prices in Lark Cove had skyrocketed in the last two decades. I'd asked Hazel to consider selling this place a year ago so she'd have some money for retirement, but she'd refused. I hadn't been surprised.

Not only did this cottage hold sentimental value from her own childhood, but it was the only home Charlie had ever known. Which meant Hazel would live here for the rest of her life.

She'd grown up in this house before setting off for New York City after high school. She'd worked for years at various places in the city, mostly at animal shelters or children's centers. One day, she came to work at the home where I was being raised. She arrived when I was eight and stayed until I turned eighteen. Not long after my birthday, her parents both passed in the span of two months and she returned home to Montana to run their bar.

Eventually, I followed.

When I rolled into town on a Greyhound bus, six months pregnant, she took me in. She moved me into this house, gave me a job and assumed the role of Charlie's grandmother.

Because that's what Hazel did.

She collected strays.

Lucky for me, I was one of her strays. So was Jackson. Together, we ran her bar after she decided to retire. Now she spent her days chasing Charlie around and volunteering in the kitchen at the Flathead Summer Camp.

A camp, I'd learned, that had just been purchased by Charlie's father.

"How are you doing?" Hazel asked.

"Shocked," I muttered, taking a deep breath of the smoky air. "I really want a cigarette."

"Too bad you quit." She took a drag. "And I don't share."

I smiled. "Yeah. Too bad."

Hazel had told me on more than one occasion to cremate her with a pack of cigarettes. Her dedication to the habit was legendary. But she'd never condoned smoking as one of my vices.

My first cigarette had been at sixteen. I hadn't even been old enough to buy them myself. But once I'd learned I was pregnant with Charlie, I'd quit cold turkey.

At times, I'd pretend to smoke. I'd hold one, unlit, between my fingers, letting the little white stick calm some nerves. I had a pack in my underwear drawer for just that reason. But tonight, I wanted more than just to pretend. Seeing Logan again had me itching for a puff.

"I can't believe he came into the bar."

Hazel hummed and turned toward the lake. "Yeah. It's, um . . . crazy."

Why did she sound guilty? Her tone was a lot like Charlie's had been earlier when I'd found that nasty frog in the bathroom after she'd promised to keep it outside.

My eyes narrowed as Hazel picked at the wood railing. "What did you do?"

"Me?" she gasped. "Nothing."

What a terrible liar. "Hazel," I warned.

She took two more drags before finally stubbing out her cigarette in the ashtray she left out here. Then she slipped off the railing and came to sit in the wicker chair across from my love seat. "It might not have been just a coincidence that he came to Montana."

My jaw slackened. "What?"

Hazel had known how to find Logan? How long had she known? Why hadn't she told me sooner? I trusted her more than any other person on the planet. We didn't keep secrets from each other. She'd let him walk into the bar today and surprise me completely. How could she keep something this important from me?

"I can hear those gears turning in your pretty head from over here, so before you make yourself dizzy, let me explain."

"Fast." I sat on my hands so I wouldn't rip a cigarette out of her pack and suck it down.

"Remember I told you that I was helping Willa try and find a buyer for the camp?"

"Yeah." It had been a few months ago, but Hazel had spent a lot of long nights hovering over her laptop as she researched charitable foundations.

"Well, while I was researching, I stumbled across the Kendrick Foundation."

The Kendrick Foundation.

Logan Kendrick.

I'd guessed a hundred potential last names for Logan, but never Kendrick. It suited him though. Much like the man himself, it was classy and strong. It was a name not easily forgotten.

Too bad he hadn't mentioned it years ago.

"His family is wealthy."

"Obviously," I deadpanned. "Anyone with two eyes can take

one look at him and see that's true. How about we get to the point where you kept a secret from me for months that involves Charlie's father?"

"Don't get pissy with me, young lady. You know I always think of you first. Just give me a minute to explain."

"Fine," I grumbled, then clamped my mouth shut so she'd continue.

"I was shocked when I saw his face on that foundation website. I recognized him immediately from the drawing in Charlie's room but wanted to be sure. So I snuck in and got it to double-check. Sure enough, I put that drawing side by side with the computer and knew I'd found him."

The drawing did look a lot like him, probably because I'd poured my heart into that sketch.

He was just as handsome as I remembered, though he had changed some. In a good way. Time was kind to men like Logan. The color of his eyes was deeper than before, more mesmerizing. His jaw seemed stronger and more refined. His hair was a bit shorter but still tamed around the inch-long part on the left.

But one thing hadn't changed. He still had the ability to capture the room. Ten minutes in the Lark Cove Bar and I'd been completely off-kilter in the one place I felt completely at ease.

"I don't think Charlie recognized him today."

I didn't want to keep her from Logan, but until I knew exactly what was going to happen, I didn't want her in the middle. I wanted the introduction to her father to be one she'd remember with a smile, not some chaotic memory that would scar her for life.

"I don't think so either," Hazel said. "She was more worried about her frog than a stranger in her gran's bar. But trust me, if you give her a quiet minute to really look at his face, she'll recognize him right away."

My daughter wouldn't need much to put it all together.

She didn't ask about her dad much. After I'd given her that sketch, she'd asked about him once or twice a year, usually around her birthday. I liked to think she didn't ask about Logan because she didn't feel like a part of her family was missing.

"Never mind Charlie," I said. "Let's get back to how you came across his identity and didn't share."

Hazel took out another cigarette from her pack and stood, going back to the railing and her ashtray. After she lit it up and took the first drag, she blew out a long stream of smoke before continuing. "It shocked me to the middle when I came across his face. I didn't sleep a wink that night, wondering what to do."

"You could have talked to me."

"I know." Her shoulders slumped. "But I love you and Charlie like you are my own. The last thing I wanted was someone coming in and causing you problems. You've had enough of those in your life. So, right or wrong, I decided to keep it quiet until I could learn more about the guy."

"You should ha—" I stopped my retort. Snapping at her wasn't going to change anything. And I couldn't be mad at Hazel when her heart had been in the right place. "Well, it's done now. Tell me what else you know."

"He's a lawyer in New York. He works for some fancy firm. He went to college and law school at Columbia. He's thirty-three. Not married. And he doesn't have other children, from what I can tell."

A lawyer. Thirty-three. Not married. I soaked up these tidbits like a dry sponge, craving any information about Logan. I'd spent too long guessing about his life.

After our night together, I spent a month working at that hotel bar with one eye on the door, willing Logan to walk through. I craved him more than I ever had nicotine. The five months after that, I watched the door, praying he'd come back for an entirely different reason.

But when my sixth month of pregnancy rolled around and I still had no earthly clue how to find Logan, I gave up hope. The manager of the hotel bar had downgraded me to day shifts, and when I complained about needing the better evening tips, he encouraged me to look elsewhere for employment. Apparently, pregnant bartenders weren't part of the image they were trying to convey in their high-class establishment. I could have refused and found a cheap lawyer to fight back, but instead, I decided to quit and leave New York.

I called Hazel and confessed my troubles. She told me to "get my ass to Montana and we'll figure it out from there." Two days later, I hopped on a bus with the entire contents of my life packed in one large suitcase and a backpack I'd bought secondhand.

I left knowing I'd never find Logan, and that Charlie would never know much about her father. The only things I could tell her were that he'd been sweet and kind. I could tell her that he'd treasured me, if only for one night.

I guess Charlie could learn a lot more about her dad now.

All she had to do was ask Hazel.

"You found all this out on the internet?"

She shrugged. "No such things as secrets in a world with Facebook."

I shook my head. "I still don't understand why you didn't tell me. After you learned all of this. How could you let him ambush me like that?"

"I'm sorry." Her face fell with her apology. "I was going to tell you but then decided to wait and see how Willa's pitch played out. I thought it would be easier if you could see him in person and explain face-to-face."

"Did you know he was coming here today?"

"No." She held up her hands. "I promise. With the Fourth last week and no camp, I hadn't seen Willa in over a week. I was running late today and by the time I showed up in the kitchen, she was already out of the office, meeting with them. I guess they called a few days ago for an impromptu visit. When she brought them into the kitchen on their tour, I almost dropped a pan of sloppy joes when I saw his face."

"A warning would still have been nice before they showed at the bar."

"I tried to call your cell five times, and the bar phone four, but it was busy."

Goddamn it. "I was on the phone with the distributor."

The company we got our liquor from was old-school, so instead of online ordering, I had to call it in each month. It took me over an hour to dictate my order and negotiate on price to get the best deal.

"Thea, when I couldn't reach you, I came down as soon as I could. But I had to finish up in the kitchen, then hunt down Charlie. She insisted on bringing that damn frog. I hustled, but they beat us to the bar by a minute."

"Okay." I sagged into the seat, trying to process everything she'd told me. "Anything else?"

"No, that's it. I'm sorry, sweetheart. I was just trying to help."

"I get it." I gave her a sad smile. "I'm just . . . scared."

My emotions were spinning faster than a tornado, but the one that stood out the strongest was fear.

Charlie was the light of my life. She was all that mattered.

I couldn't lose her.

"What if he tries to take her from me?"

"Then we'll fight," Hazel declared.

Fight. Just the idea of a custody battle made me queasy. It made me wish Logan were still a stranger and that Charlie would stay mine and mine alone. It made me wish that the simple and happy life I'd built for her wouldn't change.

It wasn't right. I wasn't proud of feeling that way. But she was my entire world.

I had no clue how to share her with a father.

That was if Logan hadn't already run back to New York City.

three

LOGAN

I'M A DAD.

A father.

I couldn't get the concept to sink in.

Did other fathers feel this whiplashed? Or dumbfounded?

Maybe other men got used to the concept of fatherhood during pregnancy. They had time to adjust to the fact a kid was coming. But I hadn't gotten nine months. I'd gotten ninety seconds for all the puzzle pieces to fit together.

I had a child.

Charlie.

I had a daughter who was five, almost six, and had my crooked pinky.

Shit. I should have taken that shot Thea had poured me. Maybe I wouldn't have run out of the bar like a coward.

Though in my defense, I'd been in dire need of some air. The cluttered walls of the bar had closed in on me and I hadn't been able to breathe.

So I'd stormed out, leaving Thea and a million unanswered questions behind. Then I'd wandered aimlessly around Lark Cove, trying to understand how I'd come to Montana this morning for business and had my entire personal life turned upside down by evening.

I didn't know how long I'd been walking or where. I'd found myself on a small, two-lane gravel road that ran along the lake. Rather than stop and get my bearings, I'd just kept walking. I'd followed the road until it curved around a point, and finally stopped walking to sit on a large rock overlooking the water.

I didn't know how long I'd been sitting here either.

When my stomach grumbled, I blinked and focused my vision to check my watch. *Four hours.* It had been four hours since I'd walked out of the Lark Cove Bar. Four hours since I'd become a father.

I ran a hand through my hair and got off the rock, brushing off the seat of my jeans. The sun was beginning to set and it cast an orange glow across the lake.

"What the hell am I going to do?" The water didn't answer.

I hated being out of control. I was *always* in control. I was the man in charge. There was surety in my every move.

Today had knocked that confidence down a peg or twenty. I'd never felt so helpless in my life.

I had no idea what to do with a daughter. I didn't know how to braid hair, buy dresses or go to tea parties. Would she even want me around? What if Charlie didn't like me?

The trees at my back were growing closer and the clouds above were closing in. I bent and gripped my knees, forcing air into my lungs before I fell over.

Fuck. I was going to pass out. I had no idea what I was doing.

But I had to figure it out. I wasn't the type of man to shirk responsibility, and the fact was, that little girl was mine. I'd been part of creating her.

I had to pull my shit together.

When my feet were steady again, I took another slow breath and stood tall. Then I turned away from the lake and headed back down the gravel road. I still had no idea what I was going to do, but hiding out here wasn't going to help. I needed to get back to Lark Cove and to Thea so we could make a plan.

And so she could explain how this had happened.

Thea and I had been safe. Hadn't we? I'd used a condom the night we were together. A lot of condoms. So how had our one-night stand turned me into a *dad*?

Thea had charmed me instantly that night. I came into that hotel bar having escaped a fundraiser in the ballroom. My mother had been relentlessly trying to set me up with a friend's daughter. I'd gotten so fed up with the matchmaking that I'd ducked out for a breather and wandered into the hotel's bar.

There, I found Thea.

I skipped the rest of the fundraiser so I could sit and talk with her. Those hours of talking and laughing about nothing were so refreshing. Thea didn't care that my last name was Kendrick. Hell, she didn't even ask. She didn't care about my money or my family's status.

And because she didn't care, I didn't offer it up. Intentionally. We were just Logan and Thea, two strangers with chemistry off the charts.

I stayed until the end of her shift. I stacked chairs on tables while she cleaned and closed the till. And then I walked her out.

Three feet out the door, I kissed her. And that kiss lasted until dawn. The attraction that had been building between us for hours combusted like a lit match.

I whisked Thea upstairs to my hotel room, the one registered under my assistant's name, where I worshiped her body until the next morning. Where one of the condoms hadn't worked.

"Goddamn it," I muttered as my strides got longer.

I'd been so desperate for some anonymity that I hadn't mentioned my last name. What a fucking mistake. Just like it had been a mistake not to go back to that bar sooner.

Thea and I had agreed on just one night. One incredible night. The next morning, we'd walked away from each other with no strings attached. She'd gone back to her life. I'd gone back to my hectic work and social schedule, just glad that I'd had the chance to meet her.

What I hadn't expected was for Thea to pop into my thoughts so often after that night. I'd think of her smile whenever I was at a hotel bar. I'd think of her laugh when I was at a boring fundraiser. I'd think of her whenever I saw a woman with long, sleek dark hair.

After months of her on my mind, I'd finally given in. I'd gone back to the bar to see her one more time.

Except she'd been gone.

With my child.

I'd waited too long.

Mistakes weren't something I made often, especially monumental ones. The knot in my gut told me that waiting to see Thea had been the biggest mistake of my life. And there wasn't a damn thing I could do about it now. There was no going backward.

All I could do was figure out where to go from here, and for that, I needed to talk to her.

I slowed my pace and looked around, hoping to find some sort of landmark to help me figure out where I was.

The homes here were larger along this road, much larger than anything I'd seen on Willa's tour through Lark Cove. All of these houses had a beach-cottage vibe, with cedar shakes and white trim. Except they were anything but cottages.

The one I was standing in front of looked almost as large as my parents' place in the Hamptons. The front was covered with large windows overlooking the lake. The front lawn was green and cut short, like the fairways at my family's country club golf course.

The gravel road separated the main house from the boathouse built right on the water. Next to it was a private dock and graveled beach area. I'd blindly walked to the one neighborhood in Lark Cove that screamed money.

There wasn't much to the town of Lark Cove. A diner and Thea's bar. A tiny grocery store next to a four-pump gas station. Two churches and a ten-room motel. There was one school for kids of all ages, from kindergarten through high school.

And a whole lot of lake.

During her tour, Willa had told us all about this area of northwest Montana. Small towns like Lark Cove were spotted all around Flathead Lake. They all had the same necessities, like a convenience store / market with the essentials. But major stores and anything of real size were found in Kalispell on the north end of the lake.

Lark Cove was basically a cluster of homes along the highway. Local people lived here to escape the city limits. "Out-of-staters" built here for two-weeks-a-year vacation homes. This road had lakefront properties most of my colleagues in New York would salivate over.

Especially this one. I'd buy this place in a heartbeat if it weren't in Montana.

Except I wasn't allowed to hate Montana anymore.

Like it or not, I'd have a tie here for the rest of my life.

To my daughter.

Maybe Thea would be willing to move back to New York. If she'd be open to a cross-country move, it would make life a hell of a lot easier.

My phone vibrated in my pocket, interrupting my thoughts. I dug it out of my jeans, assuming it was Nolan, but frowned when I saw the name Alice Leys.

"I can't deal with this right now," I muttered, declining her call.

Alice had been one of Emmeline's friends from college. She also happened to organize charitable fundraisers around the city, so we crossed paths occasionally. For years, I hadn't paid Alice much attention, not only because I'd been dating Emmeline, but because whenever Alice looked at me, there were dollar signs and sexual positions in her eyes.

But about six months ago, after Emmeline and I had broken up, I'd been in need of a release. Alice had been more than willing to take my cock.

We'd met for drinks and to fuck a few times, but I'd ended it months ago. Her affinity for childish drama had grated on my nerves, as well as the unrelenting pressure to commit to a relationship. But she still hadn't gotten the message, no matter how often I'd spelled it out.

A voicemail popped up on the screen, but I deleted it without listening. Then I hit Nolan's name.

"I was starting to get worried that you left me here," he answered.

"I'll admit, it crossed my mind." If I'd had the car keys, I probably would have made it halfway to the airport before turning around.

"Where are you?" Nolan asked.

I spun around, searching for a street sign, but all I could see were homes and trees. "I'm not really sure. I'm standing on some dinky road by the lake."

"That narrows it down," he muttered. "Do you want me to come and get you?"

"No." I sighed. "I'll pull up my GPS and find my way back to the highway. It can't be too far. Where are you?"

"Back at the motel. I wasn't sure what to do when you ran

out of the bar, so I came back here to wait."

I was in no hurry to get to the Lark Cove Motel. We'd driven by on our tour, and while it looked nice enough, I didn't need to step inside a room to know that it held only the bare essentials. Bed. Bathroom. TV. I doubted there was a minibar or room service. I could use some dinner followed by a plethora of alcohol.

"I apologize for bailing on you earlier," I told Nolan.

"It's not me who needs the apology. I mean, it wasn't me who tried to tell you that you had a secret daughter, only to have you disappear before I could explain."

Shit. I closed my eyes and blew out a breath. "How bad is it?"

Nolan chuckled. "Lucky for you, she seemed just as shocked as you were. I'd say you'll be able to recover. Just use that Kendrick charm."

"What a fucking mess."

"You had no idea?" he asked.

"None. I haven't seen Thea in six years. It was just a one-night thing."

"Damn. That's tough. What's your plan?"

"I don't know." I started walking again. "I need to find Thea."

Except I'd been in such a rush to leave the bar, I hadn't gotten anything from her. Not a phone number. A last name. Anything.

For all I knew, she was at home with her husband. Maybe she had other kids. Maybe Charlie wouldn't want a thing to do with me because she already had a dad and a family.

My stomach twisted at the thought of losing something I'd just found.

I might have only become a dad four hours ago, but that didn't mean I was going to walk away. Charlie was my daughter and I wanted to get to know her.

I just hoped she wanted to get to know me too.

"I don't know what to do, Nolan," I confessed. "What if she

hates me? What if she says she doesn't want anything to do with me? What if she's already got a dad?"

"Don't start on the what-ifs just yet." His gentle voice helped calm some nerves. "Start by talking this out with Thea."

"I don't suppose she—"

"Gave me her phone number? Yeah. I've got it and her address."

"Thanks." I was glad my levelheaded friend and coworker had been there when I hadn't. "I owe you one."

"Don't worry about it."

"What else happened?"

"Not much. We were all pretty stunned, to say the least. Thea came over and introduced herself. I told her your last name and gave her your number. She said she'd give you some time before calling. But if I could give you some advice, don't make her wait. She's just as anxious as you to talk this through."

I nodded even though he couldn't see me. "I'll call her soon. Just text me her info."

"Okay. What else do you need me to do? I've already called the hospital in Kalispell and they told me they could arrange for a paternity test to be taken tomorrow. The results will take a week or so, but you could leave your sample before we head back to the city."

During the first part of my walk around Lark Cove, I'd contemplated getting a paternity test. If not for Charlie's pinky and the fact that she looked just like a Kendrick, I probably would have insisted on one.

But I'd decided against it. Thea wasn't lying. I'd made a career out of reading people and spotting lies. An Oscar-winning actress couldn't have pulled off Thea's reaction.

"Thanks, but I don't think the paternity test is necessary."

"Logan, I don't think that's a good—"

"You saw her. You saw Charlie. You had to see the resemblance."

"Yeah, I saw it the moment she took that frog from your hands. She's the tomboy version of your sister. But your family is going to insist on proof. You might as well get it over with soon."

I ran a hand through my hair again. Nolan was right. My family and our lawyers believed in test results to prove paternity. They'd insist on a test and to know everything about Thea's life. It was the only way to ensure she wasn't a threat to the family.

The idea of fielding their questions and demands was already more than I could deal with right now. Until I had some answers, they couldn't know about Charlie.

"I need to ask a favor." I took a deep breath, hating that I was putting Nolan in this position. He worked for the entire Kendrick family, not just me. "Would you mind keeping this all a secret for now?"

"If that's what you want, then my lips are sealed."

My shoulders relaxed. "Thanks. I'll tell them soon, but I need to work some things out here first."

"Here? You're going to stay?"

"I don't think I can go yet. Not until Thea and I work some things out. That's all going to be easier if I'm here."

"And if someone asks why you're still in Montana? What do I tell them?"

My mind jumped right into planning mode and plotting logistics. "That I'm here for a vacation."

I could spend a week here, working from my phone and laptop. Today was Monday, so I'd only have four days of meetings to reschedule. Unplanned absences weren't ideal, but I could coordinate my paralegal and associate team remotely.

From my career's standpoint, finding out I had a child in Montana couldn't have come at a worse time. I was busy as hell at work right now. We'd just onboarded two new clients to my team, both of whom were in the middle of complex mergers.

My firm specialized in corporate law, mostly for prominent businesses in New York. We had a large partnership, with the senior partners focused mostly on the financial well-being of the entire firm and human resources. My role as a partner was simple: marketing. I brought in the clients.

It wasn't hard. With the last name Kendrick, I could get into meetings most other attorneys couldn't. Add to that my unparalleled reputation for negotiating contracts and closing loopholes, and I'd brought more clients to the firm in the past year than other partners had in the last five.

But I couldn't be at work this week. For the first time, my team would have to pick up my slack.

"A week," I told him. "I need a week and I'll have this all sorted."

Nolan chuckled. "You're going to need more than that."

I didn't have longer than that. I had to get back to work.

Ahead of me, I saw the intersection to the highway. I must have walked in a zigzag while I'd wandered, because I could see the sign for the gas station. Which meant I was just blocks from the bar.

"I found my way back to the highway. Just text me Thea's info, and I'll catch up with you in the morning."

"Okay. Good luck."

Luck. I never relied on luck. I put my mind to something and made it happen.

The next week would be no different.

I'd spend the week getting to know my daughter. Thea and I would figure out a custody arrangement.

I'd spend this week in Montana and then things would go back to normal.

four

THEA

"**G**ODDAMN IT!" MY PLIERS SLIPPED FROM MY PADDED glove and clanked on my worktable. I shook off my glove, then switched off the blowtorch in my other hand, setting it down to cool next to the spoon I'd just ruined.

Not long after Hazel's confession on our back porch, she'd headed inside to read and I'd escaped to my art workshop in an attempt to get my mind off Logan. But no matter how much I tried to focus on my project, all I could think about were his angry eyes as he stormed out of the bar.

My fears were getting the best of me. Every minute that passed without a call from him, I got more and more scared.

What if he wanted Charlie? What if he forced me to split custody? What if he demanded she live in New York?

I couldn't go back to the city, not after I'd escaped. Not after I'd come here and found the peace I'd craved my entire life.

But the bottom line was, I couldn't live without my daughter. I needed to see her every single day, and if Logan had her in New York, then I'd have to go too.

I'd be back to living paycheck to paycheck, hoping my Saturday-night tips would be enough to make up for what my hourly wage lacked. Charlie would have to go to a school named after a number—P.S. Whatever, Whatever, Whatever—instead of our beloved Lark Cove School. And I'd be in the city where life hadn't been all that kind.

My memories of New York were full of loneliness, insecurity and powerlessness. When I'd left, I'd found courage and confidence and control to build the life *I* wanted. A life I was proud of. Moving back to the city would be like taking an eraser to half of my accomplishments. I didn't have many on the list.

Bracing my hands on my workshop table, I breathed through the waves rolling in my stomach.

Please, Logan. Please don't make me go back there.

I'd do it if I had to. Unlike my own mother, I'd sacrifice anything to be with my child.

"Snap out of it," I scolded myself. There was no use jumping to conclusions until I had a chance to talk to Logan.

I refocused on my work, surveying the mess on my table. I'd been using the torch to heat a spoon so it would bend, but I'd been so distracted that it had gotten too hot and broken in half. Turning around to the back wall in my workshop, I rifled through the mess on one of my shelves.

With a new spoon in hand, I checked my phone for the fiftieth time in an hour.

"Come on," I whispered. "Ring."

I waited a few seconds, but a New York number didn't flash on the screen. Charlie's face on my screensaver just looked up at me with a smile.

I huffed and set down my phone. Then I took my spoon back to my blowtorch. With it burning hot and my hand regloved, I fit the spoon into my pliers.

"Okay, spoon. Cooperate."

The stem was just starting to soften under my torch when someone knocked on the open shed door behind me.

"One second!" I shouted, not bothering to turn.

Hazel had learned ages ago to knock before saying anything. Once, she'd come in jabbering about something and had scared me to death. I hadn't been handling a blowtorch that day, but I *had* ended up covering a good portion of the floor in yellow paint.

I raked the torch's flame back and forth over the metal a few more times until it was perfectly pliable. Quickly, I set the torch aside and grabbed another pair of pliers, then carefully bent the metal so it had just the right curve.

"Got it," I said triumphantly to myself before dunking the spoon in a bucket of cold water to set the arch. I shut off the torch and yanked off my glove as I turned around to Hazel. "What's up?"

But it wasn't Hazel leaning on the doorjamb.

It was Logan.

"Oh," I gasped. "Hi."

"Hi," he greeted.

A bead of sweat dripped down my side. Even though I wanted to have this conversation with Logan, I was dreading it at the same time. "Please, come in." I motioned him inside and went to my water bottle for a drink.

He pushed off the door and stepped inside. "Sorry to interrupt."

"It's no problem." I swallowed a huge gulp, then set down the water.

Logan inspected the workshop as he eased inside. His eyes ran over the many hooks and tools hanging on the walls as he avoided making eye contact. And even though his hands were casually resting in his pockets, his frame was stiff and tense.

With every passing second of him looking anywhere but at me, my heart raced faster. This was agony. Was he still mad? Was he here to tell me he didn't want anything to do with Charlie? Or was he here to deliver my worst nightmare?

"Please, don't take her away from me," I blurted.

Logan's head whipped around and his eyes snapped to mine. His straight posture relaxed and the cool façade he'd put on fell away. "I'd never do that to you. To her."

"Thank you," I whispered, sagging against the table. If that was all he said the rest of the night, it would be enough.

Logan resumed his inspection of my workshop, taking his time as he studied the small space.

My workshop was my special, albeit disorderly, space. It was just an old gardening shed that Hazel's father had built decades ago. The walls were crooked. The windows were tiny and did little to keep out the elements. And the floor wasn't even a floor, but dirt that had been worn to a semismooth and hard surface over the years.

But it was my place. Here, I could tinker without fear of burning down the house or spilling paint on the carpet.

There were some old shelves on the walls that I'd crammed full of my raw materials just waiting until the time was right and inspiration hit. Like my spoons. They were rejects from the school cafeteria, so I'd taken them two years ago before they could be trashed.

Last week, I'd finally had an idea for how to use them.

"So, you're an artist?" he asked.

"No, I'm a bartender. This is all just a hobby."

He nodded, coming closer to my table in the center of the shed. "What are you making?"

"It's going to be a bird's nest made out of spoons." I'd welded the base of the nest together already, but it just looked like a mishmash of broken spoons at the moment. When it was done, it would be a cool piece to hold jewelry or other small trinkets.

"I'll look forward to seeing it when you're finished."

I smiled. "Thank you."

Logan was just being polite, but I liked it nonetheless. There were far fewer polite people in the world than one would hope.

"Nolan, my business associate, gave me your address. I hope you don't mind me stopping by."

"Not at all. I'm glad you're here. We've got a lot to talk about."

He sighed and ran a hand through his hair. "I'm sorry for running off earlier. I just needed—"

"It's okay. You don't need to apologize. I get it."

"I should have taken that shot."

I laughed. "Probably."

He grinned and moved away from the table, leaning back against a row of cabinets on one of the walls. "I have a kid."

I nodded. "You have a kid."

Of that, I had no doubt.

Charlie had always taken after Logan. They had the same part in their hair, the one that I couldn't get to move on her head no matter how hard I tried. They had the same color eyes, a shade of brown similar to my own. Dark. The same shape of their mouth and nose.

And that crooked pinky.

"I don't even know where to start." He held up a finger. "Actually, that's not true. We used condoms."

"A lot of them," I agreed, hopping up on the table. With my feet swinging, I shook my head. "Except in the shower."

"The shower." He closed his eyes and tipped his head back. His Adam's apple bobbed as he swallowed, letting the memory come rushing back. "I forgot about the shower."

Not surprising. The sex we'd had in the shower had been amazing, just not as good as we'd had everywhere else in his hotel suite. Still, I hadn't forgotten.

Logan had carried me into the shower after hours in bed. We'd both wanted to cool off and wash away the sweat and sex. But after he'd carefully lathered up my skin, I hadn't been able to resist a long kiss. He'd hoisted me up against the tile and plunged deep, fucking me with abandon until he'd pulled out and shot his release all over my stomach. Soap and water and Logan all mixed together.

Except he hadn't pulled out soon enough.

"I assume you'll want a paternity test to be sure," I said. "We can go up to Kalispell tomorrow if you want. I don't need to tell Charlie anything until it's done."

He stared at me for a long moment. "You're sure she's mine?"

"She's yours."

"Then that's good enough."

"I—really?" I blinked. He didn't want to verify paternity? He just . . . trusted me?

He nodded. "Really."

"I swear, I tried to find you, Logan. On my life, I swear it. But the hotel wouldn't give me your name no matter how much I begged. And you paid cash for your drinks and never mentioned your last name. I tried, but I just . . . didn't know where to start."

"It's not your fault. I believe you."

The sincerity in his voice made my throat burn. *Goddamn it.* I was going to cry.

I'd worked so hard not to cry today. I'd fought to keep my emotions in check and my head from spinning out of control. But this was going to make me break.

I wanted so badly for Logan to believe that I hadn't kept Charlie from him intentionally. The fact that a man like him would trust someone like me without proof meant more than he'd ever know.

"Thank you," I choked out past the lump in my throat.

"So, um, is Charlie inside with your husband? Or boyfriend?"

The urge to cry disappeared and I barked out a laugh. "Smooth."

He chuckled. "It's been a long day for me. Give me a break, will you? This morning I was in New York, then I came to Montana for a business meeting and discovered a daughter. I'm off my game."

"Fair enough. And no, I'm not married or dating. Charlie is inside asleep. We live with a friend who Charlie calls Gran."

"Do you have other kids?"

I quirked an eyebrow. "Twenty questions?"

"More like a hundred. Do you mind?"

"Not at all. Ask away."

As much as I would like to learn more about Logan, my questions could wait. I'd tell him about Hazel's "research" later and then ask the questions I had for myself.

"Let's start with the basics. What's your last name?"

"Landry."

"Thea Landry." His deep voice saying my name sent a shudder down my back.

He took his hands from his pockets and crossed his arms over his chest. The short sleeves of his polo stretched tight across his biceps. His jeans contoured around his bulging thighs.

God, he is hot. He'd brought a heat wave into my workshop.

Over the years, whenever I'd pictured Logan, he was always in a suit. Whether he was walking down the sidewalk or climbing into a limo, my mental image always had him in an Italian suit.

It was different seeing him in casual clothes, but he was just as handsome. Though his suit held so much power, his jeans and simple white shirt showcased his muscled body better.

And in jeans, Logan didn't seem so far out of reach.

Not that I had any intention of starting something romantic with Logan again. But for Charlie's sake, he'd be easier to accept in jeans. I doubted she'd ever seen a man in a suit who wasn't on television.

Logan cleared his throat before his next question. Did he think it was as hot in here as I did? "My grandmother would cringe that I'm asking, but how old are you?"

"Thirty-one. You?"

"Thirty-three. And when is her birthday?"

"August fifth." I smiled. "She was ten days late in the heat of summer. I'd never been so miserable in my entire life. Hazel, Charlie's Gran, rented me a room at the motel because I wouldn't stop snapping at her to get air conditioning."

He smiled back. "Charlie. That's a unique name for a girl."

"It's Charlotte. Charlotte Faye Landry. But she hates to be called Charlotte. At four, she declared she was Charlie and that's all she goes by now. I'm sure you could tell, but she's a bit of a tomboy. She loves nothing more than to play in the trees or around the lake. She's always building forts in the woods and finding animals to bring home."

"Hmm." His eyebrows furrowed and his gaze drifted to the floor.

I waited for another question but it never came. Instead, a heavy silence settled in the workshop, chasing away the heat. My arms broke out in goose bumps as he stared at his shoes.

What was he thinking? Did he not like hearing about her? Charlie was my pride and joy, so I talked about her constantly. Had I said something to spook him? Maybe I'd misread his questions for interest in our daughter. Maybe he was here tonight to say he didn't want to be a part of her life. That he had no interest in being a dad.

How would I ever explain that to her?

Please, Logan. Just give her a chance.

He finally looked up and whispered, "Do you think she'll like me?"

The air whooshed out of my lungs and I wanted to cry again. He wanted to know her. Logan wanted Charlie. "She'll love you."

It would take some time. Charlie wasn't outgoing like most of her friends and she was shy when it came to strangers. She'd put Logan under a microscope, making him prove he was genuine. But once she got past the initial hesitation, she'd love him completely.

It would just take a little time.

"Can I meet her?"

I nodded. "Of course. How about tomorrow night? You can come for dinner. That will give me a chance to tell her about you first. She doesn't do great with surprises." That was an understatement, but I didn't want to scare him away.

"Tomorrow." His face lit up, filling my heart with hope. "I'll be here."

five

LOGAN

I HAD NO IDEA WHAT TO DO WITH MYSELF. SINCE LEAVING THEA'S art studio last night, I'd been a nervous wreck. Sleep had come late and short. I'd finally gotten tired of staring at the ceiling so I'd gotten up to shower.

My face was shaved, my hair combed. I was dressed and ready for the day, but I had no idea where to go next. Now, instead of the ceiling, I was standing in front of the bathroom mirror, unable to look away.

She's going to think I'm uptight.

Maybe I should just wear a T-shirt.

Would that make me look more like a fun dad?

I should have asked Thea more questions. I didn't feel prepared at all to meet Charlie.

Last night, Thea had calmed a lot of my nerves. Whether she knew it or not, the little things she'd told me about Charlie had put me at ease. There was no mistaking how much she adored our daughter. The glint in her eyes had made me excited about meeting Charlie.

But the moment I'd left that garden shed, without Thea to reassure me, self-doubt had crept back in. What if Charlie and I had nothing in common? What if she didn't like me? What if I was a bad father?

By the time I'd walked the five blocks from Thea's house to the motel, I'd all but convinced myself that Charlie was going to hate me.

In the last decade—hell, two—I couldn't remember being this nervous. Not about starting college. Not about taking the bar exam. Not about a date.

I was terrified of meeting my five-year-old.

Talking to strangers came easy for me. I was good at mingling and making conversation. But I had no idea what to say to my own kid. I tore my eyes away from the mirror to look at my watch. I had until six o'clock tonight to figure it out.

Eleven hours didn't seem like enough time.

A knock at the door forced me out of the bathroom. I crossed the small space and freed the safety chain, not bothering to check the peephole.

"Morning," I told Nolan as I swung the door open.

"Morning." He gave me a sideways glance. "You okay?"

I nodded but said, "No."

"Here." He handed me a coffee to-go cup. "I assumed you didn't sleep much so I got you a double mocha from the little coffee hut down the road."

"You'd be right about that," I muttered and took a sip. "Thanks."

He leaned against the doorjamb, studying me. His short, black hair matched the color of his suit jacket and slacks. "So? What happened last night? Did you talk to Thea?"

"Yeah." I sighed, moving back into the room to sit on the edge of the bed. "I stopped by her house and we talked for a while. I'm meeting Charlie tonight."

"That's good. Isn't it?"

"It is. If I'm only here a week, I can't afford to waste any time. But . . ."

"You're nervous."

"Terrified." I nodded. "I have no idea what to say. Do I introduce myself as her dad? Or just Logan? Should I shake her hand? Or give her a hug? And that's just the first five seconds we meet. What do I do after that? If I fuck this up, she'll remember it forever."

Other dads had it lucky. If they messed up their introduction, it didn't matter. Newborns didn't remember anything.

"You need to relax, Logan. I've seen you charm entire rooms of people before. Just be yourself. If you go in there scared, she's going to pick up on that. Kids can smell fear."

Then she was going to smell me coming from a mile away.

This would all be so much easier if they lived in New York. I could see Charlie more often. I wouldn't feel the immense pressure to make every day this week perfect.

I stood and walked to the dresser, grabbing my phone and sunglasses. "We'd better get going. Are you ready?"

Nolan let me change the subject. "Yes. I'm hoping I can get back in time to squeeze in a few hours at the office."

He was flying back to New York today, and I envied him for it. Not that I didn't want to stay to meet my daughter, but I was jealous that he knew exactly what his day would entail. He'd fly home, swing into the foundation office for a few hours, then go home to his wife and son.

"You should take the afternoon off. Go home and spend time with Kayla before Tyler gets out of school."

He chuckled. "She wouldn't even be home. Her calendar is packed tighter than mine these days."

Kayla, Nolan's wife, had invented an organic skincare line last year and it had recently been picked up by two high-end department stores. "Just promise me that when you quit to become her personal assistant, you'll give me at least a year's notice."

"Don't worry." He shook his head. "I love my wife, but we'd kill each other if we worked together. I think I'll stick with the foundation."

"Good. We wouldn't be the same without you."

"A compliment before eight? Normally you like to give me a hard time in the mornings. You really are nervous, aren't you? And it's messing with your head."

Yes, it was. I couldn't think of a time when I'd wanted so badly for someone to like me. I had no confidence. Zero. And that feeling was more unsettling than the rest.

Nolan's face softened. "You've got this, Logan."

Do I? "Thanks. We'd better get you to the airport."

I appreciated that he had faith in me. I just hoped that over the next eleven hours, I could find some for myself.

By five o'clock, I'd done everything I could think of to distract myself through the day. I'd driven Nolan to Kalispell and dropped him at the airport. I'd stopped at a small café for breakfast, then done something I avoided at all costs.

I'd gone to a mall and shopped.

The last time I'd shopped for myself had been in law school. Once I'd graduated, I'd delegated all shopping to my assistant. Whenever I needed clothes, I sent him an email and they were waiting in my closet when I came home. If they didn't fit, a tailor came over to do alterations.

But shopping today had been a necessity. Not only did I need more clothes, I also needed to stay busy. The last thing I'd wanted to do was to go back to Lark Cove and sit alone in my motel room. So I'd shopped for a week's worth of casual clothes that, hopefully, would make me seem more approachable and *dad*-ish.

With a week's wardrobe in the back of my black rental SUV, I'd finally driven back to Lark Cove. I'd found a parking lot that overlooked the lake, pulled out my briefcase, set up a hotspot, and dived right into the best kind of distraction.

Work.

From the driver's seat of the car, I spent a few hours arranging for my unplanned vacation. My team at the firm had marching orders to start drafting contracts for an upcoming merger. Both of my assistants knew to call me with urgent matters. And my parents had received a note informing them that I'd be missing the dinner we'd planned for Thursday.

But as I hit send on my last email, I realized that I'd fucked up. I'd worked too fast. Efficiency, something that had served me so well, had become enemy number one.

I still had an hour to kill.

So instead of sitting in my car, worrying for the next hour, I went to the one place in Lark Cove I hadn't planned on frequenting again.

The Lark Cove Bar.

"Hi." I nodded to Jackson as I slid into a stool at the bar.

The smile he had for the two customers he'd been talking to disappeared as he looked my way. "Thea's not here. She's at home with Charlie."

"That's fine. I just came in for a beer."

"A beer?"

"Yeah." Why was that surprising? For a bartender, you'd think Jackson would be used to people asking for beer. "Whatever you have on draft."

He scowled and picked up a pint glass. But instead of going to the row of taps along the bar, he filled the glass with ice water.

"That's a little lighter than I normally drink."

Jackson didn't think that was funny. The crease between his eyebrows deepened as he set down the water on the bar. "You're meeting your kid for the first time tonight. Is walking into Thea's house with alcohol on your breath really the first impression you want to make?"

Shit. I'd just wanted a beer to settle my nerves, but he had a good point. I didn't want to smell like beer when I met my daughter.

"Jackson," a raspy voice snapped from behind him. "Leave him alone."

From the back hallway that disappeared behind the bar, an older woman emerged. Her hair hung past her shoulders in thick white and gray strands. Her skin was tanned and leathery. The wrinkles around her lips were more fissure than fine line. All of the things my mother despised about age, this woman wore with pride. She was beautiful, especially her hazel eyes, which were light and full of life.

"You work at the camp." I'd seen her yesterday when Willa had toured us around the main lodge. She'd been working in the kitchen, but before Willa had been able to introduce us, she'd ducked out and disappeared.

"That's right. I'm Hazel Rhodes." She extended a hand over the bar and past Jackson, bumping him out of the way.

"Logan Kendrick."

"You probably don't remember, but I was in here yesterday with Charlie too. During the Great Frog Escape."

"No, sorry. I was . . . distracted."

"Understandable." She grinned and patted Jackson on the arm. "This is Jackson Page. I'm guessing he hasn't introduced himself."

I held out a hand, but rather than shake it, Jackson crossed his arms over his chest.

He had an inch or two on my six-foot frame and probably twenty extra pounds of bulky muscle, but it took much more than brawn to intimidate me. Even on days like today, when the world was spinning the wrong way.

With my hand still extended between us, I met Jackson's stare. A rush of familiar confidence sped through my veins as I refused to break first.

This. This is what I'd needed all day. A chance to put on the face I wore into intense negotiations. A chance to prove I couldn't be bested. A chance to be the powerful man I was in the city. This guy didn't know it, but he was doing me a huge favor by being an asshole.

I returned Jackson's fiery glare with ice. To his credit, he lasted longer than most. But when he began shifting his weight from one foot to the other, I knew I'd won.

He dropped his arms and held out a meaty paw.

We shook, both of us squeezing harder than necessary, until he released me and I dropped my arm. The muscles in my shoulder burned a bit from holding out for so long.

"That was interesting." Hazel smirked. "Jackson, do me a favor. Hook up that new keg of Miller Lite for me."

"Sure." He grunted and turned. But before he took a step, he spun back. With both hands placed on the bar, bracketing my water, he leaned forward to speak low. "I don't care how much money you have. Hurt them and you're dead."

I nodded. "Understood."

Jackson pushed off the bar, then disappeared down the hallway and out of sight.

"Don't mind him," Hazel said, propping a hip up against the bar. "He's just protective of Thea."

With one sentence, I was back on edge. Except now, my nerves were muddled with jealousy. A bitter taste spread across my tongue and I took a sip of water.

Thea had told me last night she wasn't in a relationship, but did she have a history with Jackson? I loathed the idea of Thea with another man. My primal instincts reared up and I swallowed the urge to tell Jackson, *I had her first.*

But Thea wasn't mine. I didn't have a claim over her. Still, I liked her.

A lot.

Being with her all those years ago had been uncomplicated and freeing. Visiting with her last night in that old shed had brought it all back.

I liked how she didn't expect anything from me. She didn't have a hidden agenda. I liked how she quirked her eyebrow when she asked questions.

I liked that, above all else, she was a good mother. She thought about our child first and foremost.

Something I needed to do too, instead of worrying about Jackson and Thea. With another sip of water, I swallowed down my jealousy. It would likely surface again—Jackson wasn't the only one possessive of Thea—but not today.

"I'm not here to hurt Thea or Charlie," I told Hazel.

"I know that," she said, getting her own glass of water. "Like I said. Don't mind Jackson. We're all just looking out for Thea."

My spine stiffened. What had happened in Thea's life that she had such fierce protectors? Was it her childhood? Or a man? Could she, or my daughter, be in danger?

"Is there something I should know? She's not in trouble, is she?" Because whatever the problem, I'd make it disappear.

"No." Hazel shook her head. "She's not in trouble. But Thea has spent her whole life fighting. Don't make her fight you."

"Why would she need to fight me?"

She sipped her water. "For Charlie."

"Ah. I see." Everyone here was worried I would start a custody battle. "I won't take Charlie from Thea. I told her the same last night."

"Good." Hazel nodded. "Don't get me wrong. If you do want a fight, my money is on Thea. You might have a bigger bank account, but that woman is fierce. She'll wipe the floor with you if it's for Charlie. But she's fought enough."

She's fought enough? What did that mean? My concern for Thea grew with every one of Hazel's vague hints. A litany of questions ran through my mind, but they would go unanswered. There would be no prying information from Hazel Rhodes. She might be here, talking to me, but her loyalties were clear.

If I wanted to learn about Thea's past, I wouldn't get those secrets from Hazel.

"Who are you, exactly?"

She laughed, her hoarse bark ringing through the air. "I'm Charlie's gran. And the closest thing to a mother Thea's ever had."

"So you look out for Thea?"

"And Charlie."

Charlie.

"What's she like? Charlie?"

"She's a sparkle." Hazel's face softened. "Her smile is the best part of my day. You'll see." She glanced over her shoulder to the clock on the wall. "Want something stronger before you head over?"

I shook my head. "No, thank you."

"Smart man."

Jackson came back into the room at that moment and shot me another glare before resuming his conversation with the customers at the other end of the bar. When I turned back to Hazel, she was walking around the end of the bar to sit by my side.

"I think you should post more photos on your Facebook page," Hazel announced as the legs of her stool scraped on the floor.

"Excuse me?"

"Your Facebook page." She set down a paper boat of peanuts between us. "You don't have many photos."

I blinked at her. Where was she going with this? "I don't manage that page. My assistant does."

"Hmm." She cracked a peanut shell and tossed it on the floor. "Tell your assistant that people like to see pictures."

I chuckled, amused that in the last twenty-four hours, Hazel had clearly spent some time looking me up. "I'll send him a note."

Her peanut cracking continued, though she hadn't actually eaten a nut yet. "Before you go over to Thea's, I think I'd better come clean."

"Okay."

"I've been—what do they call it?—cyber stalking you."

I grinned. "I don't think it's considered stalking if you've only been doing it for a day."

"I might have known you for longer than a day." She shied away an inch as she finished her sentence.

My smile vanished and my jaw clenched. "You might have known me longer than a day?"

Finally, Hazel ate a peanut and washed it down with her water. "We need to talk."

Four words I hadn't dreaded much before yesterday.

Four words that now made me crave tequila.

THEA

EVERYTHING WILL BE FINE.

> *This is a good thing.*
>
> *Tonight will be fun.*

I was sweeping the back porch, attempting to convince myself with every swish of the broom that introducing Charlie and Logan tonight was going to go well.

It wasn't working.

Ever since Logan had walked out of my workshop last night, I'd guessed at how this would go. I'd imagined every likely scenario. None of them ended with hugs and kisses.

Logan wanted so badly for Charlie to like him. I'd seen the desperation in his eyes. It would crush him if she didn't run into his arms and call him Daddy.

But I knew my daughter. She wasn't as easygoing as other children. She was a thinker. She pondered change. And a life-altering one like this would take her time to accept.

She would eventually. Someday, hopefully not too far in the future, she would adore Logan. But the chances of her embracing him tonight were slim to none. If she wasn't all smiles tonight, I didn't want him to give up on her.

I'd been given up on more times than I could count, and I didn't want that for my precious girl.

I poured my nerves into the broomstick, sweeping hard to clear the dust from the porch. I held it back for one last strong push but stopped the bristles midstroke. The hairs on the back of my neck stood.

There were eyes on me. I could feel them.

But the yard was empty. Hazel was at the bar to pester Jackson and make herself scarce. Charlie wasn't anywhere in sight, probably off in the trees to play in her fort or find some other creature to try and sneak into the house. Logan's face popped into my mind but I dismissed it immediately. It was way too early for him to be here.

So who was looking at me?

I set aside the broom and walked down the porch steps toward the middle of the yard. I turned in a circle, looking for a neighbor close by or someone in a boat out on the lake.

There was no one.

Strange.

"Charlie!" I called loud. "Time to come inside!"

"Okay!" she called back from the trees.

I went back up to the porch, scanning the yard again as I walked. Then I shook my head, giving myself a good eye roll. The nerves for this dinner were making me crazy.

I went inside and put away the broom just as Charlie rushed inside. "Hi, Mommy," she said, out of breath.

"Hello, my love. Did you have fun playing?"

She nodded. "Yeah. I'm thirsty."

"I'll get you some water." I took down one of her plastic cups from the cabinet and filled it from the sink.

She gulped down the water and set the empty cup on the counter. Then she smiled up at me from underneath her favorite baseball cap.

The hat had once been black but was now faded to a dirty

brown. The stitched logo for the Lark Cove Bar had started out white but that hadn't lasted longer than a day.

Some Lark Cove parents frowned at me for letting Charlie wear a cap advertising a bar. But Jackson had given this hat to her and she adored it almost as much as her pseudo uncle. Since I was used to getting looks of disapproval, I shrugged it off and let her keep the hat.

The bill was too large, but Jackson had curved it to cover her face. And he'd cinched the back tight so it would fit around her small head. Other than those differences, it matched his own faded bar hat.

To Charlie, that was all that mattered.

"Let's get your hat and shoes off."

" 'Kay." She used my shoulder for balance as she kicked off her tennis shoes. They were black with neon-green stripes and matching lights in the soles. She'd picked them out of the boys' section at the shoe store. When I'd offered her the same style but in pink, she'd looked at me like I'd grown two heads.

Off came her shoes and dirt bits went flying across the scuffed hardwoods. The socks she stripped off were rimmed with dust. I didn't know why I always bought white socks. Even bleach couldn't keep them from turning brown.

"Okay, now let's go wash your hands."

"Fine." She frowned and trudged past me in her bare feet to the half bathroom off the living room.

I followed, leaning against the door as she washed. As the water ran, I took a few calming breaths, reassuring myself with each one.

She would get through this. We both would. We'd find a way to work Logan into our lives.

This is a good thing.

With her hands kind of clean, Charlie shut off the water.

Her cuticles were still dirty, but that was normal. I'd bought a vegetable scrubber that was permanently located in the bathtub upstairs. Tonight, just like every night, I'd give her a thorough scrubbing and rejoice in her cleanliness until morning rolled around and she made a break for the yard.

"So," I said as she dried off her hands. "I wanted to talk to you about something exciting."

She froze. "What?"

Damn. She'd seen right through my fake, cheery voice. I should have known better than to try and spin this as an exciting surprise. Most kids loved surprises, but not my Charlie. She hated them almost as much as cleanliness.

So I dropped the act and walked over to one of the couches in the living room. "Come and sit with me."

"Are you going to make me get rid of my fort?" Her forehead was creased with worry as she climbed up next to me on the sofa.

The last time I'd had a sit-down talk with her, I'd told her that I was going to be taking down the makeshift tree house she'd constructed out of cardboard boxes and duct tape. She'd cried over it for days until Jackson had come over and built her a tiny fort between two trees.

It was her sanctuary. While I escaped to my workshop, she ran to her fort to doctor animals or fight bad guys or hide away from monsters.

"No, honey. You can keep your fort."

Her entire body relaxed as she sank into my side.

"I want to talk to you about something else."

"Something good?"

"Yeah. Something great." I wiped at a smudge of dirt on her forehead.

No matter how scuffed she was, my Charlie was gorgeous.

Her hair was long and thick, a shade closer to Logan's than my own. She had beautiful skin that was always bright and flawless. And her dark eyelashes were like mine. She'd only ever need one swipe of mascara.

"I want to talk about your dad."

"My dad?"

I nodded. "Remember how I told you about him and drew you a picture? That his name is Logan and he lives far away?"

She sat still, waiting for me to continue. While most kids were a million questions a minute at this age, Charlie was the opposite. She soaked things in. She absorbed. The questions came later.

"Well, he's here, and he wants to meet you."

She blinked her big brown eyes.

"I told him he could come over for dinner tonight."

Her eyebrows came together and she dropped her gaze to her lap.

There was a woodpecker outside, hammering into a tree. The sound echoed outside and funneled through the kitchen window I'd left open, hoping for a slight breeze to cool down the house.

As I waited for Charlie to say something, I listened to that woodpecker's unsteady rhythm. It went on and on and on. Meanwhile, she just kept mulling things over while the *tap, tap, tap* continued. That woodpecker must be trying to knock down the tree, not just build a new home.

Shut up, bird.

I wanted to get up and shut the window, but with Charlie deep in thought, I didn't dare leave. I wanted her to know if she needed me, that I was here.

I'd always be here.

I was the constant she'd have in her life, no matter what.

"Is he nice?" Charlie asked finally.

Her voice was quiet and soft. She wasn't a loud child, nothing compared to the other twelve kids on her soccer team, but right now, she was borderline hard to hear.

"Yeah." I smiled. "He's nice."

"Is he going to live here now?"

I shook my head. "No. He still lives far away."

Her forehead creased. "Do I have to live with him too? Like how Katie spends some days with her mommy and others with her daddy?"

I wanted to say no. I wanted to promise that her life wouldn't change too much. But I'd always been honest with my daughter. And I'd tried to never make promises I couldn't keep.

So as brutal as it was for her age, I went with the truth. "I don't know yet, honey."

"I don't want to go. I don't want to move."

I wrapped an arm around her shoulders, pulling her close. "I know."

We held each other for a few quiet moments. Even the woodpecker gave us some peace. But when he started up with the taps again, Charlie pulled away.

"Can I go play outside some more?"

"Sure." I sighed, hating that I'd put a burden on her young mind. "Just stay in the yard."

She nodded and slid off the couch, going straight to the door without any shoes.

Her feet would be filthy by the time I called her inside for dinner.

I didn't care.

I let her escape to her sanctuary while I got off the couch to make dinner.

I rummaged through our square kitchen for a pan to brown

some hamburger and a pot to boil water. I wasn't a gourmet cook, but my food was delicious, if simple.

"This is a good thing," I told the pot as it sat under the running faucet.

Even the damn cookware knew I was lying.

An hour later, at exactly six o'clock according to the microwave clock, the doorbell chimed. I took a slow breath and wiped my clammy hands on a dish towel before rushing from the kitchen through the living room to greet Logan at the door.

He smiled when he spotted me through the small glass window in the door, and my stomach dipped.

That smile was devastating. I bet he'd charmed many uptown socialites with that smile.

He was in jeans again, but this time they were paired with a simple blue button-up shirt, the sleeves turned up to reveal his forearms.

"Hey," I breathed as I swung open the door.

"Hi." He smiled wider and ducked inside, handing me a bouquet of baby sunflowers as he passed. "These are for Charlie. I, uh, didn't know what else to get."

"Thank you," I said as I took the flowers. "She'll love them."

My hopes lifted as I took in the yellow blooms. Maybe this would go better than I'd thought. After all, he'd unknowingly bought Charlie her favorite flower.

She loved sunflowers because the birds could eat the seeds. Every fall, we'd buy a huge bundle and she'd place them strategically throughout the yard as makeshift bird feeders.

Maybe Logan and Charlie would connect immediately and all of my worries would be for nothing.

"And these are for you." He reached into his back pocket and pulled out a small bundle of spoons. "In case you run out before your project is over."

I laughed as he handed them over. "Thank you."

These spoons were twice as thick as the industrial-grade spoons I had in the workshop. You'd never find these in a school lunchroom or hospital cafeteria. They were nicer than the spoons I had in my own kitchen drawer.

"Come on in. Make yourself at home."

Logan walked into the living room and looked around.

The cottage was the nicest home I'd ever had, but now it seemed too small and too common. Having Logan here, just like having him in my workshop last night, was a harsh reminder that he was from a different stratosphere.

For the first time, I was embarrassed for being so chemically attracted to him. Why would he want me when he probably had a fancy, rich girlfriend in New York?

Still, I had no control over how my body came to life when he was near. My blood heated. My palms ached to press against the hard planes of his chest. My fingertips itched to dig into the muscles of his sculpted ass.

But he wasn't here for me. He was here for Charlie.

I was his one-night stand gone awry.

Nothing more.

I shook off the charge of his presence, concentrating on the matter at hand. Charlie was meeting her father tonight.

"So." Logan began pacing around my small living room, his gaze sweeping over the two floral print chairs that somehow went with our celestial blue couch. "Did you, um, talk to Charlie?"

His fingers fidgeted with his watch as he spoke, and he'd run a hand through his hair twice already. Something about him was off tonight. He'd still charged the air and spiked the temperature with one step inside. He still smelled divine, thanks to his Armani cologne. But he was different.

He was nervous.

So, as gently as I could, I tried to put him at ease while hinting at how to approach Charlie.

"Yes, I talked to her. She's . . . absorbing everything. She needs time to think, so just take it slow with her, okay?"

"Slow. Got it." He nodded, staring at a canvas painting above the couch. "Did you do these?"

I nodded. "I did."

A couple of years ago, I'd decided to try painting on a whim. Hazel had cleared out most of the artwork her parents had left her, and she'd asked me to make something to fill the walls. So I'd done three paintings.

The first was of me sitting on the dock by the lake. For my first attempt with oils, it had turned out okay. My hair was too light and the details a bit fuzzy, but it had been good practice for the others. The second painting was of Hazel's beautiful profile. And the third, the one that Logan was trying to memorize, was of Charlie at one year old with her first two teeth showing through her happy smile.

I didn't know what was going through Logan's mind, but my heart squeezed for him regardless.

He'd missed all of those moments. The baby cuddles. The toddler babbles. He'd missed her first words and first steps.

For Logan's sake, I hoped Charlie would cut him a break tonight. She was notorious for her intense scrutiny. Jackson called it her superpower. Most adults had nothing on my five-year-old girl.

Please, don't let tonight be a disaster.

I wanted a good night for both of them because neither

would ever forget it.

Wanting to give Logan a moment, I cleared my throat. "I'm going to put these flowers in some water. Then I'll bring Charlie in."

He didn't turn away from Charlie's face. "All right."

I darted back to the kitchen and scrambled to put the sunflowers in a vase. As it filled with water, I peered out the window over the sink to the backyard. A streak of flying brown hair caught my eye as Charlie ran from her fort to the shoreline of the lake.

I shut off the faucet and left the flowers to hurry to the back door before she could get herself wet.

"Charlie!" I shouted. "Time to come inside."

Her feet skidded to a stop on the grass, then her frame slumped as she changed direction, plodding toward the house and up the porch steps.

"Let's get you washed up, okay?" I placed my hand on her neck as she came through the door, then steered her right for the sink.

As we both scrubbed her hands, she looked up at me. "Is he here?"

"Yes, he's in the living room."

Her tiny shoulders drooped so low my heart ached. It wasn't Logan, just his presence. My girl struggled so much with change. It was just who she was. It didn't help that her friend Katie had told her horror stories of trading homes every three days after her parents had divorced.

I shut off the water and knelt next to Charlie, caressing her cheek. "Logan is really excited to meet you and have dinner with us. Do you think you can be brave and give him a chance? We don't need to worry about all of the other stuff tonight. Okay?"

She nodded and fell into my arms.

I held her tight, hoping to give her some of the courage she often gave me. Then I let her go and stood, holding out my hand.

When her little fingers slipped into mine, I smiled and led her out of the kitchen toward the living room.

Logan was sitting on the edge of the couch, his hands steepled together by his chin as one of his feet bounced. When he saw us come into the room, he stood fast. His eyes zeroed in on Charlie. "Hi."

Her hand gripped mine harder.

"Come on, honey." I walked farther into the living room as Logan stepped around the coffee table to meet us in the middle. "Charlie, this is Logan. Logan, this is Charlie."

He knelt down in front of her and held out his hand. "Hi, Charlie."

I tensed, holding my breath as I waited for her to react.

She was staring at his hand like it was the pink headband I'd tried to get her to wear once.

Logan's eyes darted up to mine, then back to Charlie. His hand was still between them, begging for a touch.

It hurt to watch as she rejected him. My heart ached as the longing on his face grew while his hope dimmed.

Finally, the pain in my chest was too much and I pried Charlie's hand out of my own. "Charlie," I scolded, pushing her forward a step. "Don't be rude."

Reluctantly, she put her hand in Logan's.

He swallowed hard as they touched, shaking her hand. "It's nice to meet you."

She looked over her shoulder to me with panic and whispered, "What do I call him?"

Logan chuckled and let her hand go. "How about Logan?"

She nodded and met his gaze, studying him for a moment.

"Mommy said you live far away."

"That's right. I live in New York City."

"And that's why you didn't visit me before?"

Logan looked up to me for help. "I, uh . . ."

"He didn't know where we lived." I dropped to my knee next to Charlie. "That's my fault. But as soon as he found out, he came right here to visit."

Logan gave me a sad smile, then focused back on Charlie. "I'd really like to get to know you, if that's okay?"

The corner of her mouth turned up a bit. Was she actually going to smile? Could it really just be this easy?

"Do you like forts?" she asked.

He smiled and my heart started to race. *Say yes, Logan! Just say yes!* "I don't know if I've ever been in a fort. Do you have one?"

She nodded and flashed him a shy smile. "It's outside. I can show you."

"How about after dinner?" I offered.

"Sounds great." Logan and I both stood, sharing a look of pure relief.

"Okay, we'd better eat." I turned and led the way toward the kitchen.

Charlie and Logan followed in silence, sitting at the dinner table as soon as we got to the kitchen. I left them there and went to the stove to bring over the food. But the kitchen was small and with the table in the corner, I could still hear them.

"Are you going to stay here now?" Charlie asked.

"Well, um, no." I looked over my shoulder to see a rush of panic cross Logan's face. "I have to go back home in a week."

Charlie's forehead furrowed as she took a few more steps and stopped. "Then you'll be gone again?"

"I guess. But I'll come back again to visit."

"When?"

The good feeling I'd had a moment ago vanished. Like most kids, Charlie remembered promises. Every detail. If Logan committed to a visit and it fell through, she wouldn't forget.

Goddamn it. Why hadn't we talked about this more last night? Why hadn't I prepped him? We should have made a more specific plan. We should have delayed this meeting until the two of us were on the same page.

But now it was too late. He was here and she was asking the questions she had a right to have answered.

My insides started to twist. I abandoned the stove for the table, but before I could jump in and change the subject, Logan spoke up.

"I'm not sure." Logan smiled. "But soon. And maybe you and your mom can come and visit me in New York. You could even move there and live with me."

Wrong answer.

"No!" Charlie's wide eyes snapped to mine. Her chin quivered. "I don't want a dad anymore."

My feet froze as the pain hit because from three feet away, I felt Logan's heart break.

seven

THEA

AN HOUR LATER, THE MOST PAINFUL DINNER OF MY LIFE WAS over.

"Can I go?" Charlie asked, already picking up her plate.

"Did you want to show Logan your fort?" I grasped for anything that might put a smile on her face. All through dinner, I'd been trying to find a topic that would connect Logan and Charlie but nothing had worked.

Any time Logan had tried to make conversation, she'd try to hide behind her plate of noodles. Nothing either of us had said could get her to mutter more than one or two words throughout the whole meal.

She hadn't even been impressed by the sunflowers.

Charlie had shut down the minute Logan had mentioned the idea of moving. The only thing that was going to get her to emerge from her shell was time.

"I want to play in my room," she whispered, sliding off her chair.

"Okay. I'll come up in a little bit and we can do your bath."

"I'm glad I got to have dinner with you tonight." Logan forced a smile and stood from his chair. "Good night, Charlie."

"Good night."

She dropped her plate in the sink, then disappeared upstairs with sad eyes.

When the sound of her footsteps faded, I looked up at Logan. "I'm sorry."

"I think I failed that test." He ran a hand through his hair and sank back into his chair.

"She'll come around. She just needs some time." I stood and began clearing dishes from the table.

"Thank you," he said. "Dinner was delicious."

"I guess none of us was all that hungry." Our plates were all still half full. Food had been pushed around during the awkward silences instead of eaten.

"She's not like other kids, is she?"

"Not like most," I said over my shoulder as I rinsed a plate. "It takes her a while to warm up to new people and change. She's not really shy, just . . . wary. For years, her world consisted of only me, Hazel and Jackson. She just needs time."

"Time I don't have."

Because his life was in New York. And ours was in Lark Cove.

I shut off the water and turned away from the sink, leaning back against the counter. "I guess we'd better come up with some sort of plan."

"Yeah." He nodded. "Would you ever consider moving back to the city?"

I shook my head. "I'd do it if I had to, but I'm hoping you won't make us."

"Make us?"

"It's no secret you could bury me under a mountain of lawyers to get custody of Charlie."

His eyes narrowed. "I told you last night I wouldn't do that."

"I know." I held up my hands, hoping to calm the rising

tension in the kitchen. "I'm just laying it out there. If you wanted her in New York, you could make that happen. I'm hoping you won't because we're happy here."

"She could be happy there."

"Yes, she *could*. But she *is* happy in Lark Cove."

He frowned. "I can't come back and forth to Montana all the time."

My stomach sank. I knew without asking that he wouldn't consider moving an option. I didn't blame him. I knew leaving the city would be asking too much. But that hasn't stopped my foolish heart from hoping.

I wanted him to choose Charlie over everything else. I wanted him to prove that she was his most important priority.

I wanted the impossible.

"What do you want to do?" I asked quietly.

"I don't know. I wish . . ." He sighed. "I wish she would have liked me."

The ache in my chest came back with a fury. "She will, Logan. Just give it time."

"I don't *have* time, Thea." He stood from the chair and planted his hands on his hips. "I have to leave on Sunday. I have one week. One week to get to know my daughter and build something of a relationship with her. Then I need to wrap this up and get my life back to normal."

My blood pressure spiked. He wanted to *wrap this up* in a week? He thought in seven days he'd have a loving father-daughter relationship. It took me longer than a week to decide if I liked a new shampoo.

And what was normal? There was no such thing. His life, the one he was so desperate to get back to, would forever be different. As of yesterday, it wasn't about him.

"Wrap this up and get your life back to normal?" I repeated.

He shook his head. "That came out wrong."

"Good," I snapped. "I'm sorry this has disrupted your life, but you're going to need to find more than a week for your daughter."

"Which would be easier if you were in New York."

"I'm not taking her to New York! She's starting first grade in the fall. She has friends here. She has family. I can't give her the life she has here in the city."

He pointed to his chest as he stepped closer. "I am her family too. And if it's about money, you don't need to worry. You'd have the best of everything. So would she."

We were his charity case now? I pushed off the counter and met him in the middle of the kitchen. "It's not just about the money. It's about her lifestyle. It's about where I want her to grow up."

"And what about what I want?" His voice got louder. "I should get a say too, especially since I haven't so far. It wasn't my fault that I missed the first five years of her life!"

"It wasn't mine either!" I stood on my tiptoes, inching toward his face. My chest was heaving, almost touching his, and with an angry breath, I realized just how close we'd gotten.

His gaze was heated and the inch between us crackled. Even angry he was gorgeous. The pull between our bodies was just as strong as it had been years ago.

My eyes drifted to his lips. I remembered them being soft but hard. He'd used them as weapons against my skin to render me helpless.

He leaned in, just a bit, tempting me closer.

I wanted to kiss him and snake my hands up his arms. To shove all of my frustration into something raw and physical. I wanted to ignore the heap of problems at our feet and get lost in something sweaty.

But it wasn't about what either of us wanted.

It was about Charlie.

I dropped my chin and took a step backward. Then another. "She has a lot of questions, and I don't have answers."

He rubbed his forehead. "I don't either."

"We have to find them."

"I know." He nodded. "Let's talk tomorrow. I think it would be best for me to go before something happens between us that we'll regret." Without a good-bye, he turned and left me standing in the center of my kitchen.

Regret. His last word echoed off the red-speckled countertops and yellow-tinged cupboards. It burned my ears.

Logan would *regret* a kiss with me. Maybe he regretted ever stepping into that hotel bar.

And damn did that hurt. Almost as much as knowing he had no plans to change his lifestyle for our daughter.

After Logan left, while I washed the dishes and cleaned the kitchen, I pulled myself together. As I did my chores, I shrugged off the sting of his rejection. I reminded myself that only one thing mattered in all of this.

Charlie.

Then I went upstairs and down the hall to her room. She was sitting at her "art center" with her back to the door. Her center was nothing more than a short, square desk pushed into a corner, but it had a small drawer for her special drawing paper and a cup to hold her markers. These days, her legs were nearly too long for the child-sized chair.

That center was the only thing in the room that had any girly qualities. Charlie had shocked me when we'd gone shopping in

Kalispell for the table. Instead of going for the white or royal blue as I'd expected, she'd picked pale pink.

The rest of her room was decked out in items from the boys' section at Target. She had a green camo bedspread and matching sheets. Her bookshelf in the corner was in the shape of half a canoe. And there was a black teepee at the foot of her bed where she'd escape to read with a flashlight. Her bedroom resembled her fort outside more than it did a little girl's room.

Everything was tomboy.

Except for that pink table.

"Hi, honey." I knocked on the doorframe.

She looked over her shoulder and then went right back to coloring.

I crossed the room and knelt next to her chair. "What are you drawing?"

"Just a picture," she mumbled as she used brown to shade in the roof of the house she'd outlined.

Our house.

She'd drawn the cottage along with three stick figures. One was me, judging by the long black hair. The other was Hazel with gray strands around her round face. And the last was Charlie, standing between us with a big smile.

Who wasn't in the picture? Logan.

Like mother, like daughter.

Charlie used art to express her feelings when she couldn't find the words.

"That's a pretty picture," I said, stroking her hair. "Can you take a break and look at me?"

She set down her marker and turned in the seat, her chin still tipped down. When she looked up, her brown eyes flooded with tears. "I don't want to move far away, Mommy."

"Don't worry." I pulled her off the chair and into my arms.

"We'll figure something out."

She sat on my bent knees and buried her head in the crook of my neck. "Promise?"

"Promise."

The knot in my stomach tightened. If Logan forced my hand—if he made us move to the city—I'd never forgive him for making me break my promise.

"Come on." I hugged Charlie tighter, then let her go. "Let's get cleaned up for bed. Do you want a shower tonight or a bubble bath?"

"Bubble bath."

With her leading the way to the bathroom, I filled the claw foot tub with water and bubbles while she stripped off her dirty clothes and left them in a heap by the door. Then we went about our normal scrub down until Charlie was dirt-free and smelled like lavender instead of the outdoors.

As she splashed around and played with her bath crayons, I sat back against the wall, stretching my legs out parallel to the tub. I took a few breaths, fortifying myself for a heart-to-heart with my girl.

We needed to discuss her father.

I wished I didn't have to force this conversation. I wished I could put it off until tomorrow, after we'd both had a night's rest. But since Logan was adamant about being here for only a week, there wasn't time.

"We need to talk about Logan."

Her splashing stopped.

"What didn't you like about him?" I asked.

"I don't know." She shrugged and scooped up a handful of bubbles.

"You got pretty upset when he suggested that we move. Is that what scared you?"

"Yeah." She nodded, stacking her bubbles in the corner.

"Was there anything else you didn't like about him?"

She stacked two more handfuls of bubbles before she finally whispered, "No."

My back sank further into the wall. If it was just the move, I could work with that. "Honey, I think you might have hurt his feelings tonight. When you didn't want to talk to him at dinner. And when you said you didn't want a dad."

Charlie looked up from her bubbles, her eyes full of worry. "I did?"

She was so thoughtful and loving. I was exploiting those emotions tonight in hopes that they would lead to a better tomorrow. "Yeah. We'd probably better try to fix it, huh? Maybe we could try again with Logan. Would it be okay if I invited Logan to your soccer game tomorrow?"

Even though another dinner would give them more time to talk, I couldn't endure a repeat of tonight. And maybe on neutral ground, the pair would find something to connect over.

"Okay." Charlie nodded, going back to her bubbles. "He can come."

"Good." I relaxed. "Will you do something for me?"

"What?"

"Try to be extra, extra nice to Logan."

She shrugged. "Okay."

I smiled and leaned forward, skimming some bubbles into my palm. Then I carefully arranged them as a crown on her head. "That's my girl."

She giggled, filling our bathroom with her musical laugh and banishing away some of my worries. Then we spent the rest of the evening in her room, reading books, coloring orange dinosaurs and singing bedtime songs.

After an hour, she was tucked into bed and I was walking

down the stairs just as the back door opened. As I rounded the corner to the kitchen, Hazel dropped her purse on the counter. "How'd it go?"

"It went."

I crossed the cream linoleum floor, heading directly for the freezer. I yanked open the door, rifled through the frozen vegetables and ice-cube trays and moved things around until I found my coveted huckleberry vodka. With it in hand, I closed the door and sagged against the fridge.

"That bad?" she asked.

I nodded. "He suggested we move to New York."

"Oh, no," she muttered, taking a seat at the table. "I bet that didn't go over well."

"No." I scoffed. "Charlie's exact words were 'I don't want a dad anymore.' "

"Oh, my Charlie." Hazel shook her head. "I knew I should have given Logan some pointers."

"What?" My back straightened. I couldn't keep up with her these days. "You met Logan?"

"He came into the bar this afternoon when I was there visiting Jackson. I chatted with him a bit. Told him about my research with Willa. Then he left to come over here."

"Ah, I see."

At least I didn't have to explain Hazel's stalking to Logan now. We had enough on our list of discussion topics as it was.

A throb was building behind my eyes, probably caused by the stress of the last day. With my free hand, I pinched the bridge of my nose, willing the pain away. Had it really only been a day since Logan had come to Lark Cove? It felt like so much longer. I hadn't had this much happen in the course of twenty-eight hours . . . ever.

If there was a night for my special vodka, this was the one.

I opened the bottle and took a shot, wincing as it burned my throat. When the warmth reached my stomach, I tipped the bottle back and did it again.

"I think I'm going to head to my workshop for a few hours. Is that okay with you?"

Hazel nodded. "No sharp objects?"

"Not tonight." I'd have to start a new project, because I wouldn't be working on my spoon nest either. Blowtorches didn't mix well with vodka.

Hazel pushed out of her seat and went to the cupboard where we kept the glasses. "At least drink out of this." She handed me a tumbler. "Classy women don't drink from the bottle."

"On the classy spectrum, I'm near the trash end."

She frowned. "One day, I'm going to wash your mouth out with soap when you use that word. Don't run yourself down."

I gave her a sad smile. "I'm not saying that to run myself down. Honest. I'm just being real." I'd climbed far from where my life had begun, but we all had limits. Even birds knew when to stop flying higher. "I'll see you in the morning."

Then I walked out the door, leaving the tumbler behind.

eight

LOGAN

I ESCAPED THEA'S AS FAST AS POSSIBLE, HUSTLING THROUGH THEIR house, only to pick up the pace when I hit the sidewalk. My strides were long and fast, putting as many yards and trees and houses between Thea and me as possible.

Christ, I almost kissed her.

I hadn't had that strong of an urge to kiss a woman since . . . well, Thea. I'd forgotten how magnetic she was. How fast she'd pulled me under in that hotel bar. Not even Emmeline had stirred that kind of raw, primitive desire.

I wanted Thea. I wanted to taste her again and feel her thighs wrapped around my hips while my hand fisted her hair. I wanted to give into the heat and get lost in a long night of sweaty, hard, *mind-numbing* sex.

So it was a damn good thing she'd stepped away when she had because I'd been seconds from smashing my lips to hers. I'd almost kissed Thea when I should have been thinking about Charlie.

My focus needed to be on my daughter. If I got lost in Thea, I had the potential to hurt us all.

And if we caused Charlie pain, we'd both regret it.

Maybe it was because my confidence was shaken. Maybe it was because of what had happened with Emmeline. But I had no faith in my ability to manage a long-distance relationship with my daughter, let alone a girlfriend.

So like I'd done last night, I walked the streets of Lark Cove without paying much attention. I was too busy chastising myself to notice street signs or landmarks. When I finally took in my surroundings, I chuckled.

My feet had carried me to the same dirt road I'd been on last night. The one surrounded by large vacation homes.

"At least I know where I am this time," I told the lake.

Behind me stood the house I'd admired last night. The big one with all the windows and cedar shingles. The windows were all dark, like they'd been last night. And there wasn't a car in the driveway.

Maybe I should buy it.

I had ideas like that pop in and out of my head all the time, but this one stuck. Maybe I *should* buy it. Thea had made it clear tonight that moving to New York was a last resort. Charlie hadn't seemed too keen on the idea either. Which meant that for me to see my daughter, I'd be trekking to Montana.

At least if I bought this house, I'd have a place to stay other than the Lark Cove Motel.

"Gah!" My frustrated grunt echoed off the trees.

Why was Thea so against moving back to New York? That would make everything easier. They'd be close so I could see Charlie more. That was, if I got past the point of scaring her into complete silence.

I shoved a hand through my hair, pulling tight at the roots. My grandmother always said I worried too much. Well today, I hadn't worried enough. Hour after hour I'd visualized worst-case scenarios. None of it had prepared me to face Charlie's rejection.

I don't want a dad anymore.

That. Fucking. Hurt.

My daughter didn't like me at all.

And I honestly didn't know what to do about it. I didn't know how to fix this problem.

I'd been in Lark Cove for a day and my spirits were at an all-time low.

What was I going to do? I pulled out my phone from my jeans, doing the only thing I could think of at the moment.

I would buy this house.

Quickly, I snapped a couple of photos, being sure to get the numbers next to the door. Then I emailed them to my personal assistant with instructions to find out who the owners were and offer them whatever it would take to make it mine.

This could work.

I could set up this house with a remote office. That way I wouldn't get too far behind at the firm or with the foundation when I was here. Maybe I could spend a few weeks here in the summer. I could come back for the holidays, though Mom and Dad would be pissed if I missed their annual Kendrick family holiday party. They'd have to adjust.

We were all going to adjust.

This could work. This house could work.

As far as I was concerned, Thea could have the place. If she wanted a bigger house, she and Charlie could both live here. Charlie would have all this room to run around and create her forts. Maybe I'd even have a special tree house built in the forest out back. And the detached garage would work far better than a shed for Thea's art studio.

Excitement surged. This could be the start of a plan.

I smiled for the first time in hours, then turned around, going back to where I'd started. Thea's. She might not want to see my face again tonight, but I was going back.

She'd asked me for answers.

Now I had some.

My phone rang and I grimaced as Alice's name flashed. The last thing I needed was her calling all week, interrupting my time with Charlie, so reluctantly I answered. "Hello."

"Hi, stud. Want to meet me tonight?" She was purring, something I'd always hated. It was far from sexy, more desperate than desirable.

"No. I'm out of town this week."

"Bummer," she whined. "Call me when you get home so we can see each other? Maybe go on a proper date?"

A proper date? "I don't think so, Alice. If we run into each other at a fundraising event, please be sure to say hello. But I think it would be best for you to stop calling."

"Excuse me?" Her nasal tone shred the last of my nerves.

"Take care, Alice."

She snapped something but I hung up before I could hear it all.

I never should have started something up with her. Not only would she call again, but I'd also have to fend off my sister, Sofia.

Somehow, Alice had managed to worm her way into my youngest sister's good graces. They were thick as thieves these days, no doubt plotting a way for Alice to get my last name. Tomorrow, I'd likely get an irate phone call from Sofia telling me how much of a fool I was for not marrying her friend.

I silenced my phone and shoved it back in my jeans pocket, then continued my walk back to Thea's so we could try our conversation again. This time without a fight.

The sun was setting as I reached her street. Her house was the smallest on the road, sandwiched between houses that were definitely not the originals. But somehow, between two homes that were twice the size and much newer, their green cottage fit. It was the house that belonged while the others were out of place.

I went straight for the front door, ready to knock, but stopped short as a crash sounded from Thea's shed.

Déjà vu. I'd been in exactly the same place last night when I'd heard a sound in Thea's workshop. And like last night, I changed direction, forgoing the front door for her shed. When I was a few feet away, I heard her cuss.

"Goddamn it!"

I approached the doorway cautiously so as not to startle her, then peeked inside. Tonight, her back wasn't to me. She was in profile with her head tilted to the ceiling and a bottle tipped to her lips. She took a long pull, then slammed the bottle on her paint-splattered table. She swallowed, grimacing at the burn of the vodka.

I knocked on the open door. "So what's your rule for drinking vodka straight?"

"Shit," Thea gasped, clutching her heart as she spun to the door. "You scared me."

"Sorry." I stepped inside the shed, raking my eyes down her body.

Earlier, she'd been wearing a thin, long-sleeve gray top, but she'd changed after I'd left. Now she was just wearing a low-cut tank with thin crisscross straps. The way her chest heaved as she breathed made her breasts strain against the cotton.

And it made my cock jerk behind my zipper.

This woman, everything about her, was sensual. Her hair was up again, revealing the long line of her neck. Her legs were so smooth and toned, bare except for her green shorts. They hugged the curves of her hips. She was wearing rubber flip-flops, showcasing toes painted fire-engine red.

She was stunning.

My mother and sisters had always thought designer gowns and fancy jewels made a woman beautiful. They pampered themselves at the spa weekly and never left the house without makeup. Would they think differently if they saw Thea like she was tonight? Raw and natural. She was so damn gorgeous I had a hard time staying upright.

"What are you doing here, Logan?"

My head jerked up as I tore my gaze from her legs. "I owe you an apology."

Her eyebrow quirked. "For?"

"The fight." I walked farther into the room, taking my place against the far wall and leaning on the same cabinet I'd propped myself against last night.

"Oh," she muttered, dropping her gaze and picking up the bottle again. Instead of pressing it to her lips, she held it between us. "Me too."

I took the bottle and brought it to my mouth, doing my best not to think that Thea's had been on the rim not thirty seconds ago. The vodka burned but had a sweet aftertaste. What was that?

"Huckleberry," she said before I could inspect the label. "It's another one of my drinking laws. Vodka for the particularly bad nights."

I winced. "I deserved that."

"No," she sighed and took the bottle back to set aside, "it's not your fault. It's just . . ."

I waited for her to continue, but she stayed quiet. "Just what?"

She gave me a pleasant, but forced, smile. "It's just hard. We need to figure this out for Charlie."

Her eyes were on the floor. Her shoulders hunched forward. Was this just about Charlie? Because my gut was telling me there was something else. Something I was missing. I opened my mouth to push her for an explanation but stopped before a word came out.

No question I could ask would get answered. Thea wanted this to be about Charlie, so I'd make it about Charlie. Maybe after she had some answers to give our daughter, Thea would realize I wasn't the enemy. She'd realize I genuinely cared for her feelings.

She'd trust me.

"I had an idea I wanted to run past you. I'm thinking of buying a house here."

She straightened off the table, her eyes were full of hope as they lifted to mine. "Really? You'd move here?"

"Oh, no. Sorry." *Shit.* "That's not what I meant. I'd still live in New York but get a house here to stay when I visited."

"Visits. Right." She went for the bottle again. "And how often do you think you can visit?"

"I don't know. I haven't gotten that far. But I thought if I had a place to stay and work while I was here, I could extend my trips."

"Great idea. Charlie will love that."

Except she didn't sound like it was a great idea. The excitement I'd had thirty minutes ago was gone.

Thea gave me another one of her pleasant smiles. The fake smile.

I knew it well because I had one of my own. It was the same smile I used when I wanted to appease a difficult client. The one I gave my mother when she pried into my personal life. The smile I wore to fundraisers.

Most people bought that pleasant smile without question. I'd perfected it over the years.

Thea's was better.

She'd almost had me fooled.

Almost.

"If you don't think buying a house is a good idea, then just say it. Don't feed me compliments just because you think that's what I want to hear. I'm not a customer at the bar. Don't bullshit me."

Her smile vanished. "What do you want me to say? I'm glad you're going to come here to visit. If owning a house makes that easier, great. I'm sure Charlie will enjoy that once you guys get to know each other."

"But . . ."

"But I'm worried. What happens when one visit gets canceled? Then the next? I'm terrified that you'll go back to your life in New York and forget a piece of it is still here."

Forget? I would never forget about Charlie. "I'll do my best to commit to each trip, but we both know that things come up. I can't promise plans won't change. I'm doing the only thing I can think of if you're so set against moving back to New York."

"Back to that again?" she asked. "I don't want to move."

"Then I'll visit." I stepped off the cabinet, standing closer to Thea to make my point. "I want to get to know Charlie, but I live in New York. That doesn't mean I can't be a part of her life."

In twenty-four hours, Charlotte Faye Landry had become one of the most important people in my life. Maybe *the* most important. I'd already missed five years. I'd missed seeing her as a baby and toddler. Earlier tonight, as I'd stood in Thea's living room, staring at the portrait she'd painted of Charlie as a baby, I'd made a vow not to miss any more.

"Please, Thea. Give me a chance to prove that she's important before you cut me out completely."

"I'm sorry." Thea put her hands to her temples. "I'd never cut you out. I just don't want Charlie to get hurt. I don't want her to ever feel rejected."

Rejected? Why would she think I'd reject Charlie? "I'd never reject her. I promise."

Her gaze narrowed as she assessed my sincerity. My chest tightened, much like it had when Charlie had looked me up and down earlier tonight. I didn't remember a time when I'd gone through such intense scrutiny. Not in college. Not in law school. My father, who was known for his ruthless critique, hadn't inspected me this closely when I'd practiced my high school valedictorian speech for him.

These Landry women were stripping me bare.

"I want to believe you," she said quietly. "I really do. But I don't even know if you believe in yourself right now."

I staggered back as if she'd slapped me. She saw right through me, didn't she? She saw every flaw and insecurity. "You're right. I don't have the first clue what to do with Charlie. But I'll figure it out over time."

"Time? I thought you only had a week."

"I'm coming back."

"You'd better. If you make my daughter fall in love with you and then you leave her behind, I will find you and smother you in your sleep."

I chuckled. Not many people challenged me. I liked that Thea didn't back down. She met me with full force when we were fighting and when we'd had sex. I loved that she was especially scrappy when it came to our daughter. "I think you'd better hand over that vodka. You're getting violent."

She answered by grabbing the bottle and gulping down another shot. "You should see me when I drink bourbon. The last time I had Jim Beam, I decided to trim the shrubs along the sidewalk out front."

"What shrubs?"

"Exactly."

I laughed, picturing a drunken Thea going to town on some

harmless greenery. "I met Hazel today."

"She told me." Thea handed over the bottle, our fingers brushing as I took it from her grip, and my pulse quickened.

This was dangerous, the two of us together in a cramped shed, drinking and letting the awkwardness melt away. I should say good night. I should go back to the motel and spend a couple of hours working. I should leave her here before I did something rash.

Instead, I took a drink.

Thea had this way of making me ignore *should*. She inspired me to throw out logic and prudence and obligation.

"So what's next?" I asked, handing her the bottle. "Tell me what to do."

She shrugged. "You have a week. I guess let's start there. Charlie has a soccer game tomorrow night, and you're welcome to come."

"I'll be there. Just text me when and where."

She nodded. "We usually go out to dinner afterward. You're welcome to join us."

"Done."

"No more talk about moving." She pointed the bottle at my nose. "Don't tell Charlie you're thinking of buying a house here either. At least, not until she warms up to you. She's scared she's going to have to live in two places."

Yes. Now we were getting somewhere. Much like in a difficult acquisition or tense merger negotiation, I always studied my opponents. I liked to know exactly who I was facing off with on behalf of my clients. Before I sat down at any conference table, I knew everything possible about the business my client was trying to buy—financial position, staff members, any previous legal troubles. And I knew even more about the opposing counsel. It wasn't uncommon for me to take them out for a "get-to-know-you" lunch before we faced off.

It was ridiculous, comparing a soccer game and dinner with a five-year-old girl to my contract negotiation strategies. But I was desperate to get along with my daughter.

I waved Thea on. "Keep it coming."

"Don't make her any promise you can't keep. Don't let her silence scare you away. She listens more than she talks. Oh, and we can never argue in front of her. If she senses that we're not getting along, she'll pick a side and it won't be yours."

I grinned at the mental image of Charlie protecting her mother. I could relate to that feeling entirely. Something about Thea made me want to wrap her in my arms and never let go. "Anything else?"

She shook her head. "I'll let you know what I come up with."

"Thank you."

"You're welcome." She took a shot, then handed me the bottle to do the same.

We stood there in silence for a while, passing the vodka back and forth. The entire time, I studied Thea's deep brown eyes. They were so bold and large, the color of dark chocolate. The night we'd spent together, I'd spent hours getting lost in her eyes as I'd moved inside of her.

Drunk and unable to fight the pull, I stepped away from the cabinet, holding her eyes as the space between us disappeared. I walked right into her space, trapping her against the table. The heat from her heaving breasts warmed the front of my shirt.

"Logan," she whispered when I pressed even closer. "This is stupid." Still, her hands came to my waist, gripping my shirt.

"You're probably right. But I'm going to kiss you anyway."

nine

THEA

MY ENTIRE BODY HUMMED AS LOGAN PRESSED HIS HIPS closer. The hardness behind his jeans sent a wave of scorching heat to my core. I hadn't been kissed in a really, *really* long time.

Why was this stupid? I couldn't think of a reason. All of the worries and concerns I'd had in the kitchen after he'd stormed out were a hazy blur at the back of my mind. They vanished as my eyelids drifted shut, waiting for the soft brush of his lips.

The heat from his breath feathered across my cheek. He was so close I was dizzy. I gripped his shirt tighter, waiting for his mouth. He was almost—

"Wait."

No! My stupid, tiny, infuriating brain. I should have had another shot or two. Maybe then, my good judgment wouldn't have been able to reengage at the last second and send that awful word through my mouth.

I opened my eyes to see Logan had moved back, just an inch. Enough that I could make out the disappointment on his face.

"Sorry." My shoulders sagged. "I want you to kiss me."

"But?"

"But," I dropped my hands from his shirt, "it will only complicate things even more."

There were too many hurdles between us. Lifestyle. Geography. Responsibilities. Even drunk on vodka and Logan's scent, the obstacles were just too big to ignore.

He grumbled under his breath and backed away, resuming his place against the cabinets. "Are you always this logical when you've been drinking?"

I smiled, glad he wasn't angry. "No. Only when it comes to Charlie. She's all that matters."

"As disappointed as I am, she's a lucky girl to have such a good mom."

My heart swelled. Since the moment I'd held the positive pregnancy test in my hand, all I'd wanted was the best for my baby. I was proud to admit that despite having no guidance from my own biological mother, I was a good mom. Still, it meant the world that Logan thought so too.

He took a long breath and ran a hand through his hair. "I think I'd better go."

"I'll text you the details for the soccer game."

"Thanks. Good night." With a wave, he strode out of my workshop and into the night.

I counted to twenty, then rushed to the door, peeking around the side to see him walking down the street.

My house was only five blocks from the motel, three from the bar. I'd noticed earlier that he hadn't driven over, so as he walked down the sidewalk, I took a long look at him from behind.

No woman in the world would look at Logan and not think he was gorgeous. Add to that his charisma, and he was mouthwatering.

And he'd wanted to kiss me.

Six years ago, I hadn't hesitated a second when he'd asked me to spend the night with him. I'd let him whisk me away to his hotel suite for the best sex of my life.

But the Thea from six years ago was still learning. She hadn't given birth to a little girl who would become her entire life.

Charlie had given me unconditional love and a real family, two things I'd craved my entire life. But the most important thing she'd given me was confidence. Because of her, I demanded more from life and more than I'd been given as a child.

I demanded more, so I could give it to her.

The Thea from six years ago would have let Logan kiss her senseless tonight. She would have taken that kiss and locked it away, cherishing the memory when she was alone.

Present-day Thea wanted more than a memory. She wanted a man who would kiss her every morning. A man who would kiss her before falling asleep every night. She needed a man who would share in the life she'd worked hard to build in Lark Cove.

The man disappearing around the block—the one who lived a world away—wasn't him.

I woke up the next morning with a hangover. After Logan had left my workshop, I'd gone down to the dock to watch the sunset. I'd stupidly taken my vodka along.

I'd powered through the headache and nausea, getting Charlie ready for her day at camp with Hazel. With a kiss goodbye, I'd sent her on her way, then walked to work.

On days like this, working in a bar was a curse. I gagged at the smell of stale beer and the sight of liquor bottles made my stomach roll. How did Jackson come here with a smile on his face after a long night of drinking? I needed to learn his tricks if I was going to keep having vodka-soaked conversations with Logan.

I spent the morning in my office, doing paperwork and

paying bills. I slugged down coffee and aspirin, willing my head to stop pounding. When we opened at eleven, I went out to the bar, where I spent the first hour breathing through my mouth so I wouldn't puke.

Finally, around three o'clock, after the lunch crowd had left me to an empty room and the regulars had yet to come in for the evening, I braved some food and a Coke. By the time Wayne and Ronny came in for their early evening beer, I was feeling human again.

Barely.

"Hey, guys." I set down napkins in front of them both. "Same as usual?"

"Yep," Wayne answered for them both.

"Are you feeling okay, Thea?" Ronny asked.

"No," I confessed with a smile, then went to the taps to pour them each a red beer. "Too much vodka last night."

Wayne chuckled. "That'll do it."

"Can I get you some aspirin?" Ronny asked.

"I'm okay." I winked at him. "Thanks, though."

Wayne and Ronny were as opposite as they came, other than both being single. Wayne was in his fifties, had been divorced for years and worked at the school doing maintenance. Anything and everything you might want to know about his life, he'd share without hesitation.

Ronny was closer to my age, and though he wasn't as chatty as Wayne, he was just as much of a sweetheart. He worked from home, so he came into the bar often to socialize. Mostly he listened, but on the dead nights, he and Wayne would talk to me about nothing and everything until I closed down the bar. Ronny always made sure I was okay.

"Here you go, guys." I set down their beers. "Holler if you need anything." I smiled and turned to leave but stopped to look over my shoulder. "I take that back. Don't holler. My headache can't take yelling. Maybe just wave me over silently."

They each laughed, sipping their drinks as the back door opened and Jackson walked in, ready to take over for the night.

"You look like shit," he teased. "Rough night?"

"Don't make fun of me." I whipped his side with my bar rag. "I'm still not sure I'm going to live."

"If you were going to tie one on last night, you could have at least come in here and kept me company."

"Was it slow?" I'd been so miserable this morning, every task had taken me twice as long, so I hadn't finished reconciling the deposits from last night.

"Yeah. I had a couple of folks come in for a few hours but by eleven it was dead, so I closed down early."

"Maybe tonight will be busier."

"Hopefully." He opened the dishwasher and let the steam escape. "Are you coming in after Charlie's game?"

"Yeah." It was our tradition to have pizza after soccer. "I invited Logan to come too."

Jackson slammed the dishwasher closed and crossed his arms over his chest. "You need to be careful. I don't trust that guy."

I rolled my eyes. "You don't trust anyone."

"And neither should you."

"Well, I don't really have a choice this time, do I? Charlie deserves a chance to get to know her father. Logan is asking for some time with her, so I'm letting him have it."

"I hope that's all you're letting him have," he muttered.

"What are you talking about?"

"He might want to spend time with Charlie, but he's also here to get laid. I didn't miss the way he looked at you."

"That's ridiculous."

Logan probably had ample opportunities for sex in New York. He might even have a girlfriend. *Goddamn it.* What if he had a girlfriend? I'd almost kissed him last night.

My head started pounding again. I'd been so focused on sharing details about my life and Charlie's that I hadn't bothered to ask Logan about his.

"Whatever." Jackson went back to the dishwasher. "Don't say I didn't warn you."

"Instead of being a prick, you could be supportive. You know, act like my best friend? And it would help Charlie too if you didn't bust his ass when we come in here tonight."

Jackson frowned as he lifted out the warm pint glasses. "Tell you what. For Charlie's sake, I won't say anything tonight. But I'm not going to be *supportive* until after he leaves and comes back."

I had faith that Logan would come back and be true to his word, so I smiled. "Good."

"For a year."

My smile fell. "What?"

"He comes back here, makes it a point to visit Charlie throughout the *entire* year, then I'll be supportive. And by visit Charlie, I mean he's not coming here so he can fuck you. Has he made a move on you yet?"

I narrowed my eyes. "That's none of your business."

"That's a yes."

I didn't have the time or energy to deal with this. "I'm leaving. We'll see you later."

Tossing my rag on the counter, I walked behind him and down the bar. But before I got to the hallway, I stopped and turned. "Charlie is having a hard time with this. I'm asking you, Uncle Jackson, not to be a dick to her *dad*."

He shrugged. "We'll see."

"I'm warning you, if you make this hard for her, I'll make sure that every one of those plastic out-of-staters you're so fond of taking home after closing thinks you have crabs."

We scowled at each other. He lasted a while, but just like always, he was the first to break.

His mouth stretched in a slow grin. "Fair enough."

"Good." I huffed and spun back around, grabbing my things from the office before stomping the three blocks home. I used my ten minutes of quiet time alone to sit on the couch and get my blood pressure back to normal.

I loved Jackson. He was my best friend and the closest thing I had to a brother. And I knew his heart was in the right place. He was just wary of strangers. We had that in common. Life had taught us that, more often than not, other people would let you down.

But having Charlie and leaving the city had softened me. I wasn't constantly looking for ulterior motives with the people I met. Sure, I was on guard. But I wasn't so untrusting that I never let anyone close.

Not Jackson.

He trusted two adults: me and Hazel. Everyone else was kept at arm's length. He hooked up with out-of-staters so he could send them packing the next morning. He was "friends" with the regulars at the bar but didn't see them outside of work.

Besides me and Hazel, his only other true emotional attachment was to my daughter. I had no doubt that if Logan broke Charlie's heart, or mine, Jackson would dump his dead body in the middle of the lake.

Was I being too trusting with Logan? Over the last two days, I'd weighed every one of his words, assessing them for sincerity. They'd all seemed genuine. Were my feelings for him clouding my judgment? Had I gotten so caught up in his allure that I'd been blinded?

Okay, brain. You're forgiven.

Last night, I'd tossed and turned in my drunken haze, pissed at my better judgment for not letting Logan kiss me. Now I was determined more than ever not to let that kiss happen. Logan had to prove that he was in this for Charlie, not for sex with me.

He had to prove that he was coming back for our daughter.

"Mommy!" Charlie called as she ran through the door with Hazel on her heels.

"Hi, honey." I stood from the couch, giving her a hug. "How was your day?"

"Good." She smiled over her shoulder at Hazel. "Gran made me and the other kids a huge tub of slime."

"That sounds like fun." And it explained why her normally dirt-covered cheeks were clean and her fingers were tinged with blue.

"It was something," Hazel said and plopped into the spot on the couch I'd just vacated. "I've been cleaning up slime for an hour."

"Are you coming to the game?"

She laughed. "Do I ever?"

"No." I smiled. "But you know I always offer."

Hazel had come to three of Charlie's soccer games last year, then declared she was done. She said it was too hot and uncomfortable sitting on the grass. I'd offered to buy lawn chairs but she'd still refused.

Really, I think that after volunteering at the camp all day and playing with Charlie, Hazel was exhausted by the time she came home. Since Charlie didn't seem to mind her missing the games, we left her to some peace and quiet.

"Come on, my love." I took one of my daughter's hands. "Let's get ready for your soccer game."

"Is Logan still coming?" she asked as we climbed the stairs.

"He's going to meet us there."

"I hope we win," she whispered from behind me.

I smiled to myself. She never cared if they won, which meant she wanted to win with Logan there. This was progress. Like I'd told Logan, she just needed time.

Thirty minutes later, I parked my black Mazda hatchback on the street by Lark Cove School. Soccer games and all other town sports were played on the large lawn next to the children's playground.

Charlie, wearing her shin guards and neon orange jersey, unbuckled from her seat and hurried out. She was waiting by the back hatch when I got there to collect her soccer ball. I handed it to her, then unloaded a patchwork picnic blanket Hazel had made from old jeans.

"Thea." I spun around at Logan's deep voice. He came right up to us and took the heavy blanket from my arms. With his free hand, he pushed his sunglasses up into his hair and bent to greet our daughter. "Hi, Charlie."

"Hi, Logan," she whispered, inspecting her cleats.

"Ready for the game?"

She nodded.

"Don't forget your gloves." I took them out of the back and handed them over.

"You play goalie?" Logan asked. "I was a goalie too when I played soccer in high school."

Charlie's head snapped up. "You were?"

"I wasn't very good." He exaggerated a grimace. "Maybe one of these days you can teach me some of your moves."

She nodded. "Can I go, Mommy?"

"Yes. Have fun."

Charlie spun around and raced for the soccer field to join her teammates, her ponytail whipping behind her as she ran.

"Hi." Logan stood and leaned down to kiss my cheek. "How are you?"

Tingles broke out across my skin and my chest flushed red. "I'm good."

Damn you, Jackson.

As much as I just wanted to enjoy the sensation of Logan's lips on my cheek, I couldn't. Thanks to Jackson's speech earlier, I was doubting every one of Logan's moves.

It didn't make it easier that Logan looked unbelievable today. He was wearing a simple gray T-shirt, khaki cargo shorts and flip-flops. All fancy brands, I was sure. This was probably something he'd wear to a beach house in the Hamptons.

But even with the laid-back attire, he was still classy. It had nothing to do with his clothes. It was just him.

"Shall we?" Logan gestured for the grass and slid down his sunglasses.

I stepped onto the grass and we walked side by side at a leisurely pace. "Were you really bad at soccer?" I couldn't imagine Logan being bad at anything, certainly not a sport. I knew from experience how athletic his body could be in the bedroom.

"No." He looked over and grinned. "I was pretty good."

"I figured." I smiled back, leading Logan to my regular spot.

I waved at a few of the other parents who came into the bar on occasion. Behind my sunglasses, I glared at a couple of the moms who were practically drooling over Logan.

Tomorrow, I'd have an unusually large lunch crowd at the bar. People would come in who hadn't been there in years just to pester me about the handsome stranger at the soccer game.

I didn't care. If it bumped up my revenue, they could ask all they wanted. I would be staying quiet.

Jackson and I had always agreed that the Lark Cove Bar wouldn't be a gossip mill. If our patrons wanted to talk about their neighbors, they sure could. But they wouldn't get any information from us. We'd always been tight-lipped and we were staying that way.

Especially when it came to our personal lives.

"Here's good." I stopped Logan as we reached the sidelines at the far end of the field.

"You don't want to sit closer to the middle?"

"No, Charlie will be on this end." That, and I didn't want to have to dodge questions tonight.

I took the blanket from his arm and laid it out on the grass. Then I kicked off my own shoes and took a seat, hoping that a little sunshine would fight off the lingering headache from my hangover.

"Is it normal?" Logan asked as he sank down onto the blanket at my side.

"Is what normal?"

"To feel this nervous for her." He nodded to Charlie, who was taking her position in front of the net.

"Yes." I smiled and leaned over to bump his shoulder with mine. "She really wants to win because you're here."

His jaw went slack. "Really?"

"Really."

"Thank you." His hand came to my knee as he looked back to the field. His thumb stroked my bare skin once before he lifted it away.

Sweat beaded at my temple. Logan's touch had spread across my skin like fire, settling right in my center.

Damn it, Jackson.

His warning was ruining my evening.

I wanted to savor the tingles on my skin. I wanted to delight in the heat coming off Logan's shoulder that was just an inch away from mine. But I couldn't. Not until Logan had proved this wasn't about me or sex. I needed to back away from Logan until he proved his loyalty to the little girl standing on the soccer field.

The little girl who was about to make her father proud.

ten

LOGAN

"Yes!" I clapped as one of the kids on Charlie's team stole the soccer ball and kicked it down the field.

A few feet behind me, Thea was lying on the blanket. My hands were on my knees and my eyes glued to Charlie as she stood stoically in front of the net.

"Will you sit down?"

I looked over my shoulder at Thea. She looked so beautiful, stretched out on the blanket. The tendrils of her hair were floating in the breeze. Her skin was glowing under the sun. It was tempting to sit down, to cozy up to her, but I was too into the game.

"I can't sit." We were up by one goal and the game was almost over. I was practically coming out of my skin, wanting Charlie's team to win. I couldn't remember a time when I'd been this keyed up for a game. Any game.

Thea huffed. "Then will you move out of the way so I can see?"

I shuffled down a foot, not taking my eyes off the game. Just then, the opposing team stole the ball and kicked it down the field toward Charlie's goal.

"No! Where's the defense? This whole team is a bunch of

ball watchers. The coaches need to start getting these kids to play their positions. The only one sticking to her zone is Charlie."

Thea laughed behind me. "After the game, I'm sure Susan and Melinda would appreciate your input. Volunteer moms who coach peewee soccer really love getting tips from other parents on how to run the game."

I shot her a glare. "You're teasing me? For taking an interest in Charlie's team?"

"Someone should. You look ridiculous pacing along the sideline and barking soccer terms."

"You know, not many people tease me." Except for Nolan and my assistant at the foundation.

She laughed. "Trust me. If all the people who you normally intimidate into silence were sitting in my spot, they'd tease you too."

"I—forget it." I swallowed my retort and focused on the game.

One of the forwards on the other team was dribbling the ball toward Charlie's goal and it sent an uneasy feeling up my spine. For five, the kid's footwork was impressive. He knew how to handle the ball, and if he scored on Charlie, the game was over. It would end in a tie, which was still losing in my book.

My hands extended past my sides as I mirrored Charlie's stance. She was ready and waiting to make the save.

The kid with the ball had a cluster of others behind him, all trailing along and not trying to do anything but watch and see what happened. Parents and coaches on the other side of the field were cheering and clapping the enemy on.

Come on, Charlie. Come on.

My heartbeat roared in my ears as everything else went silent. I blocked everything out, focusing only on the ball and my daughter.

The kid moved in range and swung back his leg, hammering his foot into the ball and sending it flying over the grass.

Charlie made the right move, leaping left for the ball. She held out her hands, stretching her small body. Her knee hit the ground first as she fell to the side, with her arms still extended. Her fingertips had just enough reach to swat the ball away from the net right before her body collided with the grass.

No score.

"Yes!" My arms shot in the air. I punched the air a couple of times before clapping and shouting, "Way to go, Charlie! Nice save!"

I was so damn proud. I hoped she could hear me yelling. Her success felt better than any I'd ever had personally, and I'd known her for just a couple days.

Parental pride was incredible.

And I wasn't alone in my feelings. When I stopped cheering for my daughter, I looked to my side to see that Thea had gotten off the blanket and was cheering too. Her smile was beaming, brighter than any I'd seen before.

"Couldn't stay seated?" I nudged her elbow with mine.

"Quiet, gorgeous."

Gorgeous.

I'd been given nicknames in the past by women. My girlfriend in high school had called me Lo-Lo. Emmeline used to call me darling. Alice had annoyed the fuck out of me by whispering *stud* in my ear. I hadn't really liked any of them, not even Emmeline's.

But Thea's *gorgeous* was hot as hell.

Mostly because she said it with that smile.

She could call me an asshole or a douchebag with that smile and I wouldn't care.

I stepped a little closer so I could feel the warmth from her arm on mine. She sucked in a tiny breath, tensing a bit at the electricity between us. When she looked up, her smile was gone but her cheeks were flushed.

I wished she wasn't wearing those mirrored sunglasses. I'd do anything to see her eyes darken with the same desire they'd shown in her workshop last night.

The whistle blew on the field, breaking us apart. Thea's face whipped back to the game and she took a step away before sitting back down on the blanket.

As much as I hated it, I understood her reason for keeping some distance and for stopping me before I'd kissed her last night. We'd burned hot six years ago, and that fire between us was still hard to ignore. But it would be best for Charlie if she was the focus.

Kicking thoughts of sex and Thea aside, I focused on the game. The kids were all lined up to shake hands. Charlie was getting high fives from a couple of her teammates, and just like her mother, the smile on her face was blinding. It made breathing difficult to see that little girl so happy.

My little girl.

"She's a natural between the goal posts," I told Thea, taking the seat beside her. "She could be an Olympian. Maybe we should look at getting her a professional coach. Or at least getting her into some bigger leagues."

Thea shook her head but smiled. "Let's give it a few years, okay? If she still likes soccer when she's ten, we can discuss the Olympics."

I grinned. Thea was worried that I would disappear and forget Charlie, yet she'd just admitted we'd be talking about Charlie at age ten. On the surface, she might be hesitant. But deep down, I think she knew I'd keep my promise. I'd be here to discuss Charlie's life when she was ten. And fifteen. And thirty-five. I wasn't going anywhere.

I'd be around for her entire life, and if Charlie wanted the Olympics, I'd do what I could to make it happen.

The kids were huddled with their coaches on the field and after a team cheer, they were all dismissed. Charlie turned from her team and sprinted toward us.

Her hair bounced behind her as she ran. The smile on her face hit me hard again and I couldn't stay seated.

I hopped up from the blanket and jogged a few steps forward, holding up my hand for a fist bump as she got close. "You did awesome! That last save was amazing."

"Thanks." She tapped her knuckles on mine, her smile still bright, but shied back a few feet. "I heard you a couple of times."

Oh, shit. Had I embarrassed her? Was that why Thea kept teasing me? Why hadn't she told me that Charlie wouldn't like my cheering?

"Sorry. I was too loud, wasn't I?" I was messing up everything. "I didn't mean to embarrass you."

Charlie shrugged. "It's okay. Katie's dad yells a lot too, and you weren't as loud as him."

I was taking that as a win. At the next game, I'd be sure to tone it down—if I could. I was also going to find Katie's dad and sit closer so I could make sure I didn't get any louder than him.

Thea stood up and ran her hand down Charlie's ponytail. "Good job, honey."

"Thanks, Mommy. Can we get pizza?"

"Obviously. You were the star of the game! I think it deserves a root beer float too."

Charlie's face lit up before she turned to me. "Are you coming?"

"If it's okay with you."

"Yeah," she whispered, smiling at her feet.

A rush of warmth spread over me and I fought the urge to clap again. My second win of the night: a dinner invitation from my daughter.

"Meet us at the bar?" Thea asked as she folded up the blanket.

"Sounds good. I'll follow you there."

We loaded up and got into our cars, making our way across town. I chuckled to myself as I drove.

Two days ago, I would have laughed if someone had told me I'd be in a hurry to get to the Lark Cove Bar.

"Here you go." Jackson slid a round pizza pan onto our table. "The Landry Special with extra cheese for my soccer superstar. And . . ." He set an enormous root beer float in front of her and bent to kiss her forehead. "Good job, Chuck."

She leaned into his side. "Thanks, Uncle Jackson."

"You guys need anything else?" he asked Thea.

"We're good. I'll get it if we need something. Looks like you've got your hands full tonight."

"Yeah. Busy night."

He winked at her before leaving to take care of the other patrons.

I didn't miss the way he squeezed her shoulder as he walked behind her back. Or the glare he shot me from over her head.

The asshole had made it a point to constantly touch Thea and Charlie, like he was marking his territory. When we'd arrived, he'd made a huge show of coming around the bar and scooping Charlie up into his arms. Then he'd given Thea a hug that had lingered on too long before she'd patted his back and stepped away. When we'd ordered beers—Thea had reminded me that it was a law to get beer with pizza—Jackson had put his arms on the back of each of their chairs.

The show was getting old.

I got the message. He was here first. He had something with Thea and Charlie that I didn't.

But I was about done with Jackson Page.

And judging by the way Thea had dismissed him to wait on others and how she'd been rolling her eyes at him all night, she was about done too.

The bar was packed full of other families from the soccer game as well as some people who didn't seem local. With a full place, he needed to back off and concentrate on work.

Thea and Charlie were mine tonight.

I was the one who'd cheered Charlie on at her game. I was the one sitting next to Thea, occasionally brushing my knee against hers. And I was the one sharing pizza with them tonight.

"So this is the Landry Special?" The thing was huge, at least sixteen inches in diameter. Half was only cheese. Half was piled with meat and veggies.

"Mmhmm." Charlie nodded, sucking down her root beer float.

"Okay, honey." Thea dished up a slice of the cheese pizza for Charlie. "Enough of that until you eat."

Charlie swallowed a gulp, then pushed her glass away to load her small hands up with the slice.

"Which kind would you like?" Thea asked.

Before I could answer, Charlie spoke up with her mouth full. "He can have one of mine."

My eyes snapped to Thea. She was trying to pull in her smile, not make a big deal about Charlie's declaration, but we both knew it was a big deal.

I was making progress.

"Thanks," I told Charlie, taking one of her cheese-only slices. Then I took a bite, surprised at how good it was. The thin crust had a delicious char. The sauce and cheese were perfect, better than a lot of the pizzas I'd had in the city. "This is great."

"Mommy invented pizza," Charlie said before taking another bite.

Thea laughed. "Not all pizza, just the pizza here. We have a brick oven in the back, so it's kind of become our specialty."

"So you're an artist. A mixologist. A pizza chef. I'm guessing you're the one managing this place. Is there anything else you do?"

She nodded to our daughter. "Just try and keep this one mostly clean."

Charlie giggled and took another bite.

"Maybe tonight I can see that fort." I held my breath, waiting to be rejected. I knew I was pushing it. I'd done the soccer game and now dinner. Thea had warned me to take it slow, but I couldn't help it. I wasn't asking because I felt rushed that my week was ending.

I was asking because I really wanted to see Charlie's fort.

"Okay." Charlie nodded and took another bite as I nearly fell off my stool.

The smile on my face stayed through dinner, until after the pizza was demolished and Charlie was jittery from all the sugar in her float. I was still grinning as I followed Thea's car back to their cottage and parked on the street.

The minute I opened my car door, Charlie was racing into the trees, waving for me to follow.

I waved at Thea as she walked to the front door, then jogged across the grass, trying to catch my daughter.

When I hit a clump of tall trees close to the shoreline, I followed a trail of cleats, shin guards and socks until I heard

Charlie's voice.

"Come on, Logan!" She poked her head out of a small opening, waving me toward her fort.

Between three tall evergreens was her little hideaway. The trees were clustered together enough that she'd been able to build walls from plywood boards. Someone, my guess was Thea, had painted them in a mix of browns and greens, like camouflage. Tacked on top was an old army-green canvas tarp that acted as both the ceiling and door flap.

"Wow," I said, ducking down to shuffle inside. "Cool fort."

"Thanks." Charlie was standing barefoot in the middle of the dirt floor, ready to show me her sanctuary. "You can sit there." She pointed to an old stump against one wall.

I sat, crouching forward a bit to keep my head from brushing against the tarp ceiling. On the wall opposite the door, a small square window had been cut to overlook the lake.

"What's all that stuff?" I pointed to a small bookshelf leaning against one wall. She had tin lunchboxes stacked neatly on the top shelf, and on the bottom were two green plastic totes.

"My supplies." She went to the shelves and began setting down the lunch boxes, opening them one at a time to tell me what was inside. "I've got forks and spoons in this one and a cup. This one has my shovel and a couple strong sticks. This one usually has my snacks but it's empty now because Mommy needs to go to the grocery store. And this one has ropes and my favorite rocks."

There wasn't one single toy.

I loved that about Charlie. She was different from any child I'd ever met.

"That's an awesome collection of supplies." I pointed to the tubs. "What's in those?"

"My books and coloring stuff." She pushed the lunchboxes

aside to drag out a tote. "I have to keep them in there so they don't get wet."

"Do you like to read?"

"Yeah." She nodded, taking off a lid. Then she dug through the books until she found the one she'd been searching for and handed it over.

The cover was of a tadpole transforming to a frog.

"You really like frogs, don't you?"

"They're my favorite besides dogs and cats and birds." She grabbed the wooden kid-sized chair next to the bookshelf and brought it over to sit by my side. Then she took the book from my hand and started going through it page by page.

My daughter was reading me a book.

I spent the next hour learning all about frogs and tadpoles and then about cats and dogs from her other books. I could have sat on that stump for hours, if not for the fading light.

Finally, when the pages were getting hard to see, Thea called us inside.

Charlie and I packed up her things, making sure lids were on securely, and then walked toward the house, collecting her strewn clothes as we went.

"Thanks for showing me your fort tonight," I told Charlie, snagging a cleat from the ground.

"I have another one at camp. It's not as good because I had to make it myself without Mommy or Uncle Jackson's help. But it's still cool. Want to come see it?"

I smiled, ignoring the burn of jealousy that *Uncle Jackson* had helped her build her fort. "I'd love to see it."

And I'd help her make it even better. I didn't know shit about constructing outdoor forts, but how hard could it be? I graduated at the top of my undergraduate class from Columbia and was a distinguished graduate from law school. I could figure out a fort.

"See what?" Thea asked as we approached the porch.

Charlie stopped next to Thea on the bottom step. "My fort at camp."

"If it's okay with you." I hadn't even thought to ask Thea for her permission first.

I wasn't used to asking permission, for anything. I gave orders, people followed them. I came and went as I pleased in New York.

But here, I was out of my element. Here, Thea was in charge. And it was strange how that didn't bother me.

Much.

"It's fine by me." Thea smiled. "You don't need to ask. See her whenever you'd like."

Damn, that was nice to hear. It meant she trusted me with Charlie and she knew how hard I was trying.

I bent down to Charlie's level. "I'll see you tomorrow. Good job at your game today. You were awesome." I dropped her cleats and shin guards on a step, then held up my hand for a high five.

She slapped her palm to mine. "Night, Logan."

"Good night, Charlie."

"Go on upstairs," Thea told her. "I'll be up to do your bath in a minute."

When the screen door slammed closed behind her, Thea leaned against the railing on the steps. "So? How'd it go?"

I smiled like I'd just won the lottery, not even trying to play it cool. "Fucking incredible."

eleven

LOGAN

MY PHONE WAS GOING TO VIBRATE A HOLE IN MY POCKET.

The damn thing had been ringing all day.

This morning, my team at the firm had called five times. There had been an issue with a client accelerating the timeline on a high-profile tech merger, so instead of having a month to tie up all the contracts, we now had eleven days. It was pure chaos and I was in Montana, unable to dive in and help. I trusted my team to get it done, but there were some issues that'd simply needed my guidance and expertise.

Besides the team at the firm, my personal assistant had called twice with information on the lake house I was trying to buy. Then my cousin had called to ask if I'd write her a recommendation letter to Columbia Law. When I'd finally hung up with her, thinking I had everyone handled for ten minutes, Nolan had called to talk about a five-million-dollar donation request for the foundation.

An hour later, one of the founding partners at the firm called me, wanting to know if I could take on a well-known real estate developer as a new client. I'd never said no to William Abergel in my life and hadn't started today.

Two minutes after I hung up on him, my mother had called. I hadn't answered. Then my father. Again, I hadn't answered.

Then it had been my sister, Sofia. Three times. I'd pushed those straight to voicemail. When I'd ignored her for the last time, she'd reverted to text messages, telling me between emojis how horrible I was for dumping Alice.

She'd been at it for days.

I just wanted to shut off my phone and spend my Saturday with Charlie, giving her my full attention before I left. But I couldn't ignore calls for work.

I'd busted my ass this week, getting up before dawn to work so I could spend my afternoons and evenings with Charlie. I'd worked in the morning and had fun in the afternoon.

The two of us had been bonding. We'd hung out at the camp each afternoon, then eaten dinner together.

Thea had rearranged her schedule to have her evenings free all week, but today she had to work. So while she was at the bar, I'd volunteered to stay with Charlie for the afternoon so Hazel could go to the fair in Kalispell.

I was leaving tomorrow and wanted to be with Charlie as much as possible before my early morning flight. We'd spent a good amount of time at her house, playing outside in the fort and then inside doing some art projects. It would have been perfect except that the entire time, my phone had been buzzing, forcing me to step away from playtime.

By the time five o'clock had rolled around, Charlie had nearly finished an entire coloring book, while I'd absently colored in a half a page.

"What should we do for dinner?" I dug my phone out of my pocket to see another text message from my sister. I turned my phone screen down on the table. I'd had enough. "We could go get a Landry special."

"Okay." She smiled and nodded. "Can we get floats too?"

"Anything for you, peanut."

She blushed a bit, looking back to her coloring book. I'd started calling her *peanut* yesterday. It had been just an accidental slip when we'd been throwing rocks in the lake, but today, I'd been slipping it in on purpose.

I loved the shy smile it always got me.

I glanced at my watch as she cleaned up crayons. "We've got about an hour before dinnertime. What do you want to do?"

"Can we go fishing?"

I nodded. "Sure. I—"

My phone vibrated on the table, interrupting us again.

Charlie's shoulders fell with the buzz.

"Sorry." I turned it over, this time glad for the picture on the screen. "Look." I held my phone to Charlie so she could see the picture.

"Who's that?"

"That is Granny."

"She looks older than Gran."

I chuckled. "That's because she's *my* gran. And she's probably going to spoil you rotten with candy and presents."

That got me a wide smile.

"You go get the fishing stuff and I'll be right behind you. Get our stuff ready."

She nodded and slid off her chair at the kitchen table at the same time I stood, following her through the screen door, taking the call as Charlie darted down the porch steps.

"Hello, Granny."

"Logan, where are you? Your parents are looking for you."

I grinned. "I'm ignoring them."

"I wish I could," she said, "but they ambushed me during afternoon tea. Why, exactly, are you ignoring them?"

I took a deep breath before proceeding to tell Granny all about coming to Montana, seeing Thea and learning that Charlie was my daughter. I hadn't planned on telling her over the phone, but as soon as I'd answered, I knew I couldn't keep it a secret.

Out of everyone in my family, I wanted Granny to be the first to know about Charlie. I wanted to share my excitement with the one person I knew wouldn't be worried about paternity tests or custody discussions. Granny was the person I'd always trusted to give honest advice.

"I have a great-granddaughter." I didn't need to see her to know she had a teary smile. "What's she like?"

"She's . . . god, she's fantastic." I smiled as Charlie came through the trees, carrying her fishing pole. "She's unlike any child I've ever met. She's thoughtful. Smart. She's quiet until you get to know her but then she opens up and you just want to soak up every word she says."

Granny hummed. "Your grandfather was like that. When are you bringing her home?"

"I don't know." I ran a hand through my hair as Charlie walked down the dock. She looked over her shoulder and smiled, holding up the pole, a Styrofoam container of worms tucked underneath her arm. "I haven't thought that far ahead yet. This week, I've just been trying to get to know her and Thea."

"That's all well and fine, but she can't live in Montana while you're in New York. What's your plan?"

"I'm buying a house here in Lark Cove. I think we've finally reached a price and I should be able to close on it within the next few weeks. Then I'll travel back and forth. I'm going to put an office in my place here so I won't fall behind on work. I might even hire an assistant here to—"

Granny laughed before I could finish. "Oh, Logan. Traveling back and forth isn't going to be enough. You're going to need to give some things up."

Give things up? Why?

"It will be okay," I assured her. "I can fit it all in." I just needed to juggle things around. There was no reason I couldn't fit trips to see my daughter into my life.

She laughed at me again. "One of these days, you'll figure it out. Your father never did, but I have hope for you."

"Figure what out?"

"The secret to life."

I chuckled. "I'm a busy man these days, Granny. Why don't you just tell me?"

"No, it will be more fun for me to watch you struggle for a while. Sally forth, grandson. I have faith you'll find the right path."

I grinned as I walked down the porch and headed for the dock to meet Charlie.

Granny had always been a driver, pushing me to keep going until I reached the summit of whatever mountain I'd been climbing. Each time she sent me off to a daunting challenge, it had come with a *sally forth*.

"Come and visit me when you get home and bring a picture of Charlie."

"I will. See you soon." I hung up and shoved my phone back in my jeans, determined not to answer it again until I was back at the motel tonight. The rest of the evening, I was spending with Charlie.

She'd get my undivided attention until bedtime because come tomorrow, I'd be gone.

And I didn't know when I'd be back.

"Mommy, I caught a fish." Charlie was kneeling on a stool, leaning across the bar.

"You did? Way to go." Thea put her palms on Charlie's cheeks, then kissed her nose. "How big was it?"

Charlie sat back and held out her hands, spreading them apart about a foot. "This big."

I chuckled from behind her and held up my own hands, showing Thea the fish had only been about five inches.

Thea smiled and played along with Charlie. "Wow. That's huge!"

"That's what she said." Jackson laughed at his own joke as he joined us from down the bar.

"You're awful," Thea scolded, trying not to laugh.

He shrugged and high-fived Charlie. "Good job, Chuck. What are you guys doing here?"

"Dinner," I answered.

"That's right." Jackson gave me a smug grin. "A good-bye dinner. You're leaving tomorrow."

Asshole.

"Jackson, hush," Thea hissed, swatting him in the gut before nodding to Charlie.

Her warning was pointless. My daughter didn't miss much.

Charlie spun on her stool and stared at me with wide eyes. "You're leaving tomorrow?"

My heart sank at the shock on her face. Thea and I had decided not to tell Charlie the exact day I was leaving. Thea had said it would just make Charlie pull away. She'd be more worried about the calendar than enjoying our time together.

So we'd kept my departure date vague all week.

But tonight, we'd agreed to tell Charlie I had to go. Our plan was to get a pizza, then tell her I was going back to New York in the morning.

Gently.

But then *Uncle Jackson* had ruined the plan by surprising her.

"Yes," I told Charlie. "I have to leave tomorrow, but I'll be back."

Jackson scoffed, earning another smack from Thea.

I ignored them to focus completely on Charlie and the worry lines on her forehead. "Hey." I placed my hand on her shoulder. "I'm coming back. But I have to go back to work for a while."

She nodded and dropped her chin, studying her hands in her lap. An invisible cloud shrouded Charlie, breaking my heart into pieces.

I looked up at Thea, her hand pressed against her chest. *Sorry*, she mouthed.

"It's okay." This had to happen tonight, though I would have preferred to be the one to tell Charlie. "Let's eat. We can talk more over pizza."

Thirty minutes later, Thea had all but kicked Jackson out of the deserted bar and was sitting with Charlie and I at a tall table in the middle of the floor.

"Quiet night."

Thea nodded. "Most everyone in town is up in Kalispell for the fair."

We both looked to Charlie as she sat in silence, swinging her legs to kick the footrail of her stool.

"What's running through your head, peanut?"

She shrugged and kicked again.

"Honey," Thea tucked a loose strand of hair behind Charlie's ear, "you know you can always talk to us. What's wrong?"

Charlie's eyes were flooded with tears when she looked up to her mother. "Logan is going to miss my birthday."

Fuck. It felt like someone had just taken a hammer to my chest. I'd all but forgotten her birthday was coming. August fifth was only two weeks away, and there was no way I'd be caught up at work enough to take another vacation. But that didn't matter.

"I'll be here."

Charlie's face spun to me. "You will?"

"I promise." I stretched across the table and stuck out my pinky.

When Charlie and I had been at camp the other day, she'd made a pinky promise with Hazel to stay out of the lake. I'd watched, surprised at how seriously they had taken the gesture.

If hooking our pinkies together made the tears stop, I'd do it a million times.

Charlie sniffled and wiped her nose with the back of her hand. Then her crooked pinky looped around mine.

"I'll go grab the pizza." Thea stepped off her stool and went back to the kitchen. She rolled her neck as she walked, trying to shake the weight on her shoulders.

Thea had retreated these last few days, ever since the soccer game. I wasn't sure if she was trying to give Charlie and me one-on-one time, or if she was just busy. But she'd been distant, making sure she and I never had much alone time. She gave me just enough attention to discuss Charlie before running away.

Charlie and I sat quietly waiting for Thea. It only took her a minute to return with our pizza. Her posture had straightened and she was faking that pleasant smile.

I hated that smile.

I wanted the real one back. The one that reached her eyes and made my heart skip.

"What's this?" I asked as she set down the hot pan.

Charlie and Thea looked at each other. "This is the Landry-Kendrick special. Charlie and I invented it this morning."

I grinned at the pizza. Two slices were cheese only, for Charlie. Three were loaded for Thea. And the other three were extra cheese and greasy pepperoni.

My favorite.

I'd told Charlie the other day how much I liked pepperoni pizza. We'd been pretending to make pizzas in the fort at camp—the fort I'd made exponentially better this week by nailing up industrial camouflage tarps I'd special ordered and had shipped overnight. I guess after that, she'd come home and told Thea how I preferred my pizza.

Now I was a part of the family special.

I rode the pizza high all the way through dinner. Thea declared she was going to close down the bar for the night and we all walked back to the cottage together. I waited on the couch while Thea gave Charlie her bath, then my daughter came down and asked if I'd tuck her in for bed.

I shot off the couch, smiling and nodding like a bobble-head doll.

"Can we read three books?" Charlie asked as she climbed into her bed.

"Sure." I went to her boat-shaped bookshelf. "Which ones?"

"You can pick."

I grabbed three books from the middle row and brought them back to her bed. I hadn't spent much time in Charlie's room before. We'd always stayed downstairs or been outside playing. But it was exactly what I would have expected for my daughter.

A tomboy's room through and through, except for a small pink table in the corner.

I sat down on her camouflage comforter, leaning against the headboard, barely able to fit by her side on the twin bed. Much like the rest of this house, her room was cramped. Every available surface had special sticks and rocks from Charlie's outdoor explorations. Her bookshelves were nearly overflowing. And her bedside table was full of framed pictures.

"Is this my picture?" I twisted to the side and picked up the biggest of the frames on her nightstand. It was the drawing Thea had done, the one Hazel had recognized me from.

"Yeah." Charlie snuggled closer, the smell of her lavender shampoo filling the air. "Mommy did it for me."

"Your mom is quite the artist."

In the sketch, I was looking off to the side, not quite in profile, but not straight forward either. I had an easy smile. My hair was longer than it was now, more like how I'd worn it when I'd met her. But Thea had captured my features perfectly.

All from memory.

This drawing proved that the connection between us was real and lasting.

She'd felt it just as strongly as I did.

And damn, I wanted that again. But this time, I wanted more than just a physical relationship. I wanted to see just how deep our feelings went.

My gut was telling me they ran to the core.

"Let's read this one first." Charlie thrust a book onto my stomach, so I set the drawing back down to read my daughter her bedtime stories. She was yawning as I closed the last book.

"Good night, Charlie." I pulled her closer into my side and kissed her forehead.

"You're coming back?"

I rested my cheek against her hair. "I'll always come back for you."

"Okay," she whispered, but her voice was filled with doubt. "Night, Logan."

I kissed her again, then pried myself away from her side. She burrowed under her blankets as I shut off her lamp and walked out of her room.

"Hi," Thea whispered. She was leaning against the wall outside Charlie's door.

"Hi. What are you doing?"

"Just listening." She motioned for me to follow as she led the way downstairs and through the house to the porch.

"When's Hazel coming home from the fair?" I asked.

"I'm sure it will be late. There was a band playing that she wanted to see, so she and a couple of friends are there for the concert."

I paused when we got outside, expecting Thea to sit in one of the mismatched chairs. But she kept going, down the stairs and over the grass. I stayed close as she crossed the lawn and continued down the old dock that stretched over the lakeshore.

She padded all the way to the end, past the spot Charlie had left her fishing pole from earlier. She slipped off her flip-flops and sat on the dock's edge, dangling her toes into the water.

I'd been wearing flip-flops all week myself. My wingtips had felt too stuffy for Lark Cove. So I shuffled off my shoes too and sat in the space by Thea's side.

We sat quietly for a while, both of us just staring out at the lake. It was a calm night, the water gently rolling in glassy mounds.

"I hate leaving her," I whispered.

"But you have to."

"I do." I had overdue responsibilities waiting for me at home. "But I'll be back."

Thea stiffened.

The water was cold on my toes, my skin practically white beneath the surface, but not nearly as icy as the shoulder at my side.

What could I say that would convince Thea I'd be back? That I wouldn't abandon Charlie? Or her?

Nothing.

My words wouldn't mean anything to Thea. I'd have to prove it. I'd crush Thea's doubts by coming back and showing her that Charlie was a priority.

"I'll be back, Thea." I inched closer, brushing my jeans against hers. "I promise."

With the hand between us, I held out my pinky. She looked at it for a minute before curling her own around mine. The moment we touched, a shiver rolled down her spine. The heat between us flared, thawing her a bit.

She'd been trying to keep her distance and block me out, but her body betrayed her silence.

Thea said so much without words. She could make the best *fuck off* face I'd ever seen. When she was behind the bar, she held her shoulders and walked with a surety that made her the most powerful person in the room. But it was her softer movements, the subtle ones that most people missed, that made me want to pull her into my arms and hold her tight.

I loved the way her neck would tilt to the right whenever she talked about Charlie or Hazel. She'd take a long breath whenever I was close because she liked my cologne. I loved the times when I'd catch her studying me and she wouldn't look away.

Like now, with our pinkies locked. She held my gaze without wavering.

Soon she'd see.

I wasn't just coming back for Charlie, but for her too.

Thea stirred feelings deeper than I'd ever had for another woman, and we'd only been together for a week. I'd prove to them both that I was a new constant. They'd see that I was the missing piece to their family.

Then maybe one day soon, we could actually be a family. I could sweep them both away from here and build them the life of their dreams.

twelve

THEA

H E'D LEFT.

I'd known it would happen, but that hadn't made it any easier.

Logan had come here and made us fall in love with him—just a little—and then he'd left.

It had been two weeks since he'd sat with me on the dock and promised to return. It had taken all fourteen days for Charlie to *finally* get back to herself again.

As I'd expected, the day Logan had flown to New York had been the hardest. She'd been sad and quiet all day, basically sequestering herself to her room. She hadn't even wanted to play in her fort.

I'd known that day would be rough.

What I hadn't expected was for her sullen attitude and sad eyes to last so long. She did okay during the day, but every evening, after Logan would call, she'd get this lost look on her face that not even her favorite bedtime stories could erase.

She missed him. And like me, she feared he wouldn't keep his promise and be here for her birthday.

My childhood had been full of disappointment. I didn't want that for Charlie. I didn't want her to know that people let you down more often than not and that counting on others was usually pointless.

She didn't need to learn those lessons quite yet. I wanted her to grow up happy and face life's hard truths when she was older. When she was more equipped to handle heartbreak.

"That's a serious look on your face."

I looked over my shoulder at Hazel as she stepped out onto the porch. "Just thinking."

"About Logan?"

"Yeah." I nodded. "He missed his phone call with her tonight."

"Shit." Hazel lit a cigarette.

It was the first time since he'd left that he hadn't called before bedtime. I'd decided to just call him, but he hadn't answered my calls or texts. I'd made an excuse for Charlie's sake, but it hadn't helped. As I'd tucked her into bed, she hadn't just looked lost.

She'd looked defeated.

Tomorrow was her birthday and though Logan had promised to be here, he hadn't once mentioned his travel plans.

"If he doesn't show tomorrow, she'll be crushed."

And Jackson would be right.

His warning had been a constant plague in my mind these last two weeks. To Jackson's credit, he hadn't brought it up again. He'd actually avoided the Logan subject completely. But it was there, a constant niggling at the back of my mind.

If Logan missed this first visit, I had no confidence he'd make it through the first year.

"He could show." Hazel blew out a stream of smoke. "Let's not count him out yet."

"I don't know. He's been different since he left."

"Some people don't like to talk on the phone."

I shook my head. "It's not that. He's all over the place. Some nights, he's distracted and I can hear things in the background. Others, he's almost cold, like he couldn't get us off the phone fast enough."

He'd either been in meetings or he'd been with someone. A female someone.

The fact that I hadn't kissed Logan or had sex with him was a huge relief. I had no interest in being his Montana piece on the side while his girlfriend lived oblivious in New York.

"I wish he had never promised her that he'd be back."

Hazel's rough laugh filled the air. "I get why you're skeptical, but Thea, not everyone will disappoint you."

"You're right," I conceded. "Not everyone."

But most.

"I—" The chime of my phone cut me off. I picked it up and looked at the screen. "Speak of the devil." I shook it in the air before accepting Logan's call. "Hello."

Please don't cancel on her birthday. Please. Please.

"Hi. Did I miss Charlie?"

"Yeah. She's asleep already."

"Damn it. Sorry." He sighed. "I had a meeting run long."

A meeting. "Ohh-kay."

"Listen, I've had a change of plans."

I knew it. I'd had a sinking feeling all day that this was coming. "I figured."

"You figured?" he asked. "Figured what?"

"That you wouldn't be here. Now that you're back in the city, back to your *normal* life." I stood from my wicker chair as I threw his words from weeks ago back at him. "I figured you wouldn't be able to make good on your promise."

"Thea—"

"It's fine. I'll make your excuses, but I can't talk to you right now."

I'd just say something mean. I ended the call and tossed my phone down on the chair.

"Grrr!" I growled through gritted teeth as my hands fisted. "Asshole. Asshole. Asshole!"

"I can't believe it." Hazel took another drag, then stubbed out her smoke. "No. No way. There's no way I pegged him wrong."

"We both did."

"Did he say why he can't come?"

"No," I huffed and sat back down. "I hung up before he could really piss me off."

"So you didn't let him explain?"

"No. Why would I?" I quirked an eyebrow. "He's not coming. Charlie will be devastated, and the next time I see him, I'm going to punch him in the throat."

She frowned and crossed the porch. "Don't twist your ankle jumping to conclusions."

My mouth dropped open as she disappeared inside the house.

Hazel hadn't scolded me in years, but at that moment, I felt more like a teenager than a thirty-one-year-old woman.

I picked up my phone off the chair and followed her inside, standing next to the kitchen sink as she washed out a glass. "You're right. I'm sorry. I should have let him explain."

She shut off the faucet. "When you were a kid, I used to worry so much about you. If someone showed you just a little bit of affection, you'd cling to them for dear life. You were desperate for love, even though most of those people didn't give a shit about you."

It had taken me years of being used by others to stop trusting so easily.

"And then you came here and had Charlie," she said. "It was

like you flipped the switch. You didn't need other people any-more because you had her. If anyone tries to get close, you cut them off before they have a chance."

"I'm close to people. What about Jackson?"

She scoffed. "He's more closed off than you. You didn't let him in, sweetheart, he let *you* in."

I crossed my arms over my chest. I had friends, didn't I? There were Ronny and Wayne, two of the regulars from the bar. I saw them almost every day. And I talked to some of the moms on Charlie's soccer team whenever there was a game or practice. "I'm friends with Willa."

"You're friends, but not close. She comes into the bar and you talk to her. When was the last time you did something with a friend outside of the bar? When was the last time you went on a date?"

She had me there. I hadn't been on a date since I'd lived in New York. It wasn't that I hadn't been asked. There were guys who came into the bar all the time and hit on me and asked to take me out. But I didn't want to date. I was perfectly content coming home each night to Charlie.

"I don't want to date."

Hazel laughed. "Yes, you do. But what scares you is that the man you *want* to date is Logan."

I hated how she was always right. "It's just asking for trou-ble. If it ended badly, it could hurt us all."

"It could." She nodded. "Or it could be the best thing in the world for you and for Charlie. If it were me, I'd take that risk if it meant my baby girl could have a real shot at having her parents together. And given your upbringing, *you* of all people should be the first person willing to take that risk."

Again, she was right. I closed my eyes, pushing out a long breath. "I just wish he had shown up for her birthday."

"So do I. But I'm betting he's got a damn good reason for not being here."

"We'll see." I shrugged. "Would you care if I went for a quick walk? I'm still kind of mad and I want to burn off some steam before I call him back."

"Go." She waved me to the door. "Take as much time as you need. I've got Charlie."

I smiled at her, then escaped outside. Normally, when I needed to get my head together, the first place I ran was my workshop. But tonight, I needed to move. To burn off my anger on the pavement.

After an hour of flip-flopping up and down the quiet side streets of Lark Cove, I was heading home along the highway.

My frustration with Logan had fizzled over the last hour. I tried to see things from his perspective. A month ago, he'd had no idea Charlie even existed. It might take him time to adjust his schedule so it could include her.

He just needed to learn not to make false promises.

I'd drill that into his gorgeous head until it stuck.

The sun had set and its lasting glow had nearly faded as I strolled. I'd been meandering down Lark Cove's quiet side roads and had planned to take the same route back to the cottage. But as I passed the turn down a side street, a shiver rolled over my shoulders.

It was that feeling again. Someone was watching me.

I slowed my pace, looking all around, but I couldn't see anyone. All of the homes around were silent. People were all inside for the night.

The shiver came again and the side street I'd wanted to stroll now seemed unappealing. So I picked up my pace, walking fast back to the highway. Once I reached it, the feeling was gone. *You're losing it, Thea.* It had probably just been someone watching me from their window, wondering what I was doing out in front of their house alone at night.

So I relaxed my stride again, taking in the bar's red and yellow neon sign a couple blocks down. It was supposed to be my night to work, but with Charlie's birthday, Jackson had volunteered to trade. Besides the bar, the only other sign lit along the highway was the motel's. It buzzed as I walked past. All the other businesses in town were closed at this hour.

The motel's parking lot was full for a change. I'd heard through the grapevine that the Walters family was having a reunion this weekend.

I was scanning the license plates—Oregon, Idaho, Washington—when I saw a man standing at the vending machine with his back to me. I kept walking but did a double take as he ran his hand through his hair.

His hair looked a lot like my daughter's.

The man punched a button and bent to get a bottle of water. When he turned around, I skidded to a stop.

Logan.

My heart nearly burst.

I immediately changed direction, rushing to catch up to him. His long legs ate up the sidewalk that ran along the doors to each of the rooms. He went straight to his room, unlocking the door and pushing inside. It had almost swung closed, but I managed to slap my hand on the door's face.

Logan spun around, glaring until he saw it was me.

"You're here?" My voice was breathy, both from racing across the parking lot and from the shock of seeing Logan in Lark Cove.

He nodded and planted his hands on his hips. "I just got in."

"So when you called—"

"My jet had just landed."

"Oh." I cringed. The asshole here was me, not Logan.

"I promised you and Charlie I would be here, Thea," he snapped, coming right into my space. "But I'm glad to see you have so much faith in me."

"I'm sorry. I just . . ." *I just fucked up.* That's what I'd done. "I have a hard time trusting people. I'm working on it, but people have a habit of letting me down."

"I. Won't."

Two simple words said with so much conviction, they sank into my bones.

His chest was inches from my face, its heat chasing away the chill of the night air. He took my free hand and tugged me forward until the door swung closed at my back.

"You came back," I whispered.

"I told you I would."

I met his gaze. "Can we play a hundred questions?"

He'd asked for a hundred questions instead of twenty that first night in my workshop. I didn't need a hundred, at least not tonight. Really, I just needed one.

"Ask away."

"Do you have a girlfriend?" I blurted.

He grinned. "That's your first question? I like it. And no. I don't have a girlfriend or any romantic attachment outside the Lark Cove town limits."

The answer was barely past his lips before I attacked him. I stood on my tiptoes and flung my arms around his neck, capturing his mouth with mine.

Logan's mouth split into a grin before he tilted his head and took over. His tongue swept into my mouth, stroking against my own as his lips moved over mine.

This kiss. Oh my god, this kiss. I hadn't been kissed in so long, and Logan knew how to do it *right.* I clung to his shoulders, pulling myself closer.

His body pressed hard against mine, his hands running up and down in a frenzy. He came at me with the same intensity I threw at him, pushing me backward until I was against the door.

With something to keep me steady, I lifted even higher on my toes, practically climbing him. The pulsing in my core echoed through my body.

"Logan," I moaned into his mouth.

He answered by grinding his hard cock into my stomach, making the ache even worse.

I tugged on the sides of his cotton dress shirt, yanking the green hem from his jeans. As soon as it was free, my fingers dove for his belt buckle, fumbling before setting it free.

While I scrambled to undress him, Logan did the same to me. He twisted and turned the button on my jean shorts, ripping the zipper open so they hung on my hips. Then one hand dove right into my lace panties, and his middle finger immediately found my swollen clit.

I cried out into his mouth as my body went slack. It had been so long since a man had touched me, but then again, no man had ever touched me the way Logan did. I tipped my hips, wanting more friction from his circling finger, but he slid his hand free.

I whimpered, making him smile against my lips. His hands gripped the sides of my gray T-shirt and yanked it over my head.

"Clothes off," he panted as his lips broke away from mine and traveled down my neck. His hands came to my breasts, cupping and kneading them through my bra.

My hands went back to his jeans, tugging until I had the button free. Then I slid down the zipper that strained against his cock.

He wasn't wearing underwear.

My sex clenched, spasming to a near orgasm as I took him in my palm. I stroked his silken flesh, squeezing it tight in my small fist as Logan's hands left my breasts and shoved my shorts and panties down my legs.

In a split second, my bra was gone. Then Logan's mouth covered a nipple, sucking it into his mouth as he rolled it with his tongue.

My head lulled back, banging against the door, and my eyelids squeezed shut. My fingers threaded into his hair, pulling him closer as the heat pooled between my legs.

I'm going to come. Just from his mouth on me alone, I was seconds away from melting.

"Not yet," Logan murmured as my wet nipple popped from his mouth.

My eyes flew open when I realized I'd said that out loud.

He smirked at me before reaching for the buttons on his shirt. It was off in a flash, leaving his chiseled chest bare in front of my mouth.

Logan's body hadn't changed in all these years. If anything, it had just gotten better. I stared at his muscles, nearly drooling, as I took him in. He had a dusting of hair across his chest that trailed down his muscular abs. My palms went to his pecs, digging into his skin as my thumbs tweaked his nipples.

He hissed, closing his eyes for a moment as he collected himself. The cords of his arms flexed and his hands fisted before he relaxed his fingers and went for the wallet in his back pocket. After yanking out a condom, the rest was tossed to the floor.

His eyes locked with mine, capturing me completely, as he brought the foil packet up to my mouth. He placed it between my teeth and I bit down, holding it tight as he used my teeth to rip it open.

That was new.

I *loved* it.

He rolled the condom onto his hard cock, never once breaking my stare, even as he toed off his shoes and kicked his jeans loose.

In one swift movement, he had me pinned against the door, my thighs around his hips, his hands under my knees and his cock buried deep.

"Logan," I gasped as my back arched against the door. One thrust and I completely unraveled, clenching around him as my orgasm racked my body in jerks.

"Thea," he groaned, dropping his head into my neck. His lips sucked against my collarbone as his hips began to move.

He pounded into me, rattling the door with every thrust. The safety chain's clang mixed with the sound of his grunts, my moans and the slapping of our skin. My only warning that Logan was coming was the shudder that ran over his shoulders. He planted himself to the root, then roared, loud and long into my neck as his cock pulsed inside me.

My arms wrapped tighter around his neck when he stopped moving. I collapsed forward, giving him the weight of my boneless body. He spun us away from the door, staying inside me, as he walked over to the bed. With one arm holding me, the other whipped off the blanket.

Then he slowly pulled me off of him before setting me down on the white sheets. "Don't move."

Move? I couldn't even see straight. "Right." I collapsed back on the bed, my chest still heaving.

Logan disappeared into the bathroom to take care of the condom. When he returned, he fell onto the mattress at my side. "Fuck," he told the ceiling. "That went fast."

"Yeah," I panted, swiping stray hairs off my forehead. Fast, but incredible.

"Give me five minutes and we're going again."

I just nodded, still not able to really breathe.

I hadn't been with a man since Logan, but what a way to end my dry spell. Not only had he given me my only non-self-induced orgasm in the last six years, but he'd flipped a switch. My body, something that hadn't craved sex in years, was on fire and desperate for more.

I didn't know if I could wait five minutes.

I didn't have to.

Logan rolled off his back, covering my naked chest with his, and grinned as one of his legs pushed mine apart.

thirteen

LOGAN

"I HAVE MORE QUESTIONS," THEA DECLARED AGAINST MY chest. She was draped over my side, our legs tangled underneath the sheet. I was twirling a lock of her soft hair around my finger.

I chuckled. "I'm all ears."

"Why didn't you come to the house when you got to town?"

"You were upset, so I decided to just wait until morning."

Up until an hour ago when Thea had burst into my room, I'd had an awful day. I hadn't wanted to bring my shitty mood to her doorstep.

This morning, I'd arranged for a Saturday brunch with my parents in order to tell them about Charlie. It had gone as I'd expected. My parents' greatest concern had been Thea's motives. Mom and Dad had grilled me about Thea's background, immediately assuming a defensive stance. Their first assumption was that Thea was out to scheme a sliver of the family fortune. After they'd asked questions about her financial status, education and family history, most of which I hadn't been able to answer, my father had excused himself from the table to call the attorneys.

From there, the day had gotten worse. There'd been an accident on the way to the airport, so I'd left two hours late. I'd had to take a conference call for the foundation from the jet, which had run an hour long, like I'd told Thea.

I'd hoped to make it to Montana in time to surprise Charlie and give her a face-to-face good night. But by the time I'd landed, I'd missed her bedtime call and Thea had been so pissed, she'd hung up on me.

The thirty-minute drive from Kalispell to Lark Cove had gone fast. I'd fumed the whole way, angry that Thea hadn't had any faith that I'd keep my promise. When I'd finally pulled into Lark Cove, I'd been exhausted and all too ready for the day to end.

But now, with Thea in my arms, I'd actually go to sleep with a smile on my face.

I yawned. "Is Hazel with Charlie?"

"Yeah. I texted her while you were in the bathroom and told her where I was and that I'd explain everything in the morning."

I pulled the sheet up higher, covering her bare back.

"I'm sorry, Logan." Her arm slid farther across my stomach. "You said on the phone you had a change of plans, and I assumed that meant you weren't coming here. I shouldn't have cut you off."

"Next time, I won't try and surprise you."

She closed her eyes and sighed. "How long can you stay?"

"A week. I'll have to work during the day, but I should be able to free up my evenings."

The last two weeks had been brutal. With the new client I'd taken on at the firm along with everything else, I couldn't spend my days here chasing Charlie around and playing outdoors. This hotel room would serve as my office during the day, and I'd be Dad after five. The only thing working in my favor was the time difference. I was hoping that if I was up and working at four each morning, by the time quitting time rolled around on the East Coast, I'd at least have my evenings free.

Tomorrow would be the exception. Because for the first time, I was spending the day with my daughter to celebrate her birthday.

"I'm going to look at a house tomorrow morning," I told Thea. "I'd like to bring Charlie."

"That's fine. Her party isn't until three."

Just then, my phone buzzed. "Sorry." I reached to the end table and muted the incoming call.

"It's fine. You'd better get it. Someone has been trying to reach you for a while now." Thea tried to roll away, but I pinned her close.

"I'll call them back in a minute." I wasn't sure who had been calling for the last hour, but my phone had gone off a handful of times. It hadn't been hard to ignore with Thea in my bed. "I—"

My phone rang again. I rolled to mute it but saw it was the firm. At almost midnight in New York, something had to be wrong. "It's work. I'd better call them back."

"Okay." Thea took a long breath, holding it for a second before letting it out across my skin, then pulling away. "I should go."

I frowned and held her close. "I thought you had questions. Stay the night and you can ask them all. Just let me call them back."

"I can't." She pushed harder, rolling away and tossing her legs over the side of the bed.

"You mean won't."

She didn't respond, scooping up clothes and rushing into the bathroom.

"Damn it," I grumbled, running both hands over my face. The day wasn't going to end as well as I'd hoped.

I grabbed my phone and listened to one of five voice-mails with an urgent question from an associate on my team.

Apparently, some new tax regulation was coming down the pike and one of our larger clients was worried about the legal ramifications for a contract to be signed on Monday. I quickly shot him a text, letting him know I'd call him back in thirty minutes. Then I whipped the sheet off my legs and climbed out of bed to pull on my jeans. I was buttoning my shirt when Thea came out of the bathroom.

She kept her eyes on the carpet as she crossed the room to slide on her flip-flops. "I'll see you tomorrow."

"What's the hurry? Slow down for just a second."

She shook her head, going for the door. "Tomorrow is a big day. I need to go home and get some rest."

Bullshit. Something had happened to put her off. But what? Was it the phone calls? It wouldn't take me more than fifteen minutes to deal with them and then she'd have my undivided attention.

My palm pressed against the door before she could open it and I trapped her right in my space. "Thea, talk to me."

"I just . . . I don't know if this was smart. You and me."

My jaw clenched. "I disagree."

Being with Thea had felt nothing but brilliant and I sure as hell didn't have regrets. The way the two of us connected was unlike anything I'd ever felt. She touched me and I came alive. With my lips on hers, everything made sense. When our bodies were linked, the stars aligned.

I wasn't going to let her regret tonight either.

"Look at me and tell me you didn't feel the same thing I felt."

She turned up her chin, ready to lie, but when her eyes met mine, the fight disappeared. "I can't," she whispered.

"Then why are you running away? Stay the night."

"I shouldn't. I don't want Charlie to wake up in the morning and me not be home."

"I have an alarm." I pointed to the end table. "It's that little black box, right over there."

She shook her head. "It's not just Charlie. This happened so fast, I just need some time away to think. Okay?"

"Fine," I muttered. "I'm willing to let that be your excuse to run away, but just this once. In the future, you can do your thinking in my bed."

The last time a woman had told me she'd needed some time away to think, she'd moved to Montana and found a husband. There was no way I was going to lose Thea like I'd lost Emmeline.

She might need a night to think things through, but I didn't. Nothing about us together had been a mistake. I'd thought about her constantly while I'd been in New York. I'd missed her and Charlie like crazy. And all it had done was confirm something I'd known the day I'd left Lark Cove weeks ago.

Thea and I could be amazing together.

"Good night." She pulled on the door hard. My hand was still by the peephole, holding the door closed, so I let up and opened it for her.

"What are you doing?" she asked over her shoulder as I followed her outside.

"Walking you home."

"You don't need to. I'll be fine."

"Yes, you will because I'm walking you home." It was dark, and I didn't care if we were in Lark Cove. She shouldn't be walking around alone at night.

She quirked an eyebrow. "You don't think I can make it five blocks?"

This beautiful woman was testing my patience. If she wasn't going to stay, then I wanted to get her home safely. Except that eyebrow quirk made my cock jerk in my jeans, and if I wasn't out of condoms, I'd pull her right back inside and fuck her until she was so tired, she'd collapse in my bed.

"Thea, you can either let me walk you home or you can stay here with me. We're out of condoms, but I'm sure I could find another way to wear you out. What's it going to be?"

"I, um," her cheeks flushed, "should go home."

I grinned and placed my hand on her hip, pressing my fingertips into the small of her back. "Then lead the way."

We walked in silence the distance to her house, past the bar and across the highway. As we turned down the side street closest to the lake, she picked up her pace. Either she was cold or she didn't want me close enough for a good-night kiss.

Too bad. She had long legs but they couldn't outrun my stride.

"Thanks." She waved over her shoulder, turning up the sidewalk in front of the house. "I'll see you—"

Before she could escape, I reached out and snagged one of her wrists. Then I spun her around and slammed my mouth down on hers. Her lips were open, so I slid my tongue inside, kissing her hard and fast before tearing myself away.

I grinned at the flush I'd left on her face. "I'll see you tomorrow."

She nodded, then turned and jogged up to the house.

Tomorrow.

Thea would be mine again tomorrow. And the next day. And the day after that. She'd be mine all week long.

I'd spend these seven days breaking down her barriers, proving she could trust me. And when I left, she'd be coming too. Because there was no way I was going to leave Thea and Charlie behind again.

Which meant, starting tomorrow, I was going to find a way to get them to move to New York.

The next morning, I was back in the same place I'd left Thea last night, bent and ready to catch the little girl racing my way.

"Logan!" Charlie shouted as she flew down the sidewalk and into my arms.

"Happy Birthday, peanut." I wrapped her up and spun her around. "I missed you."

"I missed you too." She leaned back and her smile melted my heart. "You're back."

"Of course I'm back. I made you a promise. Besides, I had to deliver your present. The mailman said it was too big."

Her eyes sparkled. "What is it?"

"I guess you'd better go look in the back of the car." I tipped my chin toward the black Suburban parked on the street. My assistant had arranged for the SUV to be at the airport last night, ready and loaded with Charlie's gift.

She squirmed out of my arms and ran to the back, pushing the button to open the hatch. I followed, standing behind her with a stupid smile as the box came into view. It wasn't wrapped, so she could see the pictures on the cardboard.

"A Jeep!" she yelled. Her voice was louder than I'd ever heard.

"Your very own Jeep." Her excitement was contagious. I couldn't wait to get the toy set up and see her driving it around the yard.

The Jeep I'd picked out was red with black trim. It had an open top, seats for two kids and a row of spotlights on the roll bar. It was top-of-the-line, the best toy vehicle on the market. I hadn't even thought about asking Thea if the gift was too expensive. I'd missed five birthdays already, so if I wanted to spoil my daughter on her sixth, no one, not even her mother, was going to tell me no.

The door to the cottage opened and Thea and Hazel came down the sidewalk, joining us by the car.

"Mommy! Gran!" Charlie frantically waved them over. "Look what Logan got me."

"A Jeep." Thea smiled as she took in the box. "This is awesome! Did you say 'thanks'?"

Charlie stopped admiring the box to wrap her arms around my hips. "Thank you."

"You're welcome. Happy Birthday." I bent and kissed the top of her hair. "Come on. Let's get this thing unloaded and then I want to take you somewhere."

"Where?" She and Thea stepped back, joining Hazel on the curb.

Since Thea was doing her best to avoid eye contact, Hazel and I shared a smirk. Whether Thea liked it or not, we would be talking about last night soon.

But for now, I was spending the morning with the birthday girl.

"We're going on a birthday adventure."

"Hey." I walked into the kitchen and found Thea at the sink.

"Hi." Her eyes tracked my hands as they set down the screwdriver I'd been using to build Charlie's Jeep. She was still refusing to look me in the eye. "All done?"

"Yeah." I went right to her side and leaned against the counter, making sure to get close enough that I could bend and talk into her ear, but not so close that we were touching. "She's driving it around."

She was doing her best to act unaffected by my presence, but I heard the quick hitch of her breath as she washed a bowl. She'd been setting up for the party ever since Charlie and I had come back from our adventure.

"Sounds like you two had fun this morning."

I smiled. "We sure did."

The first place I'd taken Charlie this morning had been the lake house to meet with a realtor and get a tour. I'd assured her that I was buying the home for myself and she wouldn't have to move but that I needed her help to decide if it was a place she could come for visits.

Charlie explored the house from top to bottom, inspecting every inch of the five-thousand-square-foot home. By the time she declared it was acceptable, the realtor—a man who'd stood by patiently the entire time—had earned his commission.

After we left my future Montana home, I took Charlie to a boat store about ten miles outside of Lark Cove. We went straight to the showroom where I told her to pick one. Just like with my house, she gave every boat a thorough inspection before deciding on a blue ski boat. And I'd handed the salesman my credit card.

From there, we'd returned to the cottage for lunch and to get Charlie's Jeep assembled before the party.

"Can I help with something?" I asked Thea. It was almost three and guests were due to arrive at any minute.

"No, I think I'm all set."

The cake, a camouflage rectangle with neon-orange piping, was on the kitchen table. The snacks were all in bowls ready to take out to the card table set up on the back lawn down by the dock. And the coolers on the porch were all full.

Charlie had invited over some friends to play outside and go swimming in the lake for her party. There'd be kids with their parents along with Jackson, Willa and a couple of Thea's friends from the bar crowding their backyard.

There weren't a ton of decorations, just some balloons on the porch and tablecloths on the card tables. It was the polar opposite of the birthday extravaganzas that my sisters and I had experienced as children. There were no petting zoos or Cirque du Soleil performers. This wasn't a competition to see who could spend the most money for their child's special day.

Because it wasn't about the party at all. It was just about celebrating Charlie.

"That was a really nice gift you bought her." Thea spoke to the kitchen window as Charlie came driving around the side of the house.

"Too much?"

"No." She shook her head. "I don't care if you spoil her for a while, Logan. I get it."

She did. Thea had been nothing but supportive of the bond Charlie and I were building. If only she'd let down her own guard, then the two of us could do some more bonding too. "It's time to talk about last night. Why did you run away?"

She abandoned the sink, darting around the kitchen, looking for something to do.

I grinned as she shuffled the bowls on the counter around, then squared up the stack of army-green party napkins.

With her back to me, I crossed the floor and placed both of my arms on the counter at her sides.

"Logan," she gasped as I trapped her, my chest pressing against her back.

"Thea." My voice was low and quiet as I spoke in her neck. "You can't avoid me forever. I'm not going anywhere. Talk to me."

"Except you are going somewhere." She turned her head,

speaking to my bicep. "Back to New York. Back to being distracted."

"Distracted? What are you talking about?"

She spun around in the space between my arms, leaning back against the counter and crossing her arms. Her breasts lifted under her simple gray sundress, revealing a hint of cleavage.

I fought the urge to press my hips into hers. There was fire in her eyes, a passion that made the bulge in my jeans even worse.

"You were different these last two weeks," she declared. "Like you didn't really have time to talk to us."

My eyebrows came together as I mentally ran through our phone calls. Most of the last two weeks had been spent at the firm with my team buzzing in and out of my office with questions. Was that why she'd asked me if I had a girlfriend? Was she worried I'd been seeing someone else?

"I spent the last two weeks working fourteen-hour days at the firm. Every. Day. If I was distracted, it was because someone had barged into my office and interrupted our call. Trust me, there was nothing I would have rather been doing than talking to you and Charlie."

"Then—"

My phone rang in my pocket. *Damn it.* I'd forgotten to put it on silent.

She dropped her eyes to stare at her bare toes as I declined the call.

"Hey." I hooked a finger under her chin. "I work. A lot. My job is important to me. But that doesn't mean you and Charlie aren't important to me too. I'll try to do better."

"Thanks. Charlie will appreciate it."

I grinned. "Just Charlie?"

She fought it, but I caught a twitch on the corner of her mouth.

A mouth I was going to kiss right now.

I leaned forward, holding her gaze until our noses touched. Before I brushed my lips to hers, I licked her bottom lip and pressed my hips forward, letting her feel how much I wanted her. Thea's mouth had just fallen open with a gasp when the back door burst open.

"The—Shit," Hazel cussed. "Sorry."

Thea ripped her lips from mine, turning her head to the side, then ducking under my arms to escape. She cleared her throat, grabbing two bowls and walking right to the door as she muttered, "I better get these outside."

I took a few moments to get myself under control. Then I ran a hand over my lips before turning around to Hazel.

"Sorry." She barked out a laugh. "Bad timing."

"It's okay." I shrugged. "It's probably not the best time to be kissing her anyway. Not with a bunch of party guests on their way."

Hazel went to the sink and filled a glass of water as she scanned the backyard through the window. Thea was setting the snacks down outside on the tables.

"Come and sit." Hazel motioned to the table so I followed her over, taking the seat with my back to the door. "This town is small and people like to gossip. After today, everyone in Lark Cove is going to know about you."

"Is that a problem?"

"No. It's an opportunity."

I grinned, leaning my elbows on the table. "I'm listening."

"Thea doesn't have a ton of friends here in town. She spends her free time with Charlie, and she works at the bar. Not exactly a place to host play dates. She's never been able to really connect with the other moms in town. They just don't have anything in common except their kids."

I wasn't quite following how I fit into this, but I stayed quiet as Hazel slowly sipped her water before continuing.

"If you put Thea behind a bar, she can charm anyone on the other side. Hell, she could charm the lights off a Christmas tree. But the women in this town are cliquey and a bunch of them are coming here for the first time. I don't want to see Thea uncomfortable at her own daughter's birthday party."

Neither do I. "I'll make sure Thea has a good time today."

We nodded at each other and I stood, going straight for the door. I wanted to find Thea and do whatever I could to keep a smile on her face.

I stepped onto the porch with a smile on my own.

It dropped as I watched Jackson kiss Thea.

fourteen

THEA

CARRYING TWO BOWLS OF SNACKS, I HUSTLED ACROSS THE yard to the tables set up on the shoreline. I should be thinking about Charlie's party, but my head was in a fog.

A Logan fog.

I'd almost kissed him. Again. Something I'd sworn after last night I wouldn't do. Except I sure hadn't put up much of a fight when he'd trapped me against the counter.

Goddamn it. Going for a walk last night had been a colossal mistake. What had I been thinking, barging into his hotel room? Why had I had sex with him?

Stupid question.

I'd been so happy to see him in Lark Cove that I'd acted purely on emotion, letting my immense relief, joy and desire lead the way. I'd kissed him because I had no other way to explain how much it meant to me that he'd kept his promise.

But now, the emotions were waning and worry had filled in the gaps.

What did Logan want from me? Was he looking for a fling? A long-distance relationship? I didn't know how to ask him what *he* wanted because I didn't want to tell him what *I* wanted.

Him.

I wanted him to stay in Lark Cove. To be a full-time father to Charlie. To explore this thing between us. I wanted that damn phone of his to stop ringing.

His job was demanding. I could support and respect his commitment to work. But Logan's passion went well beyond career commitment. In the short time he'd been here, I'd discovered his only flaw.

Logan was a workaholic.

If he was so dedicated to his career, did he have room in his life for anything else?

Whatever the answer, I didn't have time to worry about it now. Today, I needed to focus on Charlie's party and entertaining a group of parents who were coming to my house for the first time ever. People who gave me polite but distant smiles at the school programs and soccer games.

I could picture the awkward afternoon now. Me, Jackson, Hazel and the bar folk on one side of the yard. The other kids' parents on the opposite. Logan would likely be mingling with them, impressing them with his small-talk skills and big-city anecdotes. Tomorrow's grapevine topic would be predictable.

Did you meet Charlie's father?

What a wonderful man. And so handsome.

How did Thea manage to trap a man like him?

Puke.

"Snap out of it," I muttered to myself, arranging the bowls of snack mix and potato chips on a card table.

I'd asked Charlie what she wanted for her birthday party food and she'd requested snacks. It was fitting that Logan had taken to calling Charlie *peanut*. She loved them. She loved all snacks. I was constantly sneaking down to her fort to replace the stashes in her lunch boxes.

So today we were having a variety of chips and crackers and

snack mixes. And since our local grocery store made delicious cakes, I'd ordered one for Charlie, just like I'd done for her other five birthdays.

There were juice boxes for the kids and mini water bottles. I'd also filled a couple of coolers with beer because my side of the lawn divide would definitely be drinking.

I was allowing myself two beers, max. Beer had a tendency to make me loose and flowy. If I had one too many, I'd be defenseless against Logan's next advance. Three Fat Tires and I'd let him drag me back to his motel room without a peep.

Just the thought of another night with him sent a wave of pleasure down my back. Last night, though a huge mistake, had been incredible. I'd forgotten what real orgasms were like.

"Earth to Thea."

I jumped at Jackson's voice, spinning around and clutching my heart. "Hi."

"You okay?"

"Oh, yeah." I shrugged him off. "I was, um, just thinking about what else I needed to do for the party. Did you get my text about putting up a sign at the bar? I forgot to make one yesterday."

One luxury of running the bar was that Jackson and I dictated hours. If it was slow, we closed early. And we did the same on days like today when we had family functions.

"It's done." He nodded, leaning past me for a chip.

I caught the smell of alcohol on his breath. It wasn't uncommon for him to have a couple of beers at the bar, but I was surprised he'd had some before Charlie's party.

"What do you need me to do?" he asked while crunching.

"Nothing." I started walking for the porch. "Want a beer?" *Or another?*

"Are they cold?"

I rolled my eyes. "Once. I served you lukewarm beer at *one* birthday party. Are you ever going to let that go?"

"Probably not." He threw an arm over my shoulder for a sideways hug.

The gesture confirmed he'd been drinking. Jackson was always playful and touchy after a few beers. But it was one of the rare afternoons where we were both free to relax, so if he wanted to get a buzz, I wouldn't hold it against him.

I was just glad he was here. One thing was for sure: even if the other parents huddled together on their own, I'd always have Jackson on my side.

"Uncle Jackson!" Charlie's Jeep came into view from behind a clump of trees. "Look at what Logan got me!" She waved at him while one hand was firmly gripping the steering wheel.

"Looks great, Chuck!" Jackson waved back with a smile, then dropped the arm he'd had around me. His good mood vanished as he looked from my daughter to me. "So, he showed?"

"He came in last night," I said, not meeting his gaze as we continued to the porch.

When I'd gotten home last night, Hazel had still been awake. She'd taken one look at my face and known I'd slept with Logan. Apparently, the I-just-had-three-orgasms look took longer than five blocks to fade. If it was still lingering, I didn't want Jackson to see.

"Hold up." He caught up to my side, gripping my elbow as we walked.

I tipped up my chin and smiled. "What? Come on. I'll get you your beer and then set out the other snacks." I squirmed out of his hold and hurried to the porch, jogging up the four steps. I'd almost reached the door when Jackson grabbed me again, spinning me around.

"Thea," he warned. "Did you fuck him?"

"Hey," I hissed, glancing toward the yard to make sure Charlie wasn't close. "Keep it down and watch the language."

"We talked about this, Thea. You're setting yourself up to get used."

I glared up at him. "It's not like that. He's not using me." I had complete faith that Logan had been honest last night when he'd told me he was single. There had been only truth in his eyes.

"So what then?" Jackson asked. "You're using him? Is that it? Haven't gotten laid in a while, so you take advantage of having Baby Daddy around? You know, if you needed to get off, you could have just asked me." He shuffled closer, right into my space. "I'd be happy to help."

"Jackson." I gaped at him. "What is wrong with you?"

He inched closer. "Nothing. I'm just offering to help you out so we can get rid of this guy."

"This guy is Charlie's father." I dug my heels in, not letting Jackson push me backward. I wasn't sure what he was playing at, but I'd had enough people push me around in my life. I wasn't going to take it from my best friend. "Logan's not going anywhere. Get used to it."

"Oh yeah?" His eyes flicked to the side, but before I could turn to see what he was looking at, his lips came right down on mine.

Jackson's kiss stunned me for a split second, but my anger kicked in. I planted both hands on his chest and shoved him back with all my might.

"Damn it, Jackson!" I shouted at the same time the door to the house flew open and Logan stormed out.

"Get away from her." Logan moved in a flash, stepping between me and Jackson and shoving me behind his back.

"Butt out, rich boy. This is between me and Thea." Jackson stood to his full height, but Logan didn't back down from my idiot of a friend.

"No." Logan stepped closer. "This is between you and me."

I'd seen this standoff at the bar more than my fair share of times. We were seconds away from flying fists and bloody lips.

No way I was letting that happen on my daughter's birthday.

"That's enough." I grabbed Logan's arm, yanking it as hard as I could to get his attention. He barely moved an inch, but it was enough to slip around him and stand between the men. "It's Charlie's birthday. Ruin this for her, and I'll kill you both."

That got through to Logan. With grinding teeth and clenched fists, he took one step back.

I spun around to Jackson and shoved my finger in his face. "Don't you ever kiss me again."

A pained gasp echoed across the porch. My head whipped down the stairs, just in time to see Willa's face pale. Blond hair streamed behind her as she ran away.

Goddamn it.

Everyone within a twenty-mile radius of Lark Cove knew that Willa Doon was in love with Jackson Page.

Everyone except Jackson.

Willa was as sweet and shy as they came. She'd worked up the courage about a year ago to ask me if there was anything between me and Jackson. I'd assured her that our love was the purely platonic kind. It always had been and always would be.

But if she'd only caught the tail end of that exchange, she wouldn't have realized that Jackson had only kissed me to get a rise out of Logan.

"Damn it, Jackson."

"What did he do?" Hazel asked, coming outside to the porch.

"He kissed me to pick a fight with this one." I jerked a thumb at Logan. "And Willa saw."

Hazel's face hardened. "Damn it, Jackson." Before he could respond, she swung her arm back and brought it up fast and hard, smacking him in the back of the head.

"Hey!" He winced, rubbing the back of his head. "That hurt."

She stuck her index finger in his face. "You deserved that."

"Gran, why did you hit Uncle Jackson?"

All our heads spun to the little girl climbing out of her Jeep at the base of the steps.

"Sometimes your uncle needs a good thumping," Hazel declared, then turned to Jackson. "All the bowls in the kitchen need to be taken down to the tables. Get on it."

His frame shrank. "Yes, ma'am."

We might be in our thirties, but neither of us ever went against that tone in her voice.

"Show me that Jeep." Hazel left Logan and me on the porch while Jackson disappeared inside the house.

He and I would have it out later. For now, I was just glad that Charlie had missed the entire kissing episode and her happy birthday wasn't in jeopardy.

"You okay?" Logan stepped up to my back and placed his hands on my shoulders.

I nodded and turned, ready to apologize and explain, but I was cut off when two of Charlie's soccer teammates came running around the side of the house followed by their parents.

My explanation would have to wait.

It was party time.

"Here." I handed Logan a tumbler of bourbon and ice. "It's not Macallan, but it'll have to do."

"Thanks." He took the glass, resting it on his knee as I sat down on the couch beside him.

I had my vodka in hand, but tonight, it was in a glass, over ice and with a lemon twist. "Thank you. For today."

He extended a hand to squeeze my knee. "You're welcome."

Logan had been amazing at the party. He'd stuck by my side all day, introducing himself to the other parents and bringing them under his spell. I'd gotten to know some of the other parents better than I ever had before, so much so, a couple of them had insisted I sit with them at the next soccer game.

Because of him, there hadn't been any awkward silences or divided groups. He'd brought us all together from the start and no one, especially me, had wanted to leave his side.

On top of that, he'd been incredible with Charlie. He'd watched proudly as Charlie had made a wish and blown out her candles. He'd fussed over all the gifts she'd gotten from her friends. When he wasn't standing by me, he was at her beck and call, getting her another drink or more snacks or another piece of cake.

The afternoon and evening had flown by in a whirl, and Charlie had fallen asleep with a smile on her face.

For the first time, both her mother and father had tucked her into bed on her birthday.

"It was a fun day." Logan sighed. "Except for the part where *he* tried to kiss you."

"Jealous?"

"Yes."

I smiled, glad he hadn't tried to deny it. "There's nothing going on between me and Jackson. He was just trying to get a rise out of you."

Jackson and I were having words tomorrow, though he already knew he'd screwed up. He'd kept his distance today, watching from the back of the crowd. Any time I found his gaze, it was full of apology.

"I still don't like it." Logan set down his glass on the coffee table, then reached across the couch. He looped his finger into the cloth belt of my dress, giving it a tug.

I didn't fight it. I scooted close so we were shoulder to shoulder. There was a lot I needed to sort out when it came to Logan, but tonight, I was too tired to resist snuggling into his side as he put his arm across the back of the couch.

"She's six." His voice was laced with regret. "I've missed so much."

My heart broke. "I'm so sorry. I wish—"

"Hey." His hand came up to cup my cheek. "Don't."

"Okay."

His hand fell away as he dropped his cheek to my hair. I sank even further into his side. "Tell me what her other birthdays were like."

"They were much less exciting. Mostly just me and Hazel fussing over her. Actually," I pushed away to stand from the couch, "I can show you."

I put down my drink, then went to the closet in the hallway, pulling down a plastic tub full of the scrapbooks I'd made for Charlie.

I hefted the tub into the living room, smiling as I set it down on the coffee table. Then I took off the lid, barely able to contain my excitement as I found the book I wanted and handed it over.

"Start with this one. It's her baby book."

Logan set his glass aside, sitting on the edge of his seat with the pink scrapbook splayed across his knees. He stroked the edge of the first photo, memorizing the picture. The one of Charlie swaddled and sleeping on my chest as I dozed in my hospital bed.

It took him a few moments to flip the page. I didn't rush him. Instead, I resumed my seat and watched as he slowly studied every detail in five scrapbooks.

I'd put hours and hours into those books. Placing pictures. Adding designs. Noting important moments. I'd compiled one every year after her birthday. Mostly I'd done it for myself, so I'd have something to look back on as Charlie grew up. It took days to put one together with hundreds of photos. Every year when I was done, I told myself I'd scale back with the next book.

The look of pure awe and joy on Logan's face made me grateful I'd never backed off.

Maybe deep down, I'd put them together not for myself, but in hopes that one day I could give them to Logan.

He studied each photo and memento, touching the ones he seemed to love most. Book after book, I sat at his side and watched him soak it all in.

I told him little stories, like how when Charlie was two, she'd only eat if I gave her ketchup, which she called her "dip." Everything got dipped. Meat. Vegetables. Fruit. Then I narrated through the Christmases and Easters. Through her first haircut and her first day of kindergarten.

Hours later, when he came to the last page, there were tears in both our eyes.

"Thank you." He sucked in a deep breath, then laced his fingers with mine. "It doesn't feel like I missed it all now."

"I'm glad." I reached up to cup his cheek, like he'd done earlier, and stroked my thumb across the stubble on his jaw.

"Fuck, I wish I would have come back to that hotel bar sooner."

Sooner? My thumb froze. "You came back? When? Why?"

"It must have been a week or so after you quit. Six months after we met. I came back to ask you out on a real date, but they'd told me you'd already gone. I should have hunted you down."

My hand fell away as my head started spinning.

All this time, I'd thought he'd walked away and forgotten about me. I'd assumed he'd moved on to other things. But if he'd come back to the bar, it meant he'd wanted more.

He'd felt it too.

My eyes flooded at the realization. It hadn't just been my silly, foolish heart believing in a one-sided fairy tale for all these years.

He felt it too.

In that hotel bar, I'd found something magical. Something more than lust and sex. Something I'd been running from for the last month, because I was worried Logan hadn't felt it too.

But he had. He was right there with me.

I opened my mouth to speak but I was at a loss for words. So instead of trying to find them, I launched myself into his arms and crushed my mouth to his.

He kissed me back, stroking his tongue against mine as his hands threaded through my hair. I swung up and onto his lap, straddling his thighs and grinding down against the hardness growing in his jeans.

I wasn't sure how long we sat there, but my lips were swollen when he finally broke away. He framed my face with his hands, holding me captive as I swayed on weak knees. "You're a dream, Thea Landry."

So are you.

"But we have to stop. I'm out of condoms."

I shook my head, climbed off his lap and stood. "I went to the gas station while you and Charlie were on your adventure earlier and bought some."

"You did?"

I nodded.

He surged off the couch and wrapped me up, kissing me breathless. Then he took my hand and led me upstairs, where the condoms were hidden under my pillow.

I'd bought them on a whim when I'd been getting ice earlier.

Just in case, I'd told myself as I'd grabbed a pack. Just in case Logan melted down my defenses.

Just in case Logan turned out to be more than just a dream too.

fifteen

LOGAN

"HI, PEANUT." I HELD OUT MY ARMS FOR CHARLIE AS SHE came into the kitchen. She rubbed her sleepy eyes, then came right to me and crawled into my lap, burrowing her head into my shoulder.

Thea came over to the kitchen table and kissed Charlie's hair. "Good morning, my love. Want some pancakes?"

Charlie nodded as she yawned.

"Chocolate chips or blueberries?"

"Chocolate chips," Charlie and I said in unison.

Thea smiled at me and went back to her bowl of pancake batter.

"Morning." Hazel came into the kitchen from the back porch, kicking off some garden clogs by the door. "Nice shirt, Logan. It's so similar to the one you were wearing yesterday."

I grinned. "Nearly identical."

Thea and I had gotten up early, wanting to beat Charlie out of bed. I'd intended to get to the motel and shower and change, but when Thea had handed me a cup of coffee, we'd ended up talking for an hour and I'd lost track of time.

So I was in the T-shirt I'd worn yesterday, the one she'd worn to sleep in after we'd used three of her condoms.

Cramped in her bed that was much too small for the two of

us, I'd slept like a rock with Thea at my side. We'd heard Hazel head outside early, then had sex again before coming downstairs.

I needed to get to work since my team at the firm had already been at it for three hours. But I couldn't seem to get my feet to walk out the door. I couldn't break away from the girl in my lap and the woman at the counter.

"What's the plan for today?" Hazel asked Thea, coming to sit at the table with a cup of coffee.

"Since I'm off, I was thinking about going shoreline picking."

Charlie's head flew off my chest. "Can I come?"

Thea twisted to look over her shoulder. "Of course."

"Yes." Charlie smiled up at me. "Can you come too?"

Damn, I wanted to. I had no idea what shoreline picking was, but I wanted to find out. I'd go Dumpster diving if that meant I got to spend the day with the Landrys. But the phone in my pocket had been vibrating all morning. Ignoring it was getting harder with each call.

"I'm not sure." I touched her nose. "I'm supposed to be working, but hanging with you sounds like a lot more fun."

She nodded. "It is. It's super fun. And we can bring snacks for a picnic."

I glanced over at Thea's back. "What time are you going?"

"Whenever. We can hang out and wait for you. Maybe leave around noon." She was trying to come across as nonchalant, but I could hear the hope behind her words. It matched Charlie's.

"Okay. Let me make some calls."

I'd been killing myself for two weeks—more like two years. I could take an afternoon off.

"Now." I gave Charlie a serious look. "What on earth is shoreline picking?"

By noon, Thea had loaded up her hatchback with some empty buckets and work gloves. She and Charlie had both changed into their swimsuits, and I'd run back to the motel to do some work and pull on a pair of shorts.

I hadn't changed my shirt, because it still smelled like Thea. She used the same lavender shampoo and lotion that she did on Charlie, but her natural citrusy scent made it entirely her own.

"What can I do?" I asked her as she carried out a handful of trash bags from her workshop.

"I think we're good to go." She scanned the yard, searching for our daughter. "Charlie!"

In the distance, a faint "I'm coming!" carried through the trees.

My phone buzzed in my pocket but I ignored it. I'd scrambled in my attempts this morning to fit eight hours of work into three. I hated being behind or leaving my team on their own, but that motel room couldn't keep me today. I was too excited about what Thea had planned.

Shoreline picking, I'd learned, was basically a treasure hunt.

Thea and Charlie had made this a special outing between the two of them, and they'd go a couple of times each summer.

Thea would pick a spot along the lake's long, winding shoreline and they'd spend the day walking around the edge. Sometimes they were right on the water. Other times they were on deserted gravel roads, like the one that wrapped around the shoreline in front of my future property.

But wherever they were, they'd walk a mile or so, searching for items that had been discarded.

"I'm ready!" Charlie joined our sides just as Thea slammed the hatchback closed.

She smiled. "I'm ready too."

Charlie turned to run toward the backseat, leaving Thea

and me alone. So before she could walk away, I grabbed her wrist, yanking her to my chest.

"What—"

I cut her off, slamming my lips down on hers in a hard, fast kiss. "There," I said, breaking away. "Now I'm ready too."

She shook her head, smiling as she turned and wiped her lips dry.

We hadn't talked about how to act in front of Charlie and whether or not we should keep our relationship a secret. But if all went according to my plan, I'd have both of them living with me before fall. Charlie would need to know something was up between Thea and me before we were all living under the same roof and her parents were sharing a bed.

I rounded the car and got into the passenger seat, turning over my shoulder to smile at Charlie. "Excited?"

"Yeah." She nodded wildly, digging a small bag of chips out of the console in the backseat. "This is my favorite."

"So what kind of things do you guys usually find?" I asked as Thea pulled away from the cottage.

"It depends. Usually when we go out in the early summer, it's mostly trash. Stuff that got buried in the snow. But this time of year, we'll find more. Tourists and visitors always lose things as the summer progresses. Last August, I found three sets of keys over a few weekends. I posted them at the bar for a month, but when no one came to claim them, I welded them all together in pipes for a wind chime. I had to buy a few plain keys so I had enough, but it turned out really cool."

"Where is it? I'd love to see it."

"I sold it."

"Yeah? I didn't realize you sold your art."

She shrugged and pulled onto the highway. "It's not the reason I do it, but if I didn't get rid of some of the stuff, we'd be overrun at the house. So I commission my extra pieces at a gift shop in Kalispell. Then I set aside the money for Charlie's college fund."

"Hmm, interesting. How many pieces do you have commissioned?"

"I don't know. Maybe twenty or thirty at the moment. But they've been taking my work for years. The owner is a good friend of Hazel's."

I wasn't a regular in the art scene, but I'd been to my fair share of fundraisers hosted at art galleries. Twenty to thirty pieces were enough that Thea could become a career artist, especially if she had a story to go behind each piece. Most of my friends would go crazy over junk turned into art, and Thea's work was incredible.

Once Thea and Charlie lived with me in New York, she wouldn't need to work. She'd have time to focus on her artwork. I'd assumed that Thea's art was just a hobby, but this could become her career. We could get a bigger place if she wanted a studio in the house. Or I'd rent her space.

She could create something other than cocktails during the day.

"It's so beautiful today." Thea's eyes swept the lake as she drove. The sun was glistening off the glassy water. There wasn't a cloud in the blue sky.

"This is a beautiful area."

We'd definitely be back to Lark Cove. This small town had grown on me and the house I'd bought was a perfect spot for summer vacations to visit Hazel.

"Have you ever been to Montana before?" she asked.

"Once." I nodded. "An ex-girlfriend moved out here for a job and I came out to visit."

"How long were you together?" Something in her tone

made it sound like she really didn't want to know the answer.

"Five years."

"Oh." The temperature in the car dropped ten degrees, despite the shining sun. "So you were serious?"

"Yes. I met Emmeline at a fundraising gala and we started seeing each other. We lived together up until she took a teaching job in Prescott and moved out here."

"Prescott," she repeated. "I've never been there. That's southwest Montana, right?"

"Right."

Prescott was more rugged than this corner of Montana. Lark Cove suited me much more than the area where Emmeline had moved.

"What happened with you two?" Thea asked.

I studied her profile. The round sunglasses on her face were huge, covering a good portion of her cheekbones, but she was stunning. The sunlight coming through the windows gave her a glow.

"I broke it off with her at Thanksgiving this last year. She kind of forgot to tell me she was married."

"Married?" Thea winced, hissing through her teeth. "And she didn't tell you? That's awful. What a b-i-t-c-h."

I laughed. "I don't think she kept it from me maliciously. She's got a good heart. She and her husband got married young and then separated. They hadn't seen each other in years, but they were still legally married. She moved to Montana for a teaching job and he turned up there. When they reconnected, I knew it was over between us."

"Sorry."

"It's okay. It all ended for the best. She's happy." I glanced behind me, seeing that Charlie was busy staring out her window, then reached across the console to touch Thea's thigh.

"And so am I."

There wasn't anywhere in the world I'd rather be than in this car. I was happier than I'd been since the breakup. If I was being honest, I was happier now than I'd ever been when Emmeline and I had been together.

The luckiest thing that could ever have happened to me was Emmeline leaving New York for Montana. If she had stayed, I would never have met Charlie. I wouldn't have found Thea.

"Do you, um . . . still talk to her? Your ex?"

"Jealous?" I threw her question from last night back at her.

She grinned. "Yes."

"No." I chuckled. "I don't talk to Emmeline. I doubt I ever will again."

"Hmm." She pushed down her turn signal. I could have sworn I heard a "good" under her breath too as we pulled off the highway to a gravel parking area beside the lake.

"We're here." Charlie's small fingers hurried to release her harness, and she was out the door almost as fast as Thea.

I got out of the car and met Thea at the back.

"Here you go." She handed Charlie a tiny red pail with a yellow handle. "For your rocks."

Then she reached into the back of the car for one of the larger buckets and gloves. "Here." She shoved them at my gut, then got out her own bucket, a trash bag and another pair of gloves. "All set." She stood and tried to scoot past me, but I caught her at the elbow.

"How are we going to handle this?"

Her eyebrows came together. "Handle what?"

"Us. There's no way I'm not going to kiss you today. I'm wondering if you want me to hide it from her. Or if you're okay with her knowing that her dad is crazy about her mom."

She smiled and looked down at her flip-flops. "Crazy?"

"Insane." I hooked a finger under her chin, tipping it up. "Hurry, baby. She's on her way back."

"Then we'd better sneak one in fast."

The inch between us disappeared, but not because I'd crossed it. She had. She stood up on her toes and pressed those soft lips deep into mine. Her tongue darted out for a quick taste before disappearing back behind her teeth. Then she moaned, making my cock jerk so hard I shuddered from head to toe.

Fuck, this woman.

She was ruining me one kiss at a time.

As fast as she'd come at me, she pulled back. The flush in her cheeks was a sexy pink that matched her lips. With the tie of her swimsuit poking out around her neck, her hair up in a messy knot and that flush, she was the most beautiful woman in the world.

"We'd better keep this between us for a while. Until we figure some things out. Let's give her a chance to adjust to the three of us spending time together. And we should see where things go."

I nodded. "All right." When it came to Charlie, I trusted Thea's judgment. Though I already knew where things between us were going to go.

She patted my stomach. "We'd better go."

"I need a second."

Behind those sunglasses, her eyes widened. She stood stunned for a moment but then she giggled.

"What are you laughing about?" Charlie called back to the car. "Come on! Let's go."

"Coming!" Thea yelled back and closed up the car. She started down the path to the lake but stopped. "Oh, and Logan?" She glanced back. "Her mom is kind of crazy about her dad too."

"Good to know." I smiled, then took a few breaths, making

sure that I had my dick under control so I wouldn't have to explain to my daughter why my shorts had an odd bulge. Then I jogged down the path, catching up to Thea and Charlie as they headed for the lake.

"What exactly am I looking for?" I asked, swinging my empty bucket at my side.

"Trash," Thea answered.

"Not trash, Mommy." Charlie stopped examining a rock to scold Thea before looking up at me. She had on her favorite baseball cap, but I could still see her smiling eyes. "We're looking for treasures."

"Trash to become treasure." Thea tilted her face to the sky, letting the sun warm her skin before smiling at me. "I like to take the tattered and lost and make it shine. Garbage doesn't have to stay garbage. Things just need to find their right place."

Their right place.

This was my right place. Being with Thea and Charlie gave me a sense of belonging I'd never felt so strongly before. I reached into my pocket to get my phone for a picture but realized it was gone. I'd left it in the car.

I hadn't left it behind in years.

Should I get it? No. I'd enjoy the afternoon in Lark Cove.

Besides, next week, I'd be back in New York and could get all caught up.

They didn't know it yet, but Thea and Charlie would be there with me.

sixteen

THEA

COULDN'T STOP REREADING THE EMAIL ON MY PHONE.

> *From: anonymous743*
> *Subject: You're a fucking whore.*

That was it. The subject line, anonymous sender name and nothing else.

It had chimed into my phone a few minutes ago. I'd been stunned at first by the email, but the shock was fading. It had been sent to the bar's account and since I was the only one who checked our emails, I'd had it set up on my phone.

It had to be spam. Didn't it? Who else would send an email like that? It was probably a scammer trying to get me to respond.

I hit delete but it didn't make me feel better. The timing was bothering me. It was odd that I'd get an email calling me a whore just days after I'd started sleeping with Logan. Wasn't it? Except no one knew that I'd been with Logan except Hazel and Jackson.

It is spam.

Somehow, the bar's account had been added to a hacker's list somewhere and I was one of many who'd gotten an offensive email.

"What's the matter?"

My head whipped to Logan as he stepped into the workshop. "Nothing." I set my phone down, shaking off the email. "Is she asleep?"

"Yep. She didn't make it through the third book." He grinned as he took up his regular leaning position against the cabinets.

"Thanks for putting her to bed."

"Anytime." He gestured to the table where I had our score from today. "How'd we do?"

"Not bad. I was just brainstorming things to do with this stuff." At least I had been before that email had come through.

We'd spent the afternoon at the lake, alternating between wandering along the shoreline, picking up our "treasures" and taking breaks to splash in the water. By the time we'd turned back for the car, it had been nearly dinnertime. The three of us had loaded up and gone to Bob's Diner, the other Lark Cove restaurant. Then we'd laughed and joked over my favorite greasy burgers and fries.

It was the best afternoon and evening I'd had in ages. And the entire time, Logan hadn't taken a single phone call or even checked his emails.

After dinner, we'd come home and spent some time visiting with Hazel. Charlie had requested Logan put her to bed after bath time, so while they'd been snuggled in her bed reading, I'd come out to the workshop to start organizing our pickings.

Charlie had added a pail of pretty rocks to her collection, while Logan and I had mostly found junk. We filled the garbage bag quickly and ended up using his bucket for more trash. But mine had come home with some real potential.

"So what are you going to do with all this?" Logan asked.

I picked up one of the two empty bottles of sunscreen we'd found. "I think I'll add these to my collection." I nodded to the box in the corner, overflowing with plastic sunscreen bottles. "I thought it might be cool to do something with the lids. Maybe melt them down into chessboard pieces. And then I could use the plastic from the bottles for the board. Cut them into squares and laminate them on plywood. Something like that."

"I call dibs on that one. I love chess." Logan grinned. "What about the cans?"

I ran my hand over one of the beer cans that I'd washed and was drying on my worktable. "Those get made into sparrows."

"Sparrows?"

I nodded and went to a drawer by his side, pulling out a couple of the birds I'd made recently.

The sparrows were small, about three inches from wing tip to wing tip. Each was different, depending on the type of can I used. And each was posed in flight, though they all varied.

"I make a bunch of sparrows from aluminum cans and then attach pins so they can be stuck into the wall. Usually I sell them in sets of fifteen or twenty so people can arrange them into wall pieces."

He studied the two birds in his hands. "These are amazing. How'd you come up with it?"

"I don't know." I shrugged. "I saw something similar but with ceramic butterflies at a fancy home decor store in Kalispell. They were all strung into a mobile for a baby's room, but I thought a wall piece could be neat. It took me forever to figure out the designs. The wings are easy, but the body and head have to be bent just right. And aluminum is a bitch to work with. I had to wash blood off the first hundred I made because I kept cutting myself."

Hazel had ordered me a case of Band-Aids.

He turned the bird over in his hand. "I love these."

"Thanks." I smiled, savoring a swell of pride. I'd always loved those tiny beer-can birds, even more now that Logan admired them too. "You can have those two."

"Are you sure?"

I nodded. "Now that I have the pattern down, these are my easy project. I can crank out a half dozen on a good night. It's what I do when I don't feel like making anything new. It's mindless, you know? And in the winter, I stock up. I'll run out of beer cans from the beach in no time, but I just swipe the empties from the bar."

"An unlimited supply." He set the bird down and stepped closer. "Your talents are wasted at that bar, Thea."

I shook my head. "This is just a hobby."

"No, this is incredible. I've been to my fair share of art exhibits and you've got something a lot of artists don't."

"Trash?" I joked.

"My daughter tells me it's not trash, but treasure."

I smiled, falling into him so I could loop my hands around his waist and rest my cheek against his heart. "Today was fun."

"It was." He wrapped his arms around my back. "The best day I've had in weeks."

I closed my eyes, taking a few deep breaths of Logan's smell. He was still in his T-shirt from yesterday. It smelled of my conditioner from sleeping in it, but I could smell him on the cotton now too. It wasn't the Armani-cologne Logan smell, but the real Logan smell. The one that was rich and spicy. The one he'd left on my pillow from last night.

The one I'd miss when he was gone.

Gone to the city. Gone to lose himself in work. Gone to be snatched up by a woman who was more suited for his lifestyle. She wouldn't mind the long hours, constant calls and social commitments.

Logan needed a woman like the one he'd lost.

Emmeline.

He'd been right earlier when he pegged me as jealous. Though not for the reason he thought. I didn't care that Logan had been with other women. I didn't like it, but I wasn't naïve enough to think I was the only one.

I'd been jealous because Emmeline had actually stood a chance. She'd had a shot at marrying Logan and building a life and family with him. A shot I'd never have.

This thing with us was fleeting. I wasn't going to move to the city. He couldn't give up the career he'd worked hard to build. I didn't blame him for that, but I was being realistic. Eventually, we'd drift apart to where our only connection would be Charlie.

So I hugged him tighter, pressing my body into his muscles, wanting to imprint his heat permanently before the time came and I had to let him go.

But not tonight or tomorrow or the next day.

The one thing I'd always wanted to be was part of a family. A real family. The illusion of Logan with me and Charlie was too tempting to pass up, even if it only lasted a while.

"Do you have more to do out here?" he asked.

I nodded, easing out of his arms. "Just a bit. Feel like hanging out in here while I finish?"

"Yeah. Would you mind if I poked around? I'd like to see more of your other pieces."

"Um . . . sure."

I felt a rush of nervous, excited energy. I wanted Logan to like my other pieces but I was working with actual garbage here. If he was going to inspect my workshop, I needed a drink.

"Want a beer?" I jerked a thumb over my shoulder toward the door. "Hazel refilled the ice in one of the coolers so there are some cold ones left over from the party."

"I'd love one. Thanks."

I nodded and walked outside, fidgeting with my fingers as

I hurried to the porch. I couldn't recall everything I'd stashed away in the workshop's drawers and cabinets. Most of it was just unfinished projects. I think I had a painting or two complete that I needed to drive up to Kalispell. And I'd finished my spoon nest while he'd been in New York.

I climbed the porch and grabbed a couple of beers from the cooler. Then I picked up my pace, practically running back to the shed.

Was my sketch pad in there?

My feet skidded on the grass. *Shit!* Yes. I'd left it out there last week. I'd had trouble sleeping one night and come out here to draw the image plaguing my dreams.

Logan's face.

In fact, during the two weeks he'd been gone, I'd filled a ten-page sketch pad with his eyes, nose and perfectly shaped ears. He did not need to see that.

I jerked out of my stupor, running back to the shed. I hit the door but Logan's back was to me. "Here," I panted, holding out his beer.

He turned, bringing something he'd taken out of a drawer with him.

"That's j—"

"What's this?"

Thank god. I nearly collapsed with relief to see him holding an old, tattered box instead of my sketch pad. "Oh, that's nothing."

He lifted the lid, revealing a stack of old Polaroids.

Hazel must have snuck them in here one day. She'd been on me to do a scrapbook with these photos for years. I guess she thought that by leaving them in my workshop, I'd be inspired.

"What are all these?" Logan asked, lifting a handful from the box.

"Just some pictures Hazel took a long time ago."

Pictures I didn't like to look at because of the memories that came with them. Hazel thought I needed to embrace my childhood and be proud of how far I'd come, considering my start in life.

I didn't agree. I preferred to block out all the lonely nights and uncelebrated birthdays.

I hated thinking about how a mother could dump a new-born baby in a pile of garbage. I'd spent the first two hours of my life with food scraps, foul odors and filth—or so I'd been told. The theory was that my mother had pushed me out, then tossed me in a Dumpster.

That was after she'd gotten me hooked on heroin in the womb.

Luckily for me, a homeless man who'd been sleeping in that Dumpster's alley had come "home" a little early that night and carried me to a nearby hospital. I'd detoxed. I'd grown. I'd made it further than most thought I ever would.

But while Hazel reveled in all that I'd become and my fighting spirit, I didn't like to think about how a mother could abandon her child. I didn't want the reminder of how the one person who'd been supposed to love me had so easily thrown me away.

I had no idea who my mother was, or my father.

I never would.

"Hey." Logan touched my arm. "Where'd you go?"

"Sorry." I forced a smile, blinking away the threat of tears. "Just thinking."

"Is this you?" He turned up a photo from the top of the stack.

I nodded, taking in the photo.

I was standing outside the home where I'd grown up. The one where I'd met Hazel.

My jeans were too short for my string-bean legs, but considering how skinny I'd been, they were probably the only ones that would fit my waist. It was winter, so I had on a stocking cap, which covered my long hair. It was freshly washed for a change and Hazel had just trimmed it that afternoon. My sweatshirt was a size too big and frayed at the hems. My tennis shoes were worn, but for hand-me-downs, they'd been some of the nicer ones I'd owned.

But I was smiling, because the twenty-year-younger Hazel had just told me a joke.

"How old were you here?"

"I think ten or eleven. Hazel would know right off the top of her head. She took that one. And all the other ones."

She came to my orphanage when I was eight. I remember walking into the kitchen one day, and there she was with a cigarette burning in the ashtray by the window. Her dark hair had been tied back with a red bandana.

"Let me see those for a sec." I took the stack from his hands, thumbing through them until I found the one I'd been searching for and handed it over. "This was her back then."

He chuckled. "She was a real-life Rosie the Riveter."

"Chambray shirt and all."

He handed back her picture and I stared at it for a long moment. While my own pictures dredged up pain, seeing her from back then was like a warm hug.

Because of Hazel, I had a few fond memories of my childhood. She'd come to work as a cook for the orphanage where I'd been raised. The home had been one of the few open orphanages in New York at the time. While most other children had gone into the foster care system, the director of my orphanage had retained a small group of us. I'd been the youngest, and after I'd turned eighteen, the place had closed.

Hazel had come back to Montana.

Jackson had followed her out here first.

Then I'd come last.

"Is this Jackson?" Logan held out one of the Polaroids.

I nodded. "We've been friends for a long time."

Jackson was sitting next to me on a park bench, glaring at Hazel behind the camera because she'd made him buzz his hair off that morning. The foster home where he'd been living at the time had been infected with lice. And she wouldn't let him near me until they'd all been killed. He'd bitched and moaned about that haircut, but he'd never grown it longer than an inch since.

Logan's forehead furrowed as he thumbed through the stack. "There are only kids in these pictures. Is this a school? Is that how you met Hazel?"

"Sort of. I guess you could call her our caretaker." *Or guardian angel.* "It's all ancient history now." I took the photos from his hands and put them back in the box. Mentally replaying my upbringing was difficult enough. I didn't want to explain it to Logan, at least not tonight.

"Thea—"

"Charlie has soccer practice tomorrow at four. Hazel was going to take her since I need to work, but I'm sure you could go if you'd like."

He frowned and took my face in his hands. "We'll play it your way tonight. But sooner or later, you're going to let me in, baby. I'll break down the door if I have to."

"Talking about the past isn't easy for me," I whispered.

"Because you don't believe I'm a safe place yet." He dropped his head to mine. "You can believe it, Thea. Always believe."

Believing in things had never been a luxury. Normally it just ended in disappointment.

Logan kissed my forehead, then let me go. "I want to talk to you about something else anyway."

"Okay." I walked around my worktable, grabbing the now empty buckets and stowing them underneath.

"I'd like you and Charlie to come back to New York with me."

I fumbled a bucket. It clanked on the floor as it tipped over. "We've had this talk. I'm not moving Charlie to New York."

He held up a hand. "I'm just asking for a vacation before school starts. Just come home with me for two weeks."

My eyes narrowed.

"One week," he countered. "I don't want to go back without you or Charlie. I'd like to show her where I live. I'd like my parents to meet their granddaughter. And it will all be easier if we're not trying to work around her school schedule."

All good points. "I need to think about it." And mentally prepare for how it would feel going back to the city.

"Okay." He grinned like he'd already won. "Think about it."

"I'm not saying yes." I glared at his smug smile. "This is the busiest time of year for us at the bar. I can't just leave it all to Jackson. That isn't fair. And Charlie gets a say in this too. If she's not ready to be inundated by the Kendrick family, I'm not going to force her."

"That's fine. I don't want to make her uncomfortable."

"Good." I crossed my arms over my chest.

He mimicked, crossing his. "Good."

Behind his long lashes, his brown eyes smiled just as smugly as his lips. I held his stare, not willing to break away.

Damn if this man hadn't perfected the intimidating stare.

It was sexy as hell.

Confidence poured off his hard body. It oozed across the workshop, making my knees weak. Desire pooled between my legs, burning and throbbing, as he held my eyes captive.

Damn him. The smug bastard knew he'd won.

Charlie and I were going to New York, but I wasn't admitting it tonight. I'd make him sweat it out a bit.

I'd make him work for it.

Starting with another night together in my tiny bed.

seventeen

THEA

"**O**H MY GOD," I MOANED AS MY EYELIDS DRIFTED SHUT. "Logan, please."

"Say yes, Thea, and I'll give you what you want."

"No," I breathed, shivering as he dragged his tongue through my slit.

It had been four days since Logan had asked me to come back to New York with him, and we'd come out to my workshop after Charlie had fallen asleep. One kiss had led to two and now he was on his knees, his broad shoulders between my legs, forcing them apart. And I was sitting on the edge of my table, gripping the sides as he tormented me.

"Say yes." He flicked his tongue over my clit twice, making me gasp. But instead of giving me what I needed, he pulled away and kissed the inside of my thighs.

"Logan," I grumbled, opening my eyes to the ceiling.

He just chuckled against my skin, peppering kisses down to my knee.

I'd been so close. Again. Logan had been taking me right to the edge of an orgasm for what felt like hours, but every time I felt the tight pull in my lower belly, he'd back off until the shaking in my legs stopped.

My entire body felt like a rubber band ready to snap. I just needed a little bit more of his talented tongue and I'd get the shattering release I was craving.

"Say yes," he commanded.

"No."

He nipped at my knee, then stood. With the taste of me on his tongue, he ran it over my bottom lip. Between us, his hands unbuttoned his jeans to free his thick cock and roll on a condom.

"Say yes," he whispered.

"No," I breathed, scooting as close to the edge of the table as I could get. But before my sex could touch him, he jerked his hips away.

"Thea," he warned. "Say it."

I shook my head, trying to hide my smile.

The last four days had been a battle of wills. He kept asking me to come to New York with him. I kept saying no. I'd given the vacation idea a lot of thought and had already decided we'd go with him. Mostly so Charlie could meet her other family. But since messing with Logan was so much fun, I'd kept denying him.

Now he was denying me.

He fisted his cock to bring it closer, rubbing it up and down my folds. He spread my wetness onto the condom, then rolled up to my clit.

Over and over he worked the hard bud while his lips latched onto the skin of my neck, kissing up and down. With his free hand, he yanked down the collar of my tank top and dove into my bra, pushing it out of the way so he could knead my breast.

"Oh, god," I hissed when he gave my nipple a wicked twist. The sensation shot straight to my core. "Don't stop," I begged.

"Not this time."

He stopped kissing me to speak in my ear. "Say yes and I won't."

With my eyes closed, I nodded. "Yes."

His grin spread across my cheek right before his cock slammed home.

That was all it took. I cried out, writhing on the table as my orgasm pulsed around his cock.

"Fuck, Thea," he groaned into my neck, staying rooted as I squeezed him tight.

The stars behind my eyes had barely cleared when his arms wrapped around my back and his hips began thrusting. With every one of his strokes, the table beneath me rocked and squeaked.

I don't know if I had the longest orgasm of my life or if he triggered one after another, but by the time Logan shot his own release, I was completely limp in his arms.

"I'm dead," I panted into his neck.

He held me upright, breathing heavy into my hair. "It just gets better."

I hummed my agreement. He'd been fucking me senseless all week and it was the best time I'd had in years. Maybe ever. We couldn't keep our hands off each other, always sneaking touches and kisses when Charlie wasn't looking. And after she was asleep, all bets were off.

He kissed my shoulder, then leaned back, holding me steady as I climbed off the table. When I nodded that I had my balance, he let me go to collect my bottoms, which were strewn on the ground. His knuckles brushed my skin as he carefully slid on my panties and shorts. Then he righted my bra and tank top, using a gentle touch that sent tingles down my spine.

"You don't play fair, Mr. Kendrick."

He tucked himself back into his jeans and zipped them up.

"I'm a lawyer, baby. Fair is up for interpretation." He stepped close, wrapping me in his arms. "But I'm glad my tactics worked."

I couldn't say I was excited about going to New York. My nerves were too high. But I was happy that we wouldn't have to say good-bye tomorrow and could prolong it for another week.

I snuggled into his chest. "I assume you've already made travel plans for me and Charlie."

"I may have." He chuckled. "Just in case."

"Right." I rolled my eyes. "Just in case." He'd probably started planning the trip before he'd even asked me on Monday. "Do I need to do anything?"

"No. Just pack a bag for you and Charlie. My assistant will have everything ready by the time we get there."

I nodded, patting his back and letting him go. "I think we need to clarify a few things before we go."

I'd been dreading this conversation, but before we left Montana, Logan and I needed to be on the same page, starting with a label for our relationship. The last thing I wanted was to show up in the city and be bombarded by his family, not sure exactly where we stood.

"What's there to clarify?" Logan stepped back and assumed his normal leaning spot. I'd never be able to look at that cabinet again without picturing him there.

"Well, for one, what exactly are we going to be doing?"

He shrugged. "Whatever you like. I'll need to work during the day but you and Charlie can explore. And then at night, we'll all be together."

"Okay." I might be able to conjure some excitement to beat out the nerves if I focused on planning fun activities for me and Charlie. "What about your family? You said you wanted them to meet Charlie."

"I do."

"And what about me? How do you want me to play this?"

"Play this?" His eyebrows came together. "What are you talking about?"

"This." I waved my hand between us, then blurted, "Am I going just as Charlie's mom? Or as your Montana piece? I don't know how you expect me to act when we're there."

The confusion on his face disappeared as his entire frame locked. "What did you just say?"

"I sa—"

Before I could finish, he pushed off the cabinet, crossing the tiny space between us in a flash to press three fingers against my lips. "That was rhetorical."

Ohh-kay. I held his angry eyes, not moving an inch.

He removed his fingers from my mouth, only to hold one up in front of my nose. "Don't you *ever* call yourself a 'piece' again. Understood?"

I nodded.

He huffed as he dropped his hand and spun around, raking it through his hair. "Is this why you've been stalling all week? Because you're worried about how I'm going to treat you when we get to the city?"

"Maybe?"

He glowered at me.

"I've never done this before and I'm nervous," I confessed. "You coming here is one thing. We're on my turf with my friends and family. But me going there is entirely different. I'm not sure how to act when we're together and I don't want to do anything that will embarrass you."

There, I'd said it. Now he knew at least one of the reasons why I was so hesitant to go to New York.

"Baby." His voice was gentle as he laid his hands on my shoulders. "You could never embarrass me."

I scoffed, but before I could give him one of a hundred examples of exactly how—use the wrong fork at dinner, say the wrong thing to his mother, wear the wrong dress to meet his sisters—he stroked his thumb across my lips.

"You couldn't. And you're coming with me as more than just Charlie's mother. Since you haven't figured it out yet, I'll just be blunt."

"Blunt is good."

He grinned. "We're in a relationship, Thea. Man. Woman. Boyfriend. Girlfriend. Call it whatever you want. But when I introduce you to my family, it will be with your hand in mine. And it's time we stopped hiding it from Charlie."

He dropped a hand from my shoulder to trail it down my arm to my hand.

The minute our fingers were laced together, a lump formed at the back of my throat. The same one I got whenever he kissed Charlie's hair and called her peanut. The same one I got whenever he tucked me into his side at night before falling asleep.

Logan and his simple gestures spoke more than a thousand words.

"I don't expect you to act like anything but yourself. The woman I'm completely falling for."

That was really, *really* nice to hear. "I'm falling for you too."

"I know." Logan smiled, then pressed his lips against mine in a sweet kiss.

I'd fallen for him the moment he'd come back to Lark Cove for Charlie's birthday. Or maybe it was all those years ago when he'd swept me off my feet in a hotel bar. It didn't matter. I wasn't foolish enough to think our relationship would last forever.

I *was* foolish enough to let him have my heart until he realized what I'd known all along.

One day, he'd understand that Thea Landry didn't fit into

the Kendrick world. One day, I'd have to let him go.

And if the hollow pit in my stomach was any indication, that day would likely come in New York City.

The next night, I was sitting at the bar drawing in my sketch pad. I'd been here all day, throwing myself into work as a distraction from the nerves. I'd been an anxious mess ever since agreeing to go with Logan to New York. Pouring drinks, wiping down tables and making pizza had given me a nice outlet for my unease.

That was until I'd found a sweet note after the dinner rush.

Someone had written SLUT on a cocktail napkin and left it for me on the bar along with a three-cent tip.

I didn't know who'd left it because we'd had a busy Saturday. My guess was the woman who'd been in earlier and hadn't liked it when I'd told her under no circumstances would I call Jackson down so he could "entertain" her.

Seriously. What did he see in those bitches? How was I the slut in this scenario?

The napkin note had pissed me off and taken away my calm. So I'd resorted to drawing to make me feel better. I'd been at it for an hour and was finally beginning to relax again.

"Hey."

I looked up as Jackson came through the back door of the bar. "Hi. What are you doing here?"

He shrugged. "I was bored at home. Thought I'd come in and keep you company."

"Want a beer?" I set down my pencil on my sketch pad and picked up a pint glass.

"Nah." He shook his head. "I'll just have a Coke."

I gave him a sideways glance. Jackson Page never turned down beer on Saturday nights. "Are you feeling okay?"

"I'm good. Just don't feel like drinking."

I left it at that and filled his glass with ice and soda. Then I set it on a napkin and leaned against the counter where I'd been drawing.

"Been busy?" he asked.

"Not bad. There was a good dinner rush tonight. Those guys in the corner booth have been here for a few hours. Wayne and Ronny were in earlier, but they both called it a night and left."

It was almost midnight, so things were winding down, but my day here had gone fast. I loved Saturdays for that reason. If I couldn't be at home with Charlie, then at least I wasn't bored at work.

And in just two hours, I could go home and crawl into bed with Logan.

"Where's Daddy Dearest tonight?" Jackson muttered.

"Hey." I frowned. How long was it going to take for Jackson to lay off Logan? "Don't be like that."

He winced. "Sorry."

"It's okay. And he's at my house with Charlie."

They'd come in with Hazel earlier for pizza. Hazel had offered to let Logan stay and take Charlie home for bed like she usually did when I was working. But Logan had declined, saying he'd go back with them too.

Mostly because Charlie had begged him to help her pack for our vacation.

"Are you sure you're okay with covering the bar all next week?" I asked.

"Like I told you yesterday when you asked me that same question ten times, yes. I can handle the bar all week."

"I know you can handle it. I just feel bad dumping it all on you short notice."

After I'd agreed to the trip last night, I'd left Logan at home and walked down to the bar to talk with Jackson. He'd grumbled about me moving too fast with Logan but had promised to take care of everything until we came back.

"It's fine, Thea. Consider it my penance for the whole kissing thing."

I grimaced. "Don't ever do that again. That was disgusting."

"Disgusting? My kisses aren't disgusting."

"Don't pout," I scolded. "I'm sure all the women who throw themselves at you think you're a great kisser. But since I'm the closest thing you have to a sister, I can say it was disgusting."

"Yeah." His face soured. "It was kind of gross."

I smiled. "Why don't you sit down? I'm going to go check on that table and then we can talk."

He nodded, grabbing his Coke and a tray of peanuts before rounding the bar.

I made quick work of refilling my customers' drinks before pulling up the stool next to Jackson. We sat quietly for a few minutes, each taking turns at cracking and eating peanuts until I asked the question that had been on my mind for weeks.

"Do you want to tell me what's been bothering you?" I already knew the answer. Ever since Logan had shown up last month, Jackson had been off. My normally playful and supportive best friend had turned into a moody brat.

"Nothing. I don't know." He scratched the scruff on his cheek. "These last few years have been the best, you know? No drama like we had as kids. We've got a good gig here at the bar. Finally don't feel like I'm scraping pennies together. I guess I'm just pissed that things are changing. This guy . . . he's a game changer."

"Is that really so awful? Logan's not a bad guy, and Charlie adores him. She deserves a father, Jackson."

"I know." He sighed. "It's just . . ."

The pieces clicked before he could finish, and I wanted to smack myself on the forehead. Before Logan showed up, Charlie did have a father figure.

Jackson.

This had nothing to do with me and my relationship with Logan. Jackson was hurting because he felt like he was losing Charlie.

"I'm sorry. I didn't think of how you'd be feeling about all this. But you'll always be her uncle Jackson. She loves you so much."

Jackson hung his head. "But I can't spoil her like he can. I don't have that kind of money."

"It's not a competition, and it's not about the things you buy her. She needs love from you both."

He sipped his soda, contemplating my words. "She'll forget me if you don't come back."

"What? We're coming back. This is just a vacation."

"You might decide to stay."

I shook my head. "No, I won't. I've already told Logan I won't be moving back to New York."

The only way I'd live in the city was if Logan forced me into a custody situation. But now that I knew him better, I couldn't imagine him doing that to me.

"This is just a vacation," I repeated.

"Hope so." He stood from his stool and went behind the bar for a refill. "While you're there, go get a Giovanni's meatball sub for me. Damn, I miss those things."

Giovanni's had been three blocks away from my orphanage and right around the corner from Jackson's foster home. I smiled, thinking of all the times the two of us would share one of those foot-long sandwiches. It was rare. We couldn't afford them often. But whenever one of us had a couple extra bucks, we'd splurge. Even when we'd both moved out of Brooklyn, he and I would take trips back for a meatball sub.

Jackson hadn't lived in my orphanage, but he'd met Hazel at a grocery store in our neighborhood where he'd been trying to shoplift a candy bar. She'd caught him before the store owner could and dragged him back to the orphanage. She'd fed him a decent meal and shoved a bag of peas on his black eye—a recent gift from his foster father.

I'd walked into the kitchen that day and the rest was history. Jackson and I became closer than most siblings, while Hazel acted like a mother to us both, making sure we were fed and that our homework was always done.

Still, we were dirt-poor, and since Hazel wasn't our legal guardian, there was a limit to what she could do. Bad things still happened to us both. Those meatball subs were most often shared when one of us was at our lowest.

And as much as I'd like to have one again, it wouldn't be the same without Jackson. After he'd moved to Lark Cove, I hadn't gone to Giovanni's again.

"I doubt we'll be spending much time in Brooklyn." I shivered at the idea of going back to that neighborhood. Besides, Logan was Upper East Side through and through.

"Probably not. I wouldn't go back either." Jackson took the soda gun and filled his glass, then he turned and grabbed my sketch pad. He set it on the bar, flipping through the pages. "You've almost got this one full."

"When I get back, you'd better have a new one waiting for me."

He chuckled. "Done."

When I'd first moved to Lark Cove, I'd complained to Jackson about how boring it was at night when the bar was slow. He'd bought me a sketch pad and told me to quit bitching. Since then, I'd filled a ton of sketch pads with my drawings of random bar patrons. Every time I ran out of pages, I'd come in to work to find a new one on my desk in the office.

"Who were you drawing tonight?" he asked, reaching the end of the book.

"You'll see."

He turned to the last page, where I'd drawn Willa's profile.

She'd been in earlier for dinner. I hadn't seen her since she'd watched Jackson kiss me and I could tell she'd been nervous. But after I'd explained to her that there was nothing there and Logan had come in with Charlie, she'd seemed relieved.

Willa had looked beautiful tonight. She'd sat in one of the booths by the front windows and the evening sunbeams had made her long, wavy hair shine like strands of gold. So, I'd picked her as my model. Mostly the drawing concentrated on her hair but I'd also made sure to highlight her high cheekbones and shy smile.

"She's hot." Jackson looked up from the book and scanned the bar like he expected her to still be here. "I'm sorry I missed her. Who is this?"

My jaw dropped. "Seriously?"

"Seriously. Who is this?" He looked back to the page. "Was she just passing through or do you think she'll be back?"

"Do I think she'll be back?" My voice rose as I stood from my stool and rounded the bar. "Give me that." I swiped the sketch pad away from him, making sure we were talking about the same drawing.

It was. So I shoved the page in his face. "That is *Willa*, you dipshit."

"No fucking way." He yanked the pad from my hands. "She doesn't look like this."

"Yes fucking way she does."

He bent closer to the paper, studying it before looking back to me. "She does?"

"Oh my god." I tossed up my hands and walked away, going to check on the guys in the corner booth. They were ready to leave, so I rang up their tab and cleared some glasses, waving good night before going back to Jackson. He was still staring at Willa's picture. "Do you see it yet? Or am I really that bad of an artist?"

"Huh?" He jerked up, forcing his eyes away from the sketch. "I, uh, gotta go," he muttered, still in a daze as he hugged me good-bye and walked out with my sketch pad.

I smiled as the back door banged closed.

He finally got a clue.

Jackson might not like change, but I had a feeling that by the time I got back from New York, he would have made a few changes of his own.

I just hoped Willa made him work for it a bit.

eighteen

LOGAN

"YOU OKAY, PEANUT?" I KNELT DOWN IN FRONT OF Charlie.

She nodded, her eyes fixed on the plane fifty feet away. Her hand was clutching Thea's, who wore the same nervous expression as our daughter.

I ran my fingers over her hair, then stood. "Are *you* okay?" I asked Thea.

She tore her eyes from the plane. "We've never been on a plane before. Are they supposed to be this tiny?"

Tiny? This was one of the larger Gulfstream models available and by far the most expensive. It was a good thing my mother wasn't here for that comment. She would have gasped, then demanded I buy something bigger when we traded up every fall.

"It will be fine," I assured them both. "This plane is as safe as they come, my pilots are the best there is, and this is a hundred times better than flying commercial."

I hadn't been on a commercial plane in over ten years, but I was sure my statement was true. We had no lines, no baggage limitations, and comfortable and spacious seating, plus I'd made sure the jet had been filled with Charlie's favorite snacks.

"Mr. Kendrick?" One of the attendants approached, gesturing to the stairs. "You're all set, sir."

"Thank you." I nodded, then took Charlie's free hand and led them to the plane.

"Whoa." Charlie's whisper echoed through the cabin the second we stepped inside. Her eyes widened as she took in the cream interior.

My mother's decorator was responsible for the interior of our plane. My sister Aubrey had asked to decorate it one year and we'd ended up with minimalist modern. Lillian Kendrick did not approve of minimalist, so from then on out, our jets had all been decorated like this one. Everything was rich, buttery leather and dark, gleaming mahogany. And the carpet was so plush, it felt like walking on a cloud.

I'd never felt uncomfortable in this plane before. Not once. Mom's taste was extravagant compared to my own, but it was what I knew. It reminded me of my parents' estate—my childhood home. It reminded me of Granny's mansion, just three plots down from Mom and Dad's.

But at this very moment, as I took in Thea's expression, I was nervous to take a seat.

Thea was far from impressed. The worry she'd worn outside was now closer to panic, and it had nothing to do with getting in the air.

This was her first step into my life and she was terrified. Her feet were stuck by the door. She glanced over her shoulder, longing to retreat down the stairs.

Fuck. Was she going to run? I'd never dated a woman who hadn't either had money of her own or had at least spent time surrounded by extreme wealth. Was this too much for Thea?

I'd been so glad when she'd finally agreed to this trip. But maybe I'd rushed it. Maybe I'd pushed too hard for her to come along. Maybe I should have given it more time.

It was too late now.

"Sir." The captain emerged from the cockpit. "We're all set."

"Thanks, Mitch."

He nodded and smiled at Charlie. "Hello, miss."

She gave him a shy smile.

He bent, waving her close. "Would you like to sit in my seat for a minute? See what it feels like to be a pilot?"

Her face whipped to Thea, silently asking, *Can I?*

Thea nodded and reluctantly let go of her hand.

"Come on." I took Thea's elbow, practically dragging her to a seat. Then I sat across the aisle so Charlie could sit by one of us. "Was this a mistake?" I asked quietly. "This trip?"

"No," she lied. Her eyes, filled with doubt, betrayed her.

"Thea, I—" Before I could tell her I'd cancel this whole thing if she was scared, Charlie came rushing out of the cockpit, her nerves erased by a moment in the captain's chair.

"Can I sit by you?" Charlie asked me.

"Of course." I helped her get buckled into the seat, then nodded at our attendant that we were set.

Five minutes of taxiing later, the captain announced we were next up on the runway.

The minute he punched the engine, forcing our backs deep into the seats, Thea's hand shot out across the aisle. Her eyes were closed tight and her other hand was gripping the armrest with white knuckles.

I took her hand and let her squeeze my fingers tight. "I've got you."

Somehow, I'd make this okay. With time, she'd get used to this kind of lifestyle, because really, there wasn't another option. I wasn't letting her go.

This lifestyle—my lifestyle—was hers now too.

We just needed to get to the city and everything would be all right.

"Whoa."

Charlie's word of the day. It had started on the plane and continued through every part of our journey. When we'd flown over the city, she'd been glued to the window, whispering *whoa*. When we'd landed and walked to my town car, *whoa*. And now, standing just inside the door to my penthouse.

"Come on in and make yourself at home." I turned to the doorman. "We've got the bags from here. Thank you."

He nodded, setting down our luggage in the foyer. "Have a good evening, sir."

When the door closed behind him, I picked up Charlie's tiny suitcase and carried it farther down the hall. "How about we do the full tour and then order in some dinner?"

"That sounds nice," Thea said, following behind with Charlie. "Logan, this place is . . ."

"Whoa?"

She smiled. "Exactly. Nice place, gorgeous."

"Thanks." I grinned. She didn't call me *gorgeous* often, but damn I liked it when she did. "I've only been here for about three months," I told them as I walked into the living room. "So I'm still getting used to the place myself."

"Three months?" Thea's frame perked up. She'd done the math and knew this place wasn't the one I'd shared with Emmeline.

"You both will be my first overnight guests."

That got me a full-blown smile. I'd never brought a woman here for sex. It wasn't like I'd done it consciously, it just hadn't happened. The only woman I'd fucked since Emmeline was Alice and she'd never been invited over. I mentally patted myself on the back for my foresight.

The only woman who had a claim on my bed was Thea.

"Whoa." Charlie's head tipped back to the ceiling, taking it all in as she spun around. She nearly crashed into a couch as she came into the living room.

The main room was situated in the corner of the penthouse with floor-to-ceiling windows lining both exterior walls. Beyond the glass was a garden terrace that overlooked Central Park and the towering Manhattan skyscrapers in the distance.

The windows had sold me on this place. The black iron between the rectangles was thick to give them an industrial feel. On the top row, the architect had kept them as squares but added some circular iron accents to break up the grid. Wood panels had been placed strategically throughout the living room to warm up the space. And in the center was a two-story, concrete fireplace. Next to the windows, it was my favorite part of the penthouse.

"This is a beautiful place." Thea ran her hands over the back of a leather couch. "But not what I was expecting."

"Really?"

She nodded. "I guess I figured it would be modern and," she shrugged, "I don't know. I guess I thought it would be like the places you always see in fancy magazines where everything is white. The kind of place where no one can actually live for fear of spilling something. But that fireplace is beautiful. And the wood accents are done so well. It's amazing."

"Thanks." I took her hand and pulled her past the fireplace and into the kitchen.

Behind the fireplace, the ceilings were lower, making room for the upstairs bedrooms. But it was still open and airy in the back part of the penthouse. The windows let in a lot of early evening light so the room was glowing.

"Would you like anything to drink?" I set Charlie's suitcase down and opened the fridge. There wasn't much inside. My cleaning service had cleared it out last week. But my assistant had filled it with some necessities, like bottled water, soda, juice for Charlie and Thea's favorite beer.

"I can see you do a lot of cooking," Thea teased, standing beside me and taking out a bottle of water.

"Me and cooking don't mix." Not that I'd ever really tried. "Delivery is the safer choice." I grinned and grabbed my own water. After a long drink, I called to Charlie, who was pressed up against a window, looking outside. "Hey, peanut. Want to see your room?"

She spun around and her jaw dropped. "I have my own room?"

"You sure do. It might not be exactly how you want it, but while you're here this week, you can get it all set up just right." I winked at Thea. "In case you decide to extend your vacation."

The second the words were out of my mouth I wanted them back. *Damn it.*

Thea's guard went right back up. She gave me a smile—the fake one—and walked out of the room, looking to the right, then left.

"Down the hall," I told her as I set down my water and picked up Charlie's suitcase.

As she disappeared toward the bedrooms, the doubts I'd had on the plane returned. Maybe I shouldn't have pushed her to come out here so soon. Maybe we should have waited until the fall.

Still, having her and Charlie in this house was incredible. Today was the first time it had felt like home.

I spent long nights at the firm, especially when I'd just been starting out. But that habit had continued and there were still times when I'd catch a few hours of sleep on my office couch and shower in the partners' lounge.

There just hadn't been any reason to come home.

"Which one is my room?" Charlie asked as she jogged after Thea.

"Third door on the left."

I walked down the hall after them, passing a bathroom and my office. Mostly, I did foundation work from home when I didn't feel like going downtown.

There were five bedrooms in this penthouse, three upstairs and two down. I'd decided to give Charlie the biggest room downstairs because it had the fewest windows. For what I'd asked my assistant to arrange, I'd needed it to be as dark as possible.

"Whoa."

I chuckled as I caught up to Charlie and Thea. They were standing in the doorway, both wide-eyed as they took in the room.

I hadn't had the chance to see the room since I'd ordered it done the day after I'd asked Thea to come back with me, but my assistant had sent pictures.

And tomorrow, I was giving him a raise.

"It's like a fort," Charlie whispered, carefully stepping inside. "The best fort ever."

"Logan, this is . . ." Thea swallowed hard. "This is wonderful. Thank you for doing this for her."

I stepped closer, bending to brush a kiss on her cheek. "It was my pleasure. I want you both to feel comfortable here. For whenever you want to come and visit."

Her frame relaxed as I threw in that last part.

As much as I wanted them to stay for good, I'd pushed enough today. If I alienated her this week, I might never get her back.

I didn't know why Thea was so resistant to being here, but there was something she wasn't telling me. As we'd flown into the city, she'd had the same look on her face as she had the night I'd found her old Polaroids.

"Mommy, look at the trees."

"I saw them! They're so cool."

The walls had been painted a dark tan, with birch trees in a lighter shade stenciled on top. Charlie's four bedposts were all made to look like branches too, their limbs extending to the ceiling, then coming together in the middle to form a canopy.

Because the room was so dark, there was a string of golden lights that ran above the crown molding, giving the space a soft glow.

The bedding was a soft cream, the floors a deep brown wood. All the room needed were a few of Charlie's touches, like her artwork or some books on the shelves.

I set down Charlie's suitcase by the wooden dresser and wandered around the room. "My assistant Sean is going to come over tomorrow while I'm at work. He'll take you shopping for anything that's missing or you want to change."

"Logan—"

I held up a hand, stopping Thea's protest. "I want this room to be just right for her. Please."

She closed her mouth and nodded.

"Besides that, I'd like you to get to know Sean. He spends a few days a week here working and I think you guys will hit it off. And if you ever need anything from me but can't track me down, he can take care of it."

My phone buzzed with a text in my pocket, so I pulled it out. "Speak of the devil. Sean wants to know what we'd like for dinner."

Charlie climbed up on her bed, jumping once, then landing

on her back. The comforter billowed at the sides as she giggled. "Snacks!"

Thea and I shared a look, then she smiled and jumped on the bed with Charlie.

The two of them laughing together gave me hope.

My plan was going to work. After a few days, Thea would relax and feel comfortable here. She'd feel at home.

Then I could ask her to stay.

"She's out." I walked up behind Thea, wrapping my arms around her shoulders.

She relaxed, leaning into my embrace, and brought her hands to my forearms. "Thanks for tucking her in. Though, I'm getting jealous that she doesn't want my bedtime stories anymore."

"Tough. I'm stealing bedtime." I kissed the back of her hair, inhaling the soothing lavender scent.

We'd spent the evening lounging in the living room. Charlie had taken over my remote for the television and found some Lego movie for us to watch. Sean had come over hefting bags of every snack available and my favorite Chinese.

After we'd done introductions, he'd excused himself and we'd enjoyed a quiet dinner. Charlie had eaten her snacks, plus some required chicken tenders, and Thea and I had decimated the takeout.

If the rest of the week went like the last three hours, I had no doubt that I could convince her to move.

"Is this your family?" She reached out and touched a picture frame. We were standing in front of a bookshelf in the living room. Mostly it held books from law school, but there were a few pictures too.

"Yes. That was for Mom's holiday card last year."

"I feel bad." She sighed. "All the time we've spent together and I haven't once asked about your family."

I often had to remind myself that we'd only been a couple for a week even though it felt like much longer. Thea had been hiding deep in my heart for years.

"Don't feel bad. We've got time to learn all about one another."

"Do we?" she whispered. "Do we have time?"

She tried to step away, but I held her tight. "There's no clock on this, Thea. I'm not going anywhere."

"But I am."

I closed my eyes, forcing my mouth to stay shut. I wanted to tell her she was staying. To declare this was her home now. But I knew exactly how that would end.

With me sleeping on the couch.

"Let's not worry about geography tonight."

She relaxed again, then pointed to the picture. "Those are your parents?"

"Thomas and Lillian. And those are my sisters, Aubrey and Sofia. That's Aubrey, next to me. She's four years younger than me. And that's Sofia, next to my dad. She's six years younger. You'll meet them all this weekend."

The plan was to let Thea and Charlie explore the city during the week while I worked. I'd chosen to delay the introduction with my family so Charlie could do fun things in the city and Thea could settle into the penthouse. I wanted them both to feel at home here without the pressure of strangers invading. Then over the weekend, we'd take a trip to my parents' place outside of the city.

"Charlie and Aubrey look a lot alike." Thea nodded to

another picture of Aubrey on the shelf.

"They sure do."

While I'd simply trusted Thea to tell me the truth about Charlie's paternity, my parents wouldn't do the same. They'd been emailing and calling regularly to pressure me into a test. I'd continually refused because once they saw Aubrey and Charlie in the same room, they'd realize what I'd known all along.

Charlie was a Kendrick.

"Tell me about them."

I let Thea go, taking her hand and pulling her over to a couch. "What do you want to know?"

She settled into my side. "Anything. Everything. What do they do?"

"Well, my dad is in charge of everything, really. He runs the business and all of the family affairs. He says he's going to retire, but we all know he's too attached to the business to step away."

"What is your family's business?"

"Investments mostly. At the turn of the century, my great-great-grandfather made a name for himself by investing in businesses throughout the city. Flower shops. Restaurants. Real estate developments. Steel factories. Shipping companies. Businesses of all sizes. You name it and he had his hand in it. He was a real go-getter."

He'd built himself up from nothing, and his hard work had built the foundation for the Kendrick fortune.

"By the time he died, he'd amassed a huge wealth for the time. It all went to my great grandfather, who doubled it. And then to my grandfather, who doubled it again. And my dad has nearly tripled it from there."

Billions of dollars, all because the original Logan Kendrick had made his first investment in a small bakery on Fifty-Seventh Street.

"But you didn't go into the family business?"

"No." I tucked Thea closer to my side. "It had always been the family plan for me to take over, but I went to college and never found a real passion for my business classes. I took one pre-law class and knew it was the right fit. So I broke the family chain. The eldest son of the eldest son went to law school instead of to work for the company."

Since then, I'd been working my ass off, trying to prove to my family, and myself, that I hadn't made a mistake. I was still business savvy. You had to be in corporate law. I just hoped that my success at the firm would show I was still worthy of the Kendrick legacy even though I hadn't gone directly into business with my father.

"I am still involved," I told Thea. "Just because I don't work side by side with dad every day doesn't mean there isn't a ton for me to do with the family's ventures. I spend a lot of time with the foundation, and I'm starting to take over some of dad's responsibilities with our family."

There was always a cousin in need of an internship or job referral. At times, Dad or I would step in to settle a squabble between my aunts or uncles. And as of a week ago, Dad had asked me to take over managing trust fund disbursements.

"Was your dad disappointed that you didn't go to work with him?" she asked.

"At first." I sighed. "But not long after I started working at the firm, Aubrey graduated college and went to work with Dad. It helped smooth things over. He named her his successor a few years ago."

"Does that bother you?"

"Honestly? No. It was a relief. I'm not as passionate about being an entrepreneur as I am about representing them. The legal aspect of business fascinates me. I love bringing two parties to a table, figuring out what they really need from each other and finding a way to give it to them. But the rest isn't as exciting. And Aubrey just fits. It's in her blood and comes so naturally for her. I do the things she doesn't love as much, like run the foundation."

Maybe it was because Granny had started it as her pet project, but the foundation and its mission had always called to me more than anything else in the Kendrick empire.

"And Sofia? Does she work too?"

I snorted. "Sofia is living her best life as a socialite. She hasn't worked a day in her life and can spend money with the best of them. My mother is good at spending money too, but she lucked out and fell in love with my father, who adores her. Sofia, on the other hand, plays games like an adolescent and has managed to land herself two ex-husbands."

Sofia's husbands had been scum, leeching off her money while fucking other women behind her back. It was unfortunate because I think she really had loved them both. I'd hoped that, after her second divorce, she would take the time to reflect on her life and the men she'd chosen.

I'd tried to convince her to stay single for a while and wait for someone nice to come along. She'd laughed at me and rumor had it she was already seeing another money-grubbing loser. This one was a professional poker player who wasn't all that good at poker.

"See this gray hair, right here?" I pointed to my temple. "That's from Sofia."

Thea giggled. "You don't have any gray hair."

"But someday I will, and it's going to be her fault."

We'd all hoped that Sofia would find an interest in one of the Kendrick businesses. But so far, she'd yet to make much of herself but a brat. And my parents did her no favors by spoiling her rotten.

"Thanks." Thea snuggled closer. "It's nice to hear about them all so I'm prepared for when we meet."

"You have nothing to worry about."

It was a half-truth. Aubrey would embrace Thea and Charlie immediately. My parents would likely be hesitant but polite. They'd come around when they realized Thea wasn't after the family fortune.

Sofia was the risk. Either she'd want to play dress-up with Charlie, or she'd throw a tantrum to make sure she stayed the center of attention.

I didn't know how she'd play this, but one thing was for certain. If she made this a bad experience for Thea, I'd take her financial freedom away with a snap of my fingers. Because while Dad and Aubrey were in control of the working capital, I had the power over the legacy money.

I had the power over Sofia's trust fund.

Dad was making the announcement next week, so with the exception of Mom and Granny, none of the family knew that, as of a week ago, I was in charge of trust fund withdrawals for the Kendrick lineage.

We had a fairly simple trust fund setup considering the size of our fortune. If you were a direct descendant of my great-great-grandfather, you were entitled to a percentage of his legacy. Once you turned thirty, the money was yours to do with as you pleased.

But until then, withdrawals required approval from Dad. Now me. It was a safeguard to ensure the younger adults didn't take hundreds of thousands of dollars to spend on hookers and blow.

After all, that would tarnish the family image.

I'd planned to follow Dad's precedents, approving all

withdrawals unless there was cause for alarm. I wanted to stay out of each individual's financial business. But if Sofia hurt Thea or Charlie in any way, I'd make an exception.

She might be in our family, but she'd learn the hard way not to mess with *mine*.

nineteen

THEA

"I WISH YOU DIDN'T HAVE TO GO TO WORK."

Nice, Thea. That sounded just as clingy and pathetic out loud as it had in my head.

I also didn't give a shit.

What I really wanted to do today was curl up with Logan on a couch, watch movies and let Charlie have a quiet day with her parents. One thing I'd learned over the past four days was that New York City was just like I'd remembered: loud, chaotic and expensive.

Logan's apartment was a haven and had quickly become my favorite place in New York.

Everything else was for the pigeons.

"Sorry, baby." Logan's arms pulled me closer, his front to my back. "I wish I didn't have to go either and we could just spend the day in bed. But I can't."

"I know," I muttered, closing my eyes to draw out these last few moments together in his bed.

Logan's bed was massive, nearly as large as my entire room at the cottage. It sat opposite a wall of windows that overlooked the city. It was still dark outside—I'd learned this week that Logan went to work before dawn—but the sun's glow was beginning to light the sky and slowly filter into his bedroom.

Just like the rest of his penthouse, this room was magnificent. His thick gray quilt was heavy, and with his warm body pressed against mine, I was in a cocoon of luxury.

"I love your bed."

"I love you," he whispered into my hair. My eyes popped open just as he added three more words. "In my bed."

I relaxed, hoping he hadn't felt me flinch.

But he had.

Without hiding his disappointment, he kissed my head, let me go and rolled out of bed. As he walked to the bathroom, the muscles of his back and shoulders were bunched. His hands were in fists.

Goddamn it. I hadn't meant to hurt him with my knee-jerk reaction.

We were there? We'd been together for such a short time. Were we at *I love you*?

He'd told me last week that he was falling for me. I'd fallen for him too. And as much as I wanted to hear those three little words in his deep voice, I wasn't ready.

I love you meant making decisions about the future. It meant changing names and talking babies.

I love you meant me and Charlie would need to move.

After Logan had talked to me the other night about his decision to go to law school, I had a better understanding of why he worked so hard.

He loved it.

His drive to succeed was stronger than I'd ever seen. And in a way, I think he was still trying to prove himself to his family. He was showing them that even though he hadn't gone the route everyone had expected, he was still worthy of taking over as head of the family.

Logan thrived on challenges and responsibilities.

Achievement fueled him. But I knew after four days that I couldn't compete with it all. He needed his career, one he wouldn't find in Montana.

The shower in the bathroom turned on and I sat up, knowing I wouldn't be able to fall back asleep. I went to Logan's closet and pulled out some clothes from my suitcase. Dressed, I headed downstairs and peeked in Charlie's room to see she was still zonked out. Then I went to the kitchen for coffee.

The first morning I'd been here, I'd offered to make Logan breakfast, but then Sean had arrived with a breakfast sandwich in hand and whisked Logan away to the firm. Monday was their early morning catch-up meeting.

The morning after that, I hadn't offered breakfast, but I'd made him coffee. He took two sips before Piper, his assistant from the foundation, showed up with a special latte and his favorite bagel. Tuesday was their meeting day because Logan filled every moment, even those commuting to and from the office, with work.

Yesterday, Wednesday, I'd woken up alone in bed. I'd come downstairs to find Logan emerging from the penthouse gym. He'd come out shirtless with his muscles bulging and glistening with sweat. I'd almost pounced on him until Yuri, his personal trainer, had followed behind carrying a protein shake.

Now it was Thursday and I had no idea who would be his first appointment of the day.

Probably another assistant.

Not long after I sat down at the extended island in the kitchen, coffee cup in hand, Logan came down the hall, fixing a cufflink.

God, he was sexy. The suits he wore to work every morning were drool-worthy. Every angle and every line were perfect. Today's was a solid black three-piece with a crisp white shirt under a fitted vest. His golden tie matched his pocket scarf.

And here I was in five-dollar gray leggings and an oversized peach sweatshirt I'd bought when I'd been pregnant.

"Want some coffee?" I asked.

"Don't get up. I've got it."

I soaked him in as he poured a cup. "No personal assistants this morning?"

He looked over his shoulder and grinned. "Thursdays I normally go into work early and meet with my assistant there. But I'm going to be late today because someone hit the snooze button three times."

I smiled. When his alarm had gone off, I'd climbed on top of him, taking advantage of his morning erection and hitting snooze until we'd both come together and collapsed in a sweaty heap. "That was a good twenty-seven minutes."

He set down his coffee and came around the bar, spinning my chair so he could stand between my legs. "Guaranteed the best meeting I'll have all day."

I wrapped my arms around his waist, hugging him tight and breathing in his cologne. He seemed to have shrugged off his disappointment from earlier, which was a relief. I didn't want our last couple of days together to be strained. Who knew when he'd have time to come back to Montana for a visit, and I'd need a long break before considering another trip to the city.

At least a year. Maybe two.

"I was thinking we could go out to dinner tonight." He toyed with the ends of my ponytail. "I'd like to take you and Charlie to my favorite restaurant."

"Sounds good."

"You'll want a cocktail dress. Maybe while you're out shopping for your gown today, you can pick up something for you and Charlie to wear tonight."

I forced my shoulders to remain relaxed so he wouldn't feel my cringe. "Sure."

Logan had invited me to a gala tomorrow night for his family's foundation, so today I was charged with finding a ball gown. I could handle buying a nice dress. But to get one for Charlie? He had no idea the challenge he'd presented.

"I'd better get to work."

"See you tonight." I let him go, tipping up my chin for a quick kiss.

His shoes clicked on the marble as he walked to the door. When it shut behind him, I took my coffee out to the terrace and sank into a wide chaise lounge.

Besides his bedroom, this terrace had become my favorite place in Logan's penthouse. His gardener had planters and pots everywhere. Green leaves and bright flowers spilled over the edges of stone and concrete. It was as close to my cottage porch as I could get, minus Hazel and her cigarette smoke, which I missed more and more every morning.

I sipped my cup, watching as the sun rose higher. There were people who loved the city skyline, but this place had nothing on the lake view from my backyard.

And today, we'd be thrust out of the penthouse and into the madness, for shopping of all things.

All I wanted to do today was hang out with Charlie and show her parts of the city she might actually enjoy, like Central Park. Because so far, she was unimpressed with New York. And while I had my reasons for not liking the city, I did want Charlie to enjoy it here, for Logan's sake.

But nothing about this trip had gone well.

The first day, Logan's assistant Sean had taken us shopping for her room. We'd gone to a large department store to find some toys and books, but it had been a zoo and she'd been completely overwhelmed. After an hour of wandering through the store, bumping shoulders and squeezing through tight spaces, she'd only chosen one stuffed lion to bring home.

When Sean had offered to take us shopping somewhere else, she'd refused, saying her room didn't need anything else.

The next day, I'd taken her to the Empire State Building, where the warp-speed elevator ride had scared her. Then yesterday, we'd gone to Rockefeller Center and Times Square. It had been an improvement, but she'd still been out of her element with the crowds and bustle.

It hadn't helped that she'd spent so little time with Logan. He left before she woke up each morning and returned in time for a late dinner and to tuck her in. We'd both gotten a firsthand look at just how hectic his schedule was here.

Shopping for dresses today, something she refused to wear at home, meant I'd get to ruin another day of her not-so-fun vacation.

"Mommy, are we done yet?" Charlie grumbled. She was sitting in the corner of a dressing room, kicking the wall.

This was the final stop on our shopping day from hell. After two stores to find cocktail dresses for me—one for dinner tonight, and another for dinner with Logan's parents—we'd gone shopping for Charlie. Three tantrums in three consecutive dressing rooms had left my patience threadbare. But the shopping fun hadn't stopped there. Now we were in a fancy boutique trying to find a ball gown for tomorrow night's gala.

"Don't kick the wall," I hissed, trying to zip up the back of my gown.

"Can I help you in there?" the saleswoman called from the

other side of the curtain.

I sighed and dropped my hands, then held the bodice of the gown to my chest. "Could you help me zip this?"

The gold curtain whipped open and in she came with a seamstress in tow. She gave the zipper a quick tug, cinching the dress tight around my ribs.

"This is just lovely." She took a step back, scanning me up and down. "You have to choose this one. It's da-vine."

She'd said that about the last five gowns, all of which I'd hated. But since I hated this dress slightly less than the others and I was desperate to be done with our shopping marathon, this would have to do.

I gave her a tight smile and nodded. "Yes, let's get this one."

The saleswoman snapped her fingers, causing a flurry of activity outside the dressing room. An hour later, after the gown's hem had been pinned and the saleswoman had been given instructions on where to deliver the dress, shoes, jewelry and lingerie, Charlie and I escaped the boutique, finally done with shopping.

Logan's credit card had been swiped more today than I'd swiped mine in a month.

"Are we done shopping yet?" Charlie whined as she slid into the back of Logan's town car.

"Yes." I breathed with relief, fastening my seatbelt, then hers. "Should we do something fun? Do you want to go to the park? We could take a walk around and feed some ducks."

She shook her head. "No, thanks."

Well, shit. My daughter had never turned down outside time.

"I know." I clapped my hands together, spouting the first thing that popped into my head. "How about we do something special for Uncle Jackson?"

That got her interest. "Like what?"

"Did you know he used to live here? Just like I did when I was a kid?"

She nodded.

"Well, there was this place where we used to get these meatball subs. They are his favorite sandwich ever. What if we went and got some meatballs to put in the fridge and then take home to him?"

"Yeah! And some for Gran too."

"You got it. We'll get a ton and we'll make a special dinner when we get home."

She smiled and leaned into my side. I wasn't sure if it was the mention of Jackson or Hazel or just going home, but it was the first happy smile I'd seen from her all day.

As the driver pulled away from the curb, my stomach clenched. Going back to Brooklyn was going to hurt, but for Charlie, I'd do it anyway.

We were going to Giovanni's.

"Is this it, ma'am?" the driver asked over his shoulder.

Was this it?

I studied the restaurant, taking in the weathered sign and faded red awning over the front door. Giovanni's was worn and so much smaller than I remembered. Had there always been bars on the windows? From the car, I could make out the same booths Jackson and I had shared once upon a time. Had there always just been the three? I couldn't remember a time when we'd come to Giovanni's and there hadn't been a line at the counter, but today, it was dead.

"We'll just be a minute," I told the driver, taking Charlie's hand as we unbuckled and climbed out of the backseat.

She clutched me tight as we pushed open the front door, ringing the familiar bell. The sound at least hadn't changed, or the smell of garlic and tomatoes.

"What can I getcha?" The waitress behind the counter didn't look up from her magazine to greet us.

"Um, I was wondering if I could get an order of meatballs, the ones you make in your subs, to go?"

"Lemme check." She rolled her eyes and set down the magazine. "Yo, Ruthie!"

"She sounds funny," Charlie whispered as the girl disappeared into the kitchen.

"It's just her accent, honey. Some people in the city have different accents."

Though, neither Jackson nor I had ever picked up a Brooklyn accent. He'd been born in Pennsylvania and had learned to talk there before being brought to New York. And since the nannies at the orphanage had all come from out of state, usually missionaries from some Midwest churches volunteering in the city for a year, I'd never picked up the accent myself.

"Are you the lady who wants meat—" A woman came out from the back but stopped before reaching the counter. "Thea?"

My mouth fell open. "Ruth?"

We stared at each other for a long moment, until the shock on her face morphed into a smug, bitchy grin. "Well, well, well. Back in the neighborhood. I always knew you'd be back."

Her voice was like nails on a chalkboard and I tugged Charlie closer to my side. "I'm just in town visiting. I was hoping to pick up some meatballs for Jackson and take them home as a gift."

"Knew you two would end up together." She eyed me up and down before nodding to Charlie. "That his kid?"

"No." I shook my head. "We're not together. Same as

always, we're just friends."

"Uh-huh." She sneered, looking past us to the car outside. "Nice ride."

"Thanks. Listen, I think we'll just go." There was no way I was ordering food from Giovanni's now, not when I knew Ruth would spit in it.

"But Mommy—"

"Not now, Charlie." I shooed her toward the door.

I twisted the knob when Ruth's shrill voice stopped me short of our hasty exit. "Just like last time, eh? Runnin' off without a good-bye? This time gettin' in a fancy car. Think you're still too good for this neighborhood, Thea? Think you're still betta than me? Cuz you're not. You're still just stupid trash."

I guess she was still bitter about how our friendship had ended.

Ruth had been my age and a classmate in school. She'd been my best friend, or so I'd thought. In reality, Ruth had used me for years. When she wanted my desk in English to sit by a cute boy, I gave it to her even though I'd sat down first. When she needed twenty dollars our sophomore year to buy a new backpack, I lent her the money even though I'd been saving it for winter shoes— she never paid me back.

But Ruth had been the friend I'd have given anything for. My meager things had been hers for the taking. And she'd taken and taken and taken. I'd let her, until the day I found her fucking my boyfriend in the supply closet of the bar where we both worked.

I let loose my temper on my asshole boyfriend. He was drunk and pretending not to realize his mistake. But Ruth knew exactly what she'd been doing. After he zipped up his pants and stumbled out of the bar, she told me it wasn't her fault, but mine. I hadn't been keeping him satisfied, so he'd strayed.

That had been the final straw.

In that moment, I realized just how toxic and selfish Ruth was and finally listened to Jackson and Hazel's advice. Cutting her out had been a long time coming. Without a word to Ruth, I quit my job and moved out of Brooklyn. I found a hole-in-the-wall apartment in Manhattan a couple blocks away from Jackson and started tending bar at the hotel where I eventually met Logan.

Where Charlie had started.

And because of the little girl clinging to my hand, wondering what was happening, I wasn't going to let this bitch talk to me like that for another second.

I turned from the door, standing tall. "I have never been and will never be trash. And I'm not too good for this neighborhood, Ruth. But I am too good for you. Have a nice life."

Her face turned a splotchy shade of fuchsia, but I ignored her and held my chin high as I led Charlie outside and to the car. When the door closed behind us, I didn't spare another glance at Giovanni's.

I didn't want to remember it like I'd seen it today.

"Anywhere else, ma'am?" the driver asked as I helped get Charlie buckled.

"Yes, would you please go down this block and take a right? I'll tell you where to stop." I was talking fast from the adrenaline in my veins, but he caught it all and pulled away from the curb.

"Where are we going now?" Charlie asked.

"You'll see." I gave her a smile and bent to kiss her forehead. It only took a minute to get where I wanted to go, and I told the driver to pull over.

"See that building?" I asked Charlie, pointing through the side window.

She craned her neck to see and nodded. "Yeah."

"That's where I grew up. That was where I lived."

"You lived there with Gran?"

I nodded. "That's right. This is where I met Gran."

The orphanage, much like Giovanni's, wasn't the expansive and towering building I remembered from my youth. It actually wasn't much bigger than Lark Cove School. It had been abandoned, all of the windows dark and boarded up. The doors were locked shut with a chain.

But it had once been home and I wanted Charlie to know where I'd come from.

I'd spent many lonely days and nights in that building. I'd had countless nights wishing for someone to love me, endless days hoping someone would want me to be a part of their family.

That's all I'd ever wished for.

A family. Unconditional love.

It hadn't happened right away, but Charlie was all of those wishes come true.

Maybe Hazel had been right. Maybe coming back here would help me put to rest the memories from the past.

Because I knew now, I wouldn't be back here again.

My phone dinged with a new email and I took it out of my purse.

From: anonymous743
Subject: You're nothing but a cheap whore.

Anonymous743 had been emailing me all week. One per day, ever since the first. I knew now they weren't spam. Even after I'd blocked the account, they still kept coming. The email gods didn't care that some unknown person was harassing me.

But like I'd done with each of the previous, I deleted it and told myself they'd stop. I'd probably just pissed off a customer traveling through Lark Cove. A couple weeks ago, there'd been a group of drunk assholes in the bar who had bitched constantly about my food, drinks and service. One of them was probably having a real laugh right now.

I looked up from my phone, staring back at the orphanage.

The joke was on Anonymous743, because if I could sit here in front of the place where I'd mostly known loneliness and not crumble, then a stupid email wasn't going to break me.

"Okay," I told the driver. "We can go."

As he drove us back to Manhattan, I replayed the afternoon. In a way, seeing Ruth at Giovanni's had been a blessing. It had pissed me off enough to go to the orphanage. And there, I'd remembered why I left New York in the first place.

To build my own life. To live by my choices. To be with the only family I'd ever known.

Logan and I had been living in a dream these past couple of weeks, but it was time to wake up and face reality. The snooze button had been pushed long enough.

When we left here on Monday, I was letting him go. I was breaking this off before we spent months or years struggling through a long-distance relationship that could only end in pain for us both.

twenty

LOGAN

STANDING IN THE LOBBY OF MY FAVORITE RESTAURANT, I NEARLY fell over when Thea and Charlie came through the door. Thea was wearing a fitted black cocktail dress with cutouts around the collar showcasing her flawless skin. Her hair was pulled up in a twist accentuating the long line of her neck. Add to that her makeup, jewelry and hot-as-hell heels, I was glad I had on a jacket to help conceal the bulge behind my slacks.

She was always beautiful whether she was in the jeans and tank tops she wore to the bar or the ratty peach sweatshirt she'd been wearing this morning. Thea always made my heart beat faster. But I loved seeing her dressed up, wearing the finest. She deserved the best there was.

"Hi," she breathed. "Sorry we're late."

"It's fine. You look beautiful."

I bent to kiss her blushing cheek, lingering for a moment to smell her perfume. Then I forced my eyes off of Thea to greet my daughter.

"Hi, peanut." I crouched down. "You look beautiful tonight too."

She glared at me and plucked at the skirt of her dress. Charlie was wearing a gray lace dress with half sleeves. Her toes wiggled in her ballet flats. And somehow Thea had tamed her hair into a sleek ponytail with waves of curls running down her back.

But it wasn't the clothes that made her look so different to-night. It was her missing smile.

"What's wrong?"

"Nothing," she muttered, studying the floor. Then she brought her hand up and yanked at the collar of her dress as hard as she could.

"Charlie, that's enough," Thea scolded, swatting her hand away from the fabric. "Knock it off. Right now."

It was the first time I'd ever heard Thea address our daughter with a firm tone. Charlie was such a good kid, she didn't need much reprimanding. Even when you were trying to corral her into the bathtub, she didn't require stern warnings.

Charlie turned up her chin and scowled at Thea, another thing I didn't like. What the fuck had happened today?

Before I could ask, the hostess called us over. "Mr. Kendrick? Your table is ready, sir."

I stood and took Thea by the elbow, escorting her through the restaurant toward my table in the back corner. David's Table only took reservations, and at times, they were booked three or four months in advance. But whenever I walked through the door, they found a way to clear a table.

I pulled out Thea's chair, then did the same for Charlie. Once they were seated, I took the seat with my back to the wall.

When the hostess went to unfold napkins, I held up a hand to stop her. "Thank you."

"Enjoy your meal, sir." She gave me a slight bow, then backed away.

Thea searched the table. "Menus?"

"It's chef's choice, but I've never been disappointed." I opened my mouth to ask what was going on with Charlie but our waiter appeared and launched into his greeting.

Had it always taken this long to hear the gauntlet of wine selections? I wanted him to disappear so I could talk to Thea, but he kept droning on and on. Finally, after he finished detailing the reds, I was able to order a bottle of wine.

"Charlie, what do you want to drink?" I asked.

She didn't answer, so Thea ordered for her. "She'll have a chocolate milk."

The waiter looked at her like she'd just blurted a string of expletives. "We don't have chocolate milk."

"Then find some," I snapped, shooting him a glare that meant he was dismissed.

Thea closed her eyes and took a deep breath.

Charlie kicked the leg of the table.

"Okay, what's going on?"

Thea shook her head. "It's just been a long day and we're hungry."

There was more behind their attitudes, but I didn't press. "I'm sorry I was running late and couldn't meet you at home."

I'd had a client meeting go long at the firm and then a junior associate stopped into my office for some advice on a contract he was drafting. By the time I'd shut everything down, I'd been forced to send a car to pick them up instead of doing it myself. Normally, the long hours didn't bother me. It was a thrill to always be in demand and the go-to guy. But tonight, all I'd wanted to do was leave and have people figure shit out on their own.

"It's fine." Thea waved it off and took a drink of her sparkling water.

"Did you have fun shopping today?" My mother and sisters loved shopping about as much as they loved talking about what they'd bought. I figured it was a safe topic until I got a nasty look from my daughter and Thea rolled her eyes.

Shit. This was not how I'd envisioned dinner going. The waiter brought our wine and a glass of chocolate milk for Charlie, setting them down without a word. Silverware clinked on plates and voices murmured around us, but my corner of the restaurant was silent.

I was guessing that Charlie's mood was because of the dress. She kept tugging at the collar.

Thea was clearly off because of Charlie's attitude, but there was something more too. It wasn't just an angry-mom mood. Her shoulders were hunched, and worry lines marred her forehead. She seemed sullen and withdrawn.

Was it because I'd slipped this morning? *I love you* had never come as naturally as when I'd blurted it to Thea. But when she'd flinched so hard the bed had rocked, I'd hastily added, "in my bed." At first, I'd been pissed off by the rebuff.

Rejection wasn't something I handled well, which was ironic considering I'd tried to propose to Emmeline twice. Yet neither of my failed attempts to marry her had ended our relationship. Really, they hadn't done anything. We'd just carried on like nothing had changed because a deep-seated part of me had actually been relieved.

Thea's reaction to an *I love you* had hurt.

But as I'd showered and taken a minute to step back, I'd realized it wasn't because she didn't have those same feelings.

She was scared.

To make this work—to say the *I love yous*—meant a lot of changes were coming.

Except whether she was ready or not, change was coming. She could try to avoid it for the rest of the week, but I wasn't letting her go.

On Saturday, while we were at my parents' estate, I was asking her to move. I was telling her how much I loved her and how much I wanted her and Charlie in my everyday life. Then I'd give her the ring I'd picked out this morning at Harry Winston.

We sat quietly until the waiter delivered our first course.

"What is this?" Thea asked him as he set down the plate in front of her first.

"Poached shrimp, melon and frisée salad." He moved to set down Charlie's, but Thea grabbed it first.

"What?" I asked.

"She's allergic to shellfish." She pushed the dish back at the waiter. "I'm sorry, she can't eat that. Do you have french fries?"

The waiter's eyes bulged, but before he said anything, he remembered his place and looked to me. "I'll discuss it with the chef."

He served my salad and rushed away from the table while I made a mental note to discuss Charlie's diet. How did I not know my daughter was allergic to shellfish? It was another reminder of how much I still had to learn about my child and how much easier that would be if we lived in the same state.

"I'm hungry, Mommy."

Thea gave her a sympathetic smile. "I know, honey. Here." She picked up Charlie's chocolate milk. "Drink more of your milk."

"It tastes funny."

"Let me see." Thea took a small sip and frowned. "It's just because they used real cocoa." She forced a smile, trying to make it seem exciting. "It's fancy. Try a little more. I bet you'll like it."

Charlie's shoulders fell as she shook her head. "No, thanks."

The silence resumed.

I looked across the table to Thea, who mouthed, *Sorry.*

It's fine, I mouthed back.

It didn't take the waiter long to come back to the table with a small plate of fries.

Charlie raised her chin, hopeful at first, but when she saw they were covered in garlic, parsley and parmesan, her eyes filled with tears.

"Just try one," Thea urged. "Let's all try one."

Thea and I both took a fry off Charlie's plate, eating them quickly. They were marginal at best; french fries weren't the chef's specialty.

"Okay." Thea chased her bite down with a sip of wine. "Let's just wait until the next course. I'm sure you'll really like it."

"You know what?" I whipped the napkin off my lap and set it on my salad. "Let's just go."

"No, Logan." Thea held out her hand. "It will be fine."

I stood and pulled back Charlie's chair. "We can do better than eating here, can't we?"

"Yeah," she slid off the chair. "This place is yucky."

At that exact moment, the waiter returned. His gasp echoed through the room.

Thea coughed, trying to cover up her laugh as she stood and set her napkin on the table. "She's only six. Too young to appreciate gourmet."

When the waiter's shocked look turned sour, it was my turn to hold back a laugh.

"Please send my regards to David." I took my wallet out of my jacket, dropping three hundred-dollar bills on the table. "The food and wine can go on my tab. That is for your trouble." Then with Charlie's hand in mine, I walked us out of the restaurant.

When we hit the sidewalk, Thea started laughing. It began as a small giggle but turned into a belly laugh. A smile spread across my face when Charlie joined in too, and after a moment, the three of us were howling.

"What are we doing for dinner?" I asked as my laughter died down. "Because I obviously can't be trusted to choose."

Thea looked up and down the street, searching for options. "Um . . . let's see."

"How about McDonald's?" Charlie asked.

"I've never eaten at McDonald's."

"What?" Thea's head whipped around to me. "You've never eaten at McDonald's?"

I smiled. *There's my Thea.* Repeating what she thought were ridiculous statements as loud questions.

"I've never been to McDonald's."

"Oh my god." She looked to Charlie. "We're definitely doing McDonald's."

"Yesssss," Charlie hissed, doing a fist bump.

I chuckled and took out my phone, calling us a car. Fifteen minutes later, I was standing in front of a neon menu the size of New Jersey. "I have no idea what to get."

"I'll order for you." She stepped up to the counter and ordered Charlie a Happy Meal—with the boy's toy—herself two cheeseburgers with fries, and me a double-something-pounder-with-cheese.

I reached for my wallet, thinking I was going to need Yuri to step up our workout in the morning, but before I could get my credit card, Thea pulled some cash from her purse.

"No, I'll pay."

"I've got it." She ignored me and handed the cash to the clerk. "I didn't protest when you gave me a temporary credit card for the dress shopping because designer gowns aren't in my budget. But McDonald's is something I can afford."

It had actually surprised me when she'd taken my credit card so willingly. I'd braced for an argument that would rival some of the most intense purchase negotiations at the firm. But Thea had agreed immediately and tucked the card into her pocket with nothing other than a thank-you and a kiss.

"Besides," she smiled at the clerk and took her receipt, "your platinum would probably break the credit card readers here."

I chuckled. "I'm pretty sure everywhere takes my platinum."

I didn't correct her that it was actually *our* platinum. Nothing about the card in her purse was temporary since I'd had Sean add her name to my account.

"So how is it that you've never been to a McDonald's?" she asked as we went to the fountain machine to fill our soda cups while Charlie trailed behind, drinking her *real* chocolate milk.

"I don't know. I've always had a chef."

"Even in college? You never wanted to try a Big Mac?"

I shrugged. "It's not like I haven't heard of McDonald's before. I just never had the urge to eat here." I patted my flat stomach. "And this doesn't happen by eating fast food."

"Well this," she laughed, mimicking my gesture on her own incredible curves, "loves McDonald's. I guess we'll just have to think of a few things you can do to burn some extra calories tonight."

"What are calories?" Charlie asked. Her smile was back, something I hadn't seen enough of this week.

"Calories are yummy," Thea answered with a laugh.

I smiled. Damn, I'd missed these two this week. Work had been brutal at the firm. Every night, I'd left a pile of papers on my desk so I could rush home before Charlie went to bed. What I really needed was a weekend spent in the office to catch up with both client demands and my overdue tasks at the foundation.

But it would all have to wait. I felt awful for not being able to spend more time with Thea and Charlie during their first week in New York. I just hoped that after a month of them living here, I'd be caught up at work and could dedicate the time to them that they deserved.

Having them waiting for me each night had forced me to

come to a realization.

It was time to reprioritize.

A teenager called our number over the loudspeaker and I went up to get our food. When I set Charlie's Happy Meal box in front of her, she tore into it, wasting no time before inhaling her food. Thea did the same and I followed suit.

"Well?" Thea asked before shoving three fries in her mouth.

"It's good. Not as good as David's Table, but the next time I want to take you there, we'll just go the two of us."

The smile on her face fell as she chewed.

All right. Forget that idea.

I'd taken many women to that restaurant over the years and each one had been thoroughly impressed by the food and atmosphere. But Thea wasn't like any woman I'd ever met, and if she wanted fast food over gourmet, then we'd come here on our date nights.

Charlie belched and slapped a hand over her mouth, then giggled. "Excuse me."

"Feeling better, peanut?"

She nodded. "My tummy was hungry."

"Now that we're back to normal," Thea set down her burger and gave Charlie a stern look, "I think you need to apologize to your dad. You weren't very nice when we were at his favorite restaurant."

Charlie's shoulders fell as she twirled a french fry in her ketchup. "Sorry, Daddy."

"It's o—" *Wait, what? Did she just call me Daddy?*

My eyes snapped to Thea, whose mouth was hanging open. Never had a word sounded so good. I'd always hoped that one day Charlie would want to call me Dad and she'd love me as much as I loved her. But I'd been prepared to wait years to get us to that place.

"I, um . . ." I paused to recover, then placed my hand on her knee. "It's okay. You don't have to apologize. I should have thought about it more before taking you there for dinner."

She peeked up from underneath her lashes.

"I like it when you call me Daddy, but you don't have to. Would you rather call me Logan?"

Say no, Charlie. Please, don't take it back.

She shook her head. "I want to call you Daddy."

Relief and pure happiness surged. I fought the urge to yank her out of that chair and crush her to my chest by eating another fry.

Oh, fuck it.

I flew out of my chair, sending it sliding backward a few feet. Then I scooped Charlie off her bench and hugged her close.

She didn't hesitate to wrap her arms around my neck.

Over her shoulder, Thea swiped her eyes dry.

"I love you, Charlie," I said into her ear.

I'd known I loved her the moment she pulled me into her fort. Or maybe the first day I'd seen her beautiful brown eyes as she'd taken a frog from my hands. I could barely remember my life before Charlie, and it was just weeks ago.

"I love you too," she whispered back.

I smiled. That was one of the Landry girls down, now I just had one to go.

"Are you all done eating?"

She nodded against my suit.

"Let's get you home."

Her legs around my waist cinched tight, so I wouldn't put her down. "Okay, Daddy."

twenty-one

THEA

ONE NIGHT LATER, I'D JUMPED FROM ONE END OF THE DINING spectrum to the other. Logan and I were at the fundraising gala, sitting in the middle of the nicest room I'd ever seen. It was as far from McDonald's as you could get.

There were no fluorescent lights here. The ballroom was lit with crystal chandeliers hanging from gold-trimmed ceilings. The gleaming floors, not littered with fallen fries, were made from Italian marble. And the tables were covered in silk linens. I wouldn't dare drop a blob of ketchup off my hand-painted plate.

"Would you like more champagne?" Logan asked, leaning over to speak in my ear.

"Yes, please." Champagne made me loose-lipped, so I normally avoided it, but since I didn't have much to say tonight, that wouldn't be a problem.

He signaled to a waiter, who brought over a tray of champagne in crystal flutes. With my new glass in place, Logan kissed my cheek, then turned to continue his conversation with the man sitting on his other side.

We were seated at an elegant round table with a tall floral arrangement in the center. The china had delicate floral patterns and was adorned with real gold. And there were enough utensils in front of me to make one of my bird's nests, maybe two.

I sipped my champagne, listening to the murmur of conversation.

We'd arrived a few hours ago, and I'd maybe said three sentences in all that time. *Nice to meet you* when I'd been introduced to a slew of people whose names I'd immediately forgotten. *Thank you* when I was complimented on my gown. *Yes, please* when I'd been offered a glass of champagne.

All through the cocktail hour, I'd forced a pleasant smile. My cheeks hurt by the time we sat down at our table and not in a good way, like when I'd been laughing for too long. After the dinner service started, I did my best to keep up with the conversation, but after thirty minutes of listening to name dropping and vacation plans to foreign countries I'd never see, I zoned out.

Logan hadn't noticed. He was currently in a deep discussion with three men on our side of the table. For an hour, they'd been discussing some change to a stock market regulation and how it would impact the foundation's investment strategy.

So here I was, silently drinking champagne and waiting for the next round of food to be delivered in hopes it would curb the major buzz I was working.

In this room full of people, smiling and laughing, I was alone.

It had been years since I'd felt this empty hole in my chest. The last time I'd been this lonely had been after Jackson had moved to Montana. But I knew this feeling well. It was the same one I'd had nearly every night of my childhood when I'd climbed into my tiny cot without anyone to tuck me in or wish me sweet dreams. The same feeling I'd had when another child in the orphanage would get adopted into a family and leave me behind.

By the time I'd turned seventeen, I'd been the only kid left in that home. Why I hadn't been sent to a foster home was still a mystery, but somehow, the orphanage had stayed open. It had just been me and the director living there, though I rarely saw her emerge from her apartment in the basement.

Hazel would come in for a few hours to make me meals. She'd spend time with me after school, helping me with homework, but eventually, she'd have to go home. Jackson could only stay until dark. So after they'd leave, it would just be me roaming the halls without anything to do but read. The director could afford electricity for the entire building but not a television to keep me entertained.

I'd finally escaped the loneliness in Lark Cove.

"You hate this, don't you?"

"Huh?" I turned to Nolan Fennessy, who was sitting on my other side. "Oh, no. Not at all," I lied. "I'm, uh . . . just taking it all in." I didn't want to confess to Logan's coworker that I'd rather be a hundred other places than in this ballroom.

He saw through my lie and grinned. "My wife hates coming to these too. She told me last year she'd approve of me finding a stand-in woman just so she could stay home in her yoga pants."

I smiled, the first real smile of the night. "I think your wife and I could be best friends."

"She accompanies me every once in a while, but normally I come with Logan. You stole my date."

"Sorry." I laughed. "You can have him back for the next one."

"Not sticking around?"

"No, I'm leaving after the weekend." I chased down a pang of guilt with another sip of champagne.

Leaving was the right thing to do, for all of us. Trying to fit square pegs into round holes never worked. But ever since I'd come to that realization yesterday, I'd had a miserable ache in my heart.

The ache twisted and tugged every time I tried to sort through my feelings. When it came time to end this, Logan would demand an explanation. For the life of me, I couldn't think of one that he wouldn't shred to pieces.

How did I tell him that I loved him, but I wouldn't uproot my life and fit it into his?

It didn't make sense in my head.

But it did in my heart.

I knew Logan couldn't give up everything here to move to Montana. I wouldn't ask him to. So for us to be together, I had to give.

It was tempting. All I had to do was change my address, but the idea of moving here made me sick. Yet so did the thought of leaving Logan.

"Where's Charlie tonight?" Nolan asked. "You didn't leave her with his family, did you?"

"Uh . . . no." I gave him a sideways glance. "She's at the penthouse with Piper. But now I'm even more nervous about meeting his parents. Thanks for that."

Nolan chuckled. "That's not what I meant. They're great people. But I'm sure Charlie will have a much better night with Piper. She loves kids and has been chomping at the bit to spend time with Logan's daughter. Charlie will have much more fun with Piper than she would at the Kendrick estate. It's, shall we say, stuffy."

Stuffy. As in rich. As in don't touch the valuables. I made a mental note to talk to Charlie in private before we went to the estate tomorrow. I didn't want her playing with anything that I couldn't afford to replace if broken.

"Ladies and gentlemen, if I could please have your attention." The emcee took the stage in the middle of the dance floor and began his spiel.

Logan had told me the fundraiser was for an organization dedicated to improving the quality of life for people below the poverty line. After ten minutes of the speaker's pitch, I'd had enough and it had just started.

On and on he droned, talking about how the poor people in the city, or "the unfortunate," desperately needed the donations from "New York's finest." The irony of my entire situation ruined my appetite. I didn't touch a bit of the *salmon sashimi with olive lemon-mustard emulsion*. When he began speaking about how there were people in the city going without phones or internet service, the "essentials," I nearly choked on my mango parfait.

"Puke," I muttered.

"What was that?" Logan asked, leaning in closer.

"Sorry." *Damn you, champagne.* "I meant to say that in my head."

Nolan must have heard me too because he chuckled. "You don't approve of the message?"

I scoffed. "You know what 'the unfortunate' need? Essentials. *Real* essentials. Enough food so they can eat three times a day, every day. They need enough quarters to go to the laundry mat every week. They need tampons, for Christ's sake. What they don't need are some rich people sitting in a ballroom feeling sorry for them because they don't have internet or cable TV."

I ended my rant on a huff, then looked up from the spoon I'd been clutching in my fist. All eyes around the table were on me.

"Thea." Logan put his hand on my knee.

Goddamn it. I knew this would happen. I knew I'd embarrass him. I didn't belong here and I had no clue how to act or what to say.

The sting of tears pricked my eyes, but I couldn't cry in front of these people.

"Excuse me," I whispered, setting down my spoon.

Before Logan could protest, I was out of my chair, walking as quickly as I could in my uncomfortable heels to the back of the ballroom. I slipped out the door, breathing a sigh of relief when the hallway was empty.

"Don't cry." I looked up at the ceiling and took a long breath. Then another. When the sting in my nose eased, I clicked down the hall toward the restroom.

I opened the door and hurried through the sitting room to the actual restroom. Then I picked the middle mirror and checked my face.

Despite the sick feeling in my stomach, at least I looked pretty.

Whoever my parents were, I owed them one bit of thanks. They'd given me thick hair and flawless skin. I didn't have to wear much makeup, usually just eyeliner and mascara. And my hair had a natural sheen most women couldn't pay for.

Logan had offered to bring in a stylist for me tonight, but I'd opted to get ready myself. Charlie had sat on the counter in his bathroom, watching as I'd carefully applied eyeshadow, blush and lipstick. Then I'd straightened my hair into shining panels that hung down my back.

And though I'd been in such a rush to pick this dress yesterday, it was gorgeous. The top had a simple, sleeveless cut with a crew neckline. It was covered with fine lace, giving it an elegant touch. Only the front had a strip of lace missing, running from the collar down my cleavage to right above my waist, making it sexy and a little badass.

The full-length skirt flowed when I walked and had a long slit up the front. There were even hidden pockets for my lip gloss. It was made by some designer who made gowns for actresses going to award shows. This poor dress wouldn't get much use, stuffed in the back of my closet in Lark Cove.

I didn't belong in this fancy dress or elegant bathroom. I might not be the right woman for Logan, but I was here for tonight. I was *his* for tonight.

And I owed him an apology.

I reapplied some lip gloss and fixed a misplaced strand of hair, then left the restroom. I opened the door to the hallway but stopped short.

Logan was standing on the opposite wall, as handsome as ever in his tuxedo. This man could make bowties sexy.

"Hi," I sighed. "I'm sorry for embarrassing you."

He pushed off the wall, meeting me in the middle of the hallway. He came right into my space and wrapped me in his arms. "Baby, I've told you this before. You could never embarrass me."

"Were you not there? Everyone at your table was looking at me funny."

"They were looking at you because you said what we were all thinking. This gala is the biggest hypocritical joke we've all been to in years."

"No fucking way." My voice echoed in the hall. "Sorry," I winced. "Too many champagnes mean too many f-bombs."

He chuckled. "Yes, fucking way. Just ask Nolan. These people aren't getting a dime from the Kendrick Foundation until they can prove it's being used for the right things."

"Like tampons," I blurted.

He laughed again and nodded. "Like tampons."

"Thank you." I fell back into his chest, holding him close. *God, I am going to miss him.* Every single day. "I'm going to miss you."

"Then stay."

"I can't."

He pulled me off his chest, framing my face with both hands. "Why?"

My eyes filled with tears. *Why?* I wasn't ready for that question yet. I hadn't figured out my answer. So I gave him the one I gave to Charlie when I didn't want to explain myself. "Just because."

His eyebrows came together as he held my face, studying my eyes. Then the creases in his forehead went away. Gone. Poof. The worry was replaced with Logan's signature look of confidence and determination. The same look he'd given me in my workshop when he'd asked me to come to New York and I'd said no.

"We'll talk about it again this weekend."

"Okay." My answer would still be the same, but maybe I'd at least have an explanation figured out by then.

"Come on." He let go of my face and held out a hand. "The speaker is done and I want to dance with the most beautiful woman in the world."

I wasn't going to miss him every single day, I'd miss him every single minute.

Hand in hand, we went back to the ballroom, where a live band had set up next to the dance floor.

I followed behind Logan as he weaved through the tables, nodding and saying hello as he passed clusters of people mingling. We'd almost made it to the dance floor when the ignorant speaker stepped in our path.

"Logan, so good to see you. Did you enjoy the presentation?"

"To be frank? No. I implore you to do some research before wasting my time or money for a table again." Without another word, Logan pushed past the speaker and led me to the dance floor.

I glanced over my shoulder to see the speaker rooted to his

spot, staring stunned at Logan's back. When I looked forward, I smiled. "Thanks for that."

Logan spun and swung me into his arms. "My pleasure."

We slowly swayed to the music for a few moments, settling into the mix of other couples dancing.

"Do you want to talk about why you have such a passion for tampons?"

I shook my head. "Let's just say I know exactly what it's like to be one of the unfortunate. Can we leave it at that?"

"Thea—"

"Please." I leaned back to meet his gaze. "Please, Logan. I don't want to talk about it tonight."

"Then when?" he asked.

"Later." Much, much later.

He spun me in a circle, pulling me close to whisper in my ear. "I hate that I don't know everything about you. I hate that I don't know who your parents were or how you grew up. I hate that I don't understand the relationship you have with Jackson. I hate that you don't trust me enough to share."

"Oh, Logan." I deflated into his chest. "It's not that I don't trust you. It's just the one topic I can't talk about tonight in this fancy room. I'm doing my best to keep it all together and pretend I belong in this ballroom with you. If we drudge up all the garbage, I'll never be able to pretend."

He stopped dancing. "You don't have to pretend. You do belong."

I gave him a sad smile, not wanting to argue. "I trust you. But let's leave my parents and childhood off the table."

"Okay," he agreed, moving to the music again. "Then how about Jackson? Why are you two so close?"

"We met in high school. His foster home was close to the place where I grew up. Neither of us had many friends or people we could rely on and I guess that just bonded us together. Since we didn't have a real family, we made one up ourselves. He's like a brother."

"Has it ever been more?"

I smiled against his tuxedo jacket. "Never. That kiss you saw was the first time he's ever kissed me anywhere other than the cheek. He loves me but not in a romantic way."

Logan's frame relaxed and he twirled us around. Had I known that my relationship with Jackson had caused him worry, I would have explained it all in more detail weeks ago, like he had with his ex, Emmeline.

"What about you?" I asked. "Should I be worried about seeing any of your exes here tonight?"

"After Emmeline, I saw a woman briefly but that ended months ago. I had a girlfriend in college who is now happily married to a good friend. But that's it. You're all caught up."

I rested my cheek against his chest. "Good. And since I went on the mother of all dry spells between our escapades, you're all caught up too."

"What?" He stopped moving. "Say that again."

"Say what again?"

"That part about a dry spell between our escapades."

"Oh." I blushed. This fancy ballroom probably wasn't the place to announce to Logan that I hadn't slept with anyone but him in the last six-something years. *Goddamn you, champagne.* "Well, there was you. Then I had Charlie and was kind of busy being a mom. Then there was you again."

"Damn it." His face softened and he lifted a hand to cup my cheek. "I wish I had come back to that hotel sooner."

I stood on my toes, brushing my lips to his without a reply.

A part of me wished that too, but the other was glad for how things had turned out. As much as I hated that he'd missed those years with Charlie, I couldn't regret leaving for Montana.

The band started a new song, this one faster than the one we'd been swaying to a moment ago, and a wave of panic hit me. I'd never danced like this before. The only dancing I'd done was at clubs or in my living room with Charlie. My high school hadn't organized formal dances because so few of the students could afford to rent tuxes or buy dresses.

"I don't know how to dance to this," I whispered.

"But I do." Logan pulled me closer. "Hold on to me and I'll take it from there. Don't let me go, Thea."

The passion in his voice and the intensity of his gaze nearly broke me.

Because his plea had nothing to do with dancing.

twenty-two

LOGAN

THEA WAS SHUTTING ME OUT AGAIN. THE GLASS DIVIDING US from the driver in the limo might as well have been between our seats.

She'd been acting off since last night. I was sure that something had happened yesterday, but I hadn't had a chance to ask because I'd been so distracted by Charlie calling me Daddy. But whatever it was, something had spooked Thea. The gala hadn't helped. She was more guarded now than she'd been in weeks.

But I wasn't letting her run away.

We rode back to the penthouse in silence, but my thumb never stopped caressing her knuckles. As we rode the elevator upstairs, I kept her firmly tucked into my side with my arm around her shoulders, not letting her go until we crossed the threshold of the penthouse.

"How was it?" Piper asked, getting up from the couch where she'd been reading.

"Nice," Thea said at the same time I muttered, "Ridiculous."

Thea looked up at me and grinned before turning back to Piper. "Okay. It was bad."

Piper shot me a smug look. "I knew it would be. The speaker is a douche. I told you not to go."

I sighed. "And I should have listened."

"He never listens to me, Thea." Piper shoved an iPad in her backpack. "You'd think he would have learned by now since we've worked together for five years. But he still thinks he's in charge."

I chuckled. "Now you're starting to sound like Nolan. Don't make me fire you."

"Ha! You wouldn't make it two days."

She was right about that. Piper handled everything for me at the foundation, and I'd be lost without her. She made it possible for me to be a lawyer and a philanthropist without completely burning myself out. And I made sure to pay her enough so she'd never be tempted to leave for a higher wage. Hell, she made more than all but two of the vice presidents, not that they'd ever know.

She might jest, but Piper was as down-to-earth as they got. She reminded me a bit of Thea that way. Piper and her husband were struggling at the moment, probably the reason she'd been so eager to watch Charlie tonight. She used every excuse these days not to go home. So if she needed evenings away to hang with my daughter, we'd let her babysit whenever she wanted.

"Charlie was a dream tonight," Piper told Thea as she shouldered her backpack, then whipped her chestnut hair into a topknot. "I love her so much. Come back soon so I can watch her again. I'll make sure this guy," she jerked a thumb my way, "plans something much better than a pretentious gala for you two."

"I, um . . ." Thea looked to her shoes, finding her fake smile. "Thank you. I'm so glad she was good and really appreciate you watching her."

Piper came over and hugged Thea, then gave me a mock salute. "Have a good weekend, boss."

Boss. "Jesus. Do you and Nolan sit around and practice

filling 'boss' with as much sarcasm as possible?"

She shrugged. "You'll never know."

I grinned. *That was a yes.* "I had the doorman call you a car. It should be waiting."

"Thanks, Logan. Bye, Thea." She waved and walked down the hall, letting herself out.

As the door closed, Thea's shoulders fell and she kicked off her shoes. "I'm just going to go check on Charlie."

I put a hand on the small of her back while the other loosened my bowtie. "I'll come too."

"I like Piper," Thea whispered as we ambled down the hall. "Nolan too."

"They're the best. Because of them, I can stay involved at the foundation."

Thea cracked open Charlie's door, peeking inside. Our daughter was sprawled out in her bed with her head and feet turned sideways from the pillows.

"Wild," I whispered. "Even in her sleep."

"She's always slept like that." Thea smiled as she carefully closed the door. "When she was three, she got in this bad habit of coming into my room at night. She'd stick her feet in my ribs, then completely pass out."

"I wish I could have seen that."

"Me too."

I kissed Thea on the forehead, then took her hand and led her to the stairs.

I wanted to know all about the years I'd missed with Charlie, and the years Thea had spent in the city. She'd surprised me at the gala tonight when she'd gotten so upset by that speaker. She'd spoken with so much passion, it had to have come from experience. How was I going to learn more about her if she wouldn't tell me? At this point, I was left to guess.

The life she'd lived hadn't been filled with luxury, that was obvious. But now I suspected it hadn't held much love either.

She'd never want for either again.

We reached the top of the stairs and I pulled her into my arms. "You look beautiful tonight."

"Thank you." She tugged at the lapels of my jacket. "You're not so bad yourself."

I kissed her nose, grazing my lips across her cheekbone to whisper in her ear. "I love this dress, but I think it would look nicer on the floor."

Her breath hitched. "Yeah?"

I nuzzled into her hair, drawing in a long breath. Then I latched my mouth onto her throat, giving the skin underneath her ear a hard suck. "Yeah."

There was a lot we needed to talk about. We had issues to hammer out and a future to plan. But right now, I didn't want to think about any of it. All I wanted was for Thea to know how much I loved her.

If I couldn't say it, I'd show her instead.

Without letting her go, I backed us into my room, dragging down the zipper on the back of her dress. With it free, I slipped it off her shoulders and let the front fall loose. The moment her perfect tits were free and under my palms, my cock was rock hard.

"What do you want?" I asked, kissing up and down her neck.

"You. Naked." Her hands gripped my lapels again, this time yanking them over my shoulders. Her needy breaths blew against my throat. Her fingers fumbled with a button on my shirt, but I trapped her hands.

"No, Thea." I held her gaze, letting her hands rest on my thundering heart. "What do you want?"

She stared at me for a long moment, letting the meaning

of my words echo in the room. When they sunk in—when she realized I wasn't talking about sex—a tear pooled in the corner of her eye. "The impossible."

Nothing was impossible.

Not for her.

Not anymore.

I swiped the tear with my thumb, then took her mouth, swallowing a cry that was part pain, part lust. Another tear fell, hitting my cheek, and I tore away from her mouth to kiss it away.

"Don't cry, baby," I whispered. "It's all going to be okay."

Once I got her and Charlie moved here for good and we were all officially Kendricks, there would be no more tears. She wouldn't have to dread the good-byes, because we'd never be apart again. Tomorrow, after we got through dinner with my parents, we'd talk and put all her fears to rest.

She nodded and sniffled, gripping my shirt by the collar. Then her sad eyes came to mine. "Make love to me, Logan. That's what I want. Give me something to remember."

She'd just slammed the door to her heart right in my face.

Why was she so quick to push me away? What about being here was so awful that she kept reminding me that she was leaving? Why wouldn't she *talk* to me?

I ran my hands up her bare back, tangling my fingers in her soft hair. I gripped it in my fist, tugging a bit so her head fell back. And then I slammed my mouth down on hers, pouring all of my frustration with this remarkable, bright and *infuriating* woman into our kiss.

Thea met my ferocity full force, pulling so hard on my shirt that a couple of buttons popped off. Her tongue dove into my mouth, dueling with mine as her fingers pulled to free my shirt from my slacks.

I stepped forward, pushing her farther into the room. With

every step toward the bed, her dress slid farther down her body until it was pooled at our feet. She stepped out of it, kicking it aside, as I toed off my shoes. Never once did I break contact with her mouth or let go of her hair.

The control I had over her body was just an illusion. We both knew exactly who was in charge tonight.

Beneath my open shirt, her fingertips skimmed up my abs. When they reached my pecs, she dug her nails in at the same time she slid her tongue from my mouth and nipped my bottom lip.

"Fuck," I hissed, breaking free from her lips. "You drive me crazy." Physically. Emotionally. She was the only person in the world who could wind me up this tight.

She smiled against my mouth. "What are you going to do about it?"

"This." One minute she was standing, the next I'd gripped her by the hips and tossed her on the bed.

She smiled as she bounced, her hair swaying behind her as she scooted toward the headboard.

"Get those panties off," I ordered as I stripped off my shirt. "Now."

She toyed with the hem, teasing me for a minute. But when I reached for the button on my pants and paused, daring her on, she wiggled them free and kicked them to the floor.

Seeing her wet pussy nearly dropped me to the floor. I swallowed hard, sucking in some air through my nostrils as I tried to get my dick under control.

Then I set the beast loose, shoving my pants and boxer briefs down to my ankles. When I stood, Thea's eyes were locked on my straining erection. Her tongue darted out to lick her bottom lip.

Fuck. I stepped up to the bed and shot out an arm,

grabbing her by the ankle. With a fast tug, I pulled her toward me as I knelt on the mattress, using my other knee to spread her legs wide. Then with my fist around my pulsing cock, I lined up at her entrance and thrust home.

Thea's back arched off the bed as she cried out, her moans echoing up to the rafters. I stayed rooted, my eyes squeezed shut tight so I wouldn't come. My hands dug into the blankets by Thea's face as I fought to get control of my body.

"Logan. Condom."

"One sec." I nodded, still not opening my eyes. Being bare inside Thea, having nothing between us, was so goddamn amazing, I couldn't give it up just yet.

She was the only woman who had ever had me raw. Not even Emmeline could claim that. It had only ever been Thea. Tonight, and the one time in the shower when we'd made Charlie. How the hell had I forgotten about this? I should have demanded Thea get on birth control two weeks ago.

"Birth control is priority one." I opened my eyes and slid out of her tight heat.

She whimpered at the loss, breathing hard as I reached for the nightstand to get a condom. I hated rolling it on, but I knew we weren't—she wasn't—ready for another kid yet. Maybe I could change her mind this weekend once we'd gotten everything else worked out.

Because having another baby and being there from day one this time was about the only thing I really wanted in my life, other than to make Thea and Charlie happy.

They were all that mattered.

I came back to the bed, this time joining with Thea slowly, inch by inch. I rocked my hips into hers, building her up until her legs were trembling around me. The entire time, I worshiped her skin, dropping soft kisses across her neck and chest.

"I'm—" Her gasp was followed by an explosion. Her inner walls squeezed me so hard, the control I'd been trying to maintain vanished.

The tightening in my spine and balls was like a vise, forcing me to let go and come as she moaned into my neck. I was breathing so hard as I recovered I didn't hear her moans turn to soft cries at first. Not until I felt a tear on my shoulder.

I leaned back, pushing the hair off her face. She turned her head into the blankets, trying to hide, but I tipped her chin toward me so she had to look at me. "Baby, what is it? These tears are killing me."

"Sorry. It's nothing." She shook her head and sniffled, bringing up a hand to wipe her face. "I'm just emotional and I had too much champagne."

"Come here." I wrapped one arm around her, holding her to my chest, as the other jerked down the blankets. Then I pulled out and lifted her farther into the bed. "Be right back."

I went to the bathroom and dealt with the condom, hurrying back to Thea's side. With her back to my chest, I inhaled the lavender in her hair as I held her close. "It's going to be okay."

She nodded, sniffling again. "I know."

Did she? Because there wasn't a hint of confidence in her voice.

She tried to roll away to her pillow, but my arms banded tighter. I never thought I'd miss her tiny bed at the cottage, but this week had proved me wrong. When we'd been in her bed, there had been no choice except for us to sleep cuddled together. But with the space of my massive king, we'd both drift in our sleep.

Not tonight. Tonight, I didn't want her going anywhere.

The way she snuggled backward, relaxing in my arms, I

thought she wanted that too.

Except when I woke up the next morning, Thea was gone.

I shot up in a panic, searching the bathroom and closet for her. Then I went downstairs, hoping she'd just gotten up early for coffee and breakfast. But when I didn't find her there, I searched every other room.

I finally found her, asleep in Charlie's bed. Charlie's feet were digging into her ribs and tears had dried on Thea's cheeks.

"Daddy?"

"Yeah, peanut?" I looked at Charlie in the rearview mirror, smiling just like I did every time she called me Daddy.

"Are you going to come to my first day of school?"

"I, uh . . ."

My shoulders sagged. How the hell did I answer this question? I hoped she'd be going to school here, and in that case, I'd be taking her to school with Thea. I'd already had Sean make arrangements to get her enrolled at a small, private school a few blocks from the penthouse.

But with the way Thea had acted last night and this morning, I wasn't as confident she'd say yes to my proposal as I had been a few days ago. Which meant there was a slim chance Charlie would have to start school in Lark Cove, then transfer once Thea and I worked everything out.

With school starting in two weeks, I couldn't swing another trip to Lark Cove right now. One of my newest clients was restructuring their business over the next month and I had to be in town to participate in the discussions.

Would I be able to take Charlie to school? Only if Thea said yes to moving and marrying me.

"Are you?" Charlie asked again.

"Honey," Thea turned in her seat, "we are going home on Monday. Remember? Logan has to stay here for work. But he'll come and visit us as soon as he can. Mommy and Gran will take you to your first day of school, just like we did last year."

"Oh." Charlie's disappointment darkened the car.

"I'm sorry," I told her. "I'd be there if I could."

Charlie nodded, then turned to look out her window.

I focused back on the road with a frown.

We were driving to my parents' estate on Long Island. It had taken us an hour to get out of the city, but once we'd hit the Nassau County line, traffic had thinned. My white Land Rover, which spent most of its time in the garage at the penthouse, was free to zoom over the highway on our way to Oyster Bay.

I reached across the console, taking Thea's hand in mine. She laced our fingers together but didn't look over. Her sunglasses remained pointed out her own side window.

"Mommy, we didn't get Uncle Jackson his meatballs."

"It's okay," Thea said to the glass. "We've got those other presents we bought for him and Gran."

"Meatballs?"

Thea sighed. "When we were kids, Jackson and I used to get these meatball sandwiches from a place in our neighborhood. I went to get some the other day but it didn't work out."

"Were they closed?"

Thea shook her head without further explanation.

"The lady was mean to Mommy."

My hand tightened over Thea's. "What lady?"

She shook her head. "Just someone I used to know. We used to be friends but had a falling out. I ran into her at Giovanni's."

Giovanni's. I made a mental note to check it out next week.

"Can we stop for a sec?" Thea pointed to a gas station ahead. "I'd like a water and to use the restroom."

"Sure." I let go of her hand, slowing to pull into the parking lot.

Thea pulled up her purse from between her feet and dug through it for her wallet. Before she got it out, I had my money clip out and a hundred between my fingers. "Here."

"Thanks." She took the money, giving me a small smile. "Would you guys like anything?"

"Snacks!" Charlie and I said in unison, making us all laugh.

"Okay. Water and snacks. Be right back."

She opened the door, setting her purse on the seat as she went inside. It fell open after she closed the door, spilling her phone on the leather.

The screen was lit with a new email. I dismissed it, but then did a double take when I made out the word *cunt.*

I grabbed the phone.

From: anonymous743
Subject: You're nothing but a filthy cunt.

What the fuck? Red coated my vision and I gripped the phone tight, stopping myself before I cracked the damn thing. Who would send that kind of email to Thea? Was it the first? Or had this been going on for a while?

Alice's face popped into my mind instantly. I could definitely see her doing something like this. Her maturity level was right on par with Sofia's and it wouldn't surprise me at all if Alice was behind this disgusting message.

I set down Thea's phone and pulled out my own, sending Sean a text.

Me: Someone is sending Thea threatening emails. Find out who. Yesterday.

He didn't make me wait. He never did.

Sean: On it.

When it came to my assistants, I hired the best there was. Just like Piper, there was no one as good as Sean. He managed almost every aspect of my personal life including purchases, travel and even my security protocols. As a former hacker who'd once lived in his mother's basement, he was now comfortable on the Upper West Side. Sean would have this asshole's information to me tonight.

A few years ago, a creep had been stalking Emmeline. Sean had tracked him down and arranged for him to get the message that she was completely off-limits. I'd been angry back then, pissed someone would want to stalk Emmeline. But having someone threaten Thea sent me into a blind rage. If not for Charlie in the back, I would have pounded my fists into the steering wheel.

I was still seething by the time Thea came back to the car. She came in with a smile, but it vanished after one look at my face.

"What?"

I tossed over her phone. All the color in her face drained away before she even opened it up.

"How long has that been going on?"

She looked at her lap. "A couple weeks. It's no big deal."

"He called you a c—" I stopped myself before I could cuss in front of Charlie. I took a calming breath, lowering my voice. "This is not okay. We're going to talk about this later."

"Fine." She nodded, her eyes turned down.

I backed out of the parking lot and pulled back onto the highway. As much as I wanted answers this instant, I had to wait. Before we talked about those emails and before I got to the bottom of why she was acting so strangely this week, we had to get through the afternoon and evening with my parents.

twenty-three

THEA

SHIT. *SHIT. FUCKING SHIT.*

The last thing I wanted was for Logan to know about those emails.

We had so many more important things to worry about than some asshole who wanted to send me messages. I was sure that in a few more days, they'd stop. And if they didn't, I'd tell Jackson. If he thought there was cause to worry, then I'd go to the sheriff. After all, it wasn't the first time a patron had called me names. I doubted it would be the last. There was always some drunk who thought cussing at a bartender was acceptable.

I dismissed the email so I could put on my game face. We needed to be all smiles and laughs today for Logan's family.

God, this is hard. Knowing good-bye was right around the corner was miserable. I dreaded it but wanted to get it over with all at the same time.

After Logan had fallen asleep last night, I'd fought hard not to cry again, but I'd lost the battle. So I'd escaped to Charlie's room, where I could cry into her pillow without worrying she'd wake up.

Logan hadn't been happy when he'd found me there this morning, but he hadn't been angry, just worried. He kept looking at me, checking on me and touching me. I'd give him small smiles, hoping to reassure him that I was fine.

We both knew I wasn't.

On top of it all, I was nervous for Charlie. She was meeting new grandparents today, and when I'd explained to her over breakfast we'd be spending the weekend with Logan's parents, she'd immediately gone quiet.

She'd barely muttered anything as we'd packed our things and said good-bye to the penthouse. The three of us were staying at the Kendrick estate this weekend, then Monday morning, Charlie and I were flying home.

"How much longer?" Charlie asked from her seat.

"Just right down this road," Logan said into the mirror. He smiled at her, then over at me, taking my hand in his.

At this point, every touch was torture. I craved them, but they stung. Still, I didn't let go of his fingers, forcing Logan to drive with one hand.

He turned off the highway and down a road that wound past gate after gate. People didn't get to just "pop in" around here. You made an appointment. You probably had to get a background check before they gave you a gate code to enter a property. Every home we passed got bigger and bigger until we reached the end of the road.

"Whoa." I was stealing Charlie's word as Logan turned down a private drive. "Is this it?"

"This is it." Logan nodded, letting go of my hand to roll down the window as he approached the gate. An oval plaque engraved with KENDRICK was in the center of the iron bars.

I looked over my shoulder to a wide-eyed Charlie. Her mouth fell open as we pulled through the gate and slowly made our way up an incline to the mansion.

The grounds were enormous. Green grass and manicured shrubs sprawled on both sides of the drive leading to the estate.

The cobblestone courtyard had enough room to fit at least ten cars, maybe more, even with the fountain in the center.

"Is this where you grew up?" I asked Logan.

"It sure is. We spent a lot of time in the city too, but this is where we lived most of the time and where I went to school."

I couldn't imagine being a child in this place. Like everything else about our lives, it was the polar opposite of the orphanage.

The gray stone exterior spoke to the home's age, but it had been meticulously well kept. The many windows were large and sparkling in the afternoon sun. Their rich, cream trim matched the ornately carved scallops along the roofline.

Logan parked and shut off the car. "Ready?"

No. I nodded anyway, unbuckling my seatbelt as he went to the backseat to help Charlie out. He took her hand, leading the way to the front door.

I smoothed down the front of my jeans, wishing I'd worn the dress I'd brought for dinner. Logan was in jeans too, but his were a dark wash. Mine were cuffed in a loose boyfriend cut. My white tennis shoes were new but totally inappropriate for a home that screamed *high heels only.* I straightened at the hem of my black cardigan, making sure it covered my white tee and that my bra wasn't showing through.

Charlie and I were wearing the same style today, except she had on her cap. I quickly swiped it off her head, earning a glare as I smoothed down her hair. "No hats inside."

That had never been a rule before.

As Logan approached the front wooden door, it opened for him. The butler bowed—an actual bow—and waved us inside. "Mr. Kendrick."

"Hello, Phil. How are you today?" Logan asked as we passed over the threshold.

"Very well, sir. Thank you. You are all set up in the

guesthouse this weekend."

"Thank you." Logan grinned down at Charlie, swinging her hand a bit. "Phil, I'd like you to meet my daughter, Charlie. And this is my girlfriend, Thea."

"Please to meet you, miss. Ma'am." Phil smiled at us both, bowing again. "If that will be all, sir, I'll take care of unpacking your belongings. Your parents have requested everyone meet in the east parlor for cocktails at five."

"Excellent. Thanks." Logan nodded and off Phil went, snapping his fingers as he walked out the door. From nowhere, two other butlers appeared, each wearing khaki pants and a white button-up shirt that matched Phil's.

I followed Logan and Charlie farther inside, taking in the estate with its tall ceilings, gleaming wood and marble floors. Everything was pristine, from the crystal chandelier to the gold-framed artwork, likely worth millions. It was the most elaborate home I'd ever seen.

"Would you like a quick tour?" Logan's voice echoed in the foyer.

Quick? Not likely. We could get lost in here. "Sure. That would be nice, wouldn't it, Charlie?"

She nodded, her eyes scanning all over as she tried to take it all in.

We spent the next hour walking through the house where it seemed there were two of everything, formal and informal. Dining room. Sitting room. Parlors. Guest rooms. Bathrooms. Ten minutes into the tour and I was completely turned around. And the entire time, we didn't see a single person.

Finally, after winding our way back to the main floor, Logan led us outside to a back patio. Right in its center was an enormous pool complete with a diving board, attached hot tub and mosaic mermaid tiled into the bottom.

"Mommy!" Charlie ran to the edge of the pool. "Can we go swimming?"

"Maybe tomorrow. We have to get ready for dinner tonight."

"Oh." She frowned, probably remembering that dinner meant another torturous dress. She shuffled back to Logan's side just as a woman rushed out of the pool house, waving.

"Logan!" Her dark hair was tied up in a bun, much like mine, and I was relieved to see she was wearing frayed denim shorts and a tank top. Without an introduction, I knew this was Logan's sister.

Just like I'd seen in the family picture at the penthouse, the resemblance between Charlie and Aubrey was even more uncanny in person. They had the same hair. The same nose. Even the same tilt of their upper lip.

"Hi, Aubrey." Logan smiled and kissed her on the cheek. "Good to see you. Meet Charlie and Thea."

Aubrey smiled at me first, then bent in front of Charlie and held out her hand. "Hi, Charlie. I'm your auntie Aubrey. Your dad has told me so much about you."

Logan nudged Charlie and she returned Aubrey's shake hesitantly before hiding behind his leg.

"We'll get to know each other one of these days soon." Aubrey winked at her, then stood again. This time she came right into my space for a tight hug. "Welcome. I'm so glad you're both here."

"Um, me too." I hugged her back, unsure what else to do. I'd been prepared for a thorough inspection, so her friendly gestures were taking me off guard. If all of Logan's family was like this, I had nothing to fear for the weekend.

"Well, I hate to say hello and run." Aubrey glanced at her delicate gold watch. "But if I'm going to be ready for cocktail hour, I'd better get going. I need to change and return a couple of phone calls."

"We should probably do the same." Logan kissed his sister's cheek once more before she disappeared inside the house. "Come on."

He took Charlie and I each by a hand to lead us through a garden trail. At the edge of the garden, the path opened up to a huge lawn that stretched to a guesthouse set in a grove of trees at the edge of the estate.

"Is that where we're staying?" Charlie asked, wiggling free of his grip to run on the grass.

"Yeah." He let go of my hand and put his arm around my shoulder. "That is our spot for the weekend."

I leaned in close, tucking my hand into the back pocket of his jeans. "This place is incredible."

"It's over the top but that's Mom."

It was over the top but still beautiful. The guesthouse ahead matched the main house, but it was much smaller and less ostentatious. It even had a porch swing by the front door. The house resembled something you might see in the wealthier neighborhoods of Lark Cove.

We walked along a paved path toward the guesthouse as Charlie ran ahead in the grass. She was making a beeline for the trees.

"Charlie!" I shouted. "Don't get too dirty!"

"I won't!" she called back over her shoulder.

"She totally will."

Logan chuckled. "We've got time to clean her up." He led me to the porch and toward the swing. "Come sit with me. We can let Charlie play for a little while."

"Okay." I sank into the wooden seat by his side, letting him gently rock us back and forth. It was cooler today, so I leaned in close.

"We need to talk."

I smiled. "You're supposed to say that and then hand me a tequila shot. Remember?"

"Sorry. I'm out of tequila at the moment." He sighed. "Why didn't you tell me about the emails? Or Giovanni's?"

I shrugged. "Neither is that big of a deal. I'm used to taking shit from people and letting it roll off."

"No, not anymore. You don't take shit from anyone."

"I work at a bar, gorgeous." I patted his stomach with my free hand. "It's going to happen."

"Those emails are serious, Thea. We need to find out who is sending them. I won't allow you to go back there if you're in danger. You'll have to stay here."

"Hold on." I sat up straight, my temper rising. Those emails were not going to be his excuse to make me stay in New York. "Let's not make this a bigger deal than it is, okay? So some asshole calls me a name or two. So some bitch thinks it's funny to write *whore* on a napkin at the bar. It's happened before, it will happen again. But just like always, it will blow over. I'm not in danger in Lark Cove. It's my home, and I am going back."

His jaw clenched. "What. Napkin?"

Shit. I hadn't meant to let that slip in there. "It's nothing. Totally unrelated."

At least, I hoped it was. There wasn't someone in Lark Cove who could be doing all this, was there? I dismissed it immediately. I knew Lark Cove. I knew the people. This was not coming from someone local.

"Sticking your head in the sand—"

"Is not what I'm doing. If it keeps up, I'll talk to the sheriff. Okay? But I'm sure they'll stop and I don't want to fight. Just let it go." I stood off the porch swing, not wanting to deal with an overprotective Logan. "I'm going to go get ready for dinner."

But before I could retreat inside, he grabbed my hand.

"If anything ever happened to you or Charlie, I'd be destroyed."

My anger evaporated. I stepped between his legs and put my hands on his face. "It's just been one note from someone immature enough to think a nasty napkin was funny and a couple of mean emails to the bar's account. I'm sure it's just a guy I kicked out or something, and this is his way of getting revenge. Logan, nothing is going to happen to us."

He covered one of my hands with his, turning it to kiss my palm. "You don't have any idea what you mean to me, do you?"

Maybe I don't.

But I knew how much I loved him. It was enough to know that if we forced this—if I laid down an ultimatum for him to move or vice versa—we'd both end up miserable.

"I better get ready." I tried to pull my hand away, but he kept it pinned, holding my gaze for a few heartbeats, until finally letting me go.

"I'll bring Charlie in soon," he said.

I nodded, turning before he could see my quivering chin.

With blurry eyes, I wandered through the guesthouse until I found the bedroom where Phil had brought our luggage. Alone and safe from being overheard, I collapsed on the bed, ruining the perfectly smoothed cream quilt. I dropped my head into my hands and let my shoulders fall.

Was I making a mistake? No. Down to my bones, I knew going home was the right decision. Because unlike fairy tales, there was more to real happiness than just being with someone you loved.

Loving yourself was just as important. So was finding a place where your soul was at peace.

I let myself be sad for a few minutes, giving in to a few tears that ruined the makeup I'd applied this morning. Then I pushed off the bed and dragged my suitcase into the adjoining bathroom to get ready for dinner with Logan's parents.

I'd just finished zipping up my dress when Logan knocked on the door. "Can I come in?"

"Sure." I flipped the lock and opened it for him.

"I just—" He stopped short, letting his eyes rake up and down my body. Then he stepped closer, resting his hands on my hips. "You're beautiful."

"Thanks." I ducked my head, having no confidence that I'd bought the right dress.

It was a simple green shift, nicer than anything I owned at home. And while I appreciated Logan's compliment, his family might not be as quick to approve.

"You look nice too," I said, touching a button on his shirt.

He'd pulled on black slacks and an ivory button-up. His newly polished wingtips matched his camel belt.

I hated this. *Hated.* I hadn't hurt him yet, but I hated that it was coming. This handsome, charming and generous man deserved so much more than the heartache I'd leave him with come Monday.

"Where's Charlie?" I asked, swallowing down the urge to cry again.

"I told her to get dressed, but she'll probably need some help."

"Okay." I stood on my toes for a soft brush of our lips just as Charlie's frustrated scream carried down the hallway.

I stepped past Logan, rushing to her room two doors down. "Hey. What's the matter?"

"I don't want to wear this dress." She balled up the light blue dress we'd bought and threw it on the floor. "Why can't I wear my jeans?"

"Sorry, honey." I went to her side, picking up the dress. "We're all going to dress up for dinner tonight."

"Don't you like dresses, peanut?" Logan asked, leaning against her bedroom's doorframe.

She crossed her arms over her chest. "No."

"Oh." He came further into the room and sat on her bed. "I didn't know that. Don't girls usually like dresses?"

When she glared at him, I couldn't help but laugh.

"Not this girl." I took Charlie's chin. "But you can make it through one more dinner in a dress."

She turned her glare on me but stripped off her T-shirt.

I slipped the dress over her head after she tugged off her jeans. Then I went to her suitcase and found her ballet flats. "Put these on and then let's comb your hair."

Twenty minutes later, her hair was tamed under a thin headband and we were all back at the mansion.

We followed Logan down a series of hallways until we reached a parlor filled with people.

Elegant people.

Aubrey was in the back corner. Her red dress was floor-length and nearly as fancy as the one I'd worn to the gala. Next to her was an older man who I guessed was Logan's father. He was wearing a suit jacket and tie, drinking what was probably Macallan.

"Logan, dear. You're finally here." A woman stood from a wingback chair in the corner, crossing the room in a teal lace dress and a champagne flute in her hand. Her brown hair was pulled back into a fancy twist, revealing strings of aqua jewels dangling from each ear. She kissed Logan on each cheek, then turned to me, her smile cooling as she looked me up and down.

What I wouldn't give to hide behind Logan.

But I couldn't because my daughter had already taken up

that spot.

"Thea, this is my mother, Lillian."

"Nice to meet you." I smiled. "You have a beautiful home."

"It is." She nodded, then peered around Logan to get a glimpse of Charlie.

"Please come and say hello." I touched her shoulder, but she didn't budge. *Come on, kid. Not tonight.*

"She's just shy." Logan laughed it off and stepped to the side, forcing Charlie into the open. Then he dropped to a knee at her side. "Charlie, this is my mom, Lillian."

Charlie's brown eyes tipped up slightly to take in her grandmother.

"Hello, Charlotte." Lillian didn't spare Charlie more than a glance before looking over her shoulder to her husband as he approached.

Charlie cringed at her full name, but with Lillian backing away a few steps, I didn't correct her.

"Hello, son." Logan's father held out his hand as Logan stood. "Thea. Welcome. I'm Thomas."

"Thank you for having us." I shook his hand as he gave me the same cautious inspection as his wife.

"This must be Charlotte?" He gave her a small smile.

"It's Charlie," Logan and I corrected at the same time.

"Right. Well, come on in." Thomas gestured for us all to join him at the small bar at the back of the room.

"Hi, again." Aubrey appeared at my side, giving me a reassuring smile, then winking at Charlie.

With the hand not holding Logan's, Charlie actually waved back.

We followed Thomas to the back of the room where two other women were standing by the bar. One I recognized as Sofia from Logan's family photo. She was wearing a strapless navy gown, just as formal as Aubrey's, and much like her sister, she was beautiful. She didn't look as much like Charlie, especially with all the makeup and her long hair dyed black, but the family resemblance was still there.

I had no clue who the other guest was, but Logan knew her. His jaw ticked and he shot Sofia an angry glare as we reached the bar.

"Sofia, what do you think you're doing?" he snapped.

"What do you mean? I'm just standing here talking to Alice. We're allowed to bring friends here, aren't we?"

Alice pushed away from the bar at the mention of her name, strutting right up to Logan in a pink minidress and six-inch sequined heels. "Hey, stranger."

The way she purred made me want to vomit. I had no idea who she was, but by the sultry gleam in her eye, she was quite familiar with Logan. Could this be the woman he'd seen briefly after Emmeline? It had to be. Clearly, Alice hadn't gotten the message that they were over.

"Alice," he clipped. "Meet Thea, my girlfriend. And my daughter, Charlie." He gave Alice a tight smile before pushing past her to the bar.

"What can I get for you?" Thomas asked, taking up post behind the bar.

"She should make the drinks," Alice snickered, returning to her place next to Sofia. "She's the bartender."

Ohh-kay. I'd never heard my occupation said with such condemnation.

As she and Sofia giggled like eighth graders, I looked up at Logan.

"Alice," he warned.

"What?" She pretended to be clueless. "Isn't she a bartender? That's what Sofia said. I was just thinking if she knows how to make good drinks, we should let her."

"Don't—"

"No, it's fine." I cut Logan off and gave both Alice and Sofia a sugar-sweet smile. "What do you like?"

Logan tried to grab my hand, but he was too slow. I made my way around the bar and stood at Thomas's side.

"A cosmopolitan." Alice smirked. "You know what that is, right?"

"Of course." I was going to make this bitch the best cosmo she'd ever had in her life.

"Thea, put that glass down."

I shot Logan a shut-up look and went about making the cocktail. "Aubrey? Sofia? Would you like one?"

"Sure. That's so sweet of you." Aubrey came behind the bar, making her allegiance clear. "Dad does his best, but he's never mastered the cosmo. Sorry, Dad."

Thomas chuckled. "I'm better at making Logan drinks than I ever was you girls."

It took me no time to fill three martini glasses, then pour a Macallan for Logan. As I handed him a tumbler, I smiled at his mother. "Mrs. Kendrick? More champagne?"

"No." She raised her champagne flute to her lips, finishing the glass.

I looked down at Charlie and smiled. She knew something was wrong, but it was too big for her to comprehend. "Want a Jackson Special?"

"Yeah." She grinned and left Logan's side to come behind the bar.

I picked her up to sit on the edge as I made her the mocktail her Uncle Jackson had invented when she was four. It was basically a Shirley Temple but he'd splash in some orange juice and double the cherries.

"Both hands. Be extra careful not to spill." I set her down and handed her the glass.

The cream carpets wouldn't recover from a Jackson Special, at least not without a lot of trouble. Since I knew Lillian didn't do the cleaning, I didn't want to cause any hassle for their staff.

"I'll make yours." Logan came behind the bar, setting down his tumbler and practically knocking me out of the way.

Meanwhile, Alice and Sofia had retreated back a few feet to whisper to one another, probably about me.

"What would you like?" Logan asked.

"Vodka and soda with a twist, please."

After all, vodka was for the particularly bad nights.

twenty-four

THEA

THE COCKTAIL HOUR WAS THE LONGEST HOUR OF MY LIFE.

As Charlie and I huddled together, sipping our drinks, conversation with the Kendricks carried on as if we weren't here. I flip-flopped between listening to the business conversations between Aubrey, Logan and Thomas, then to Alice and Sofia gossiping about their friends. Meanwhile, Lillian stood quietly, watching me with a careful eye.

Charlie had traded Logan's legs for mine, leaning against me as she kept her eyes on the floor. I hated that she was so uncomfortable, and I was pissed that her grandparents hadn't tried at all to get to know her. It made my own misery even more difficult to bear.

"Am I late?" The conversation stopped as an elderly woman waltzed into the parlor, then answered her own question. "Of course not. Granny is never late. You're all early."

She crossed the room wearing cream slacks and a matching sweater. She was dripping in gold and diamonds, but the fact that she wasn't in an evening gown made me feel much more comfortable about my own attire.

She paid no attention to anyone other than Charlie as she came our way with a warm smile. Her eyes flickered to me briefly but went right back to my daughter as she bent at the waist and held out a hand.

"You must be my most special great-granddaughter, Charlie. My name is Joan, but everyone calls me Granny."

Charlie looked past her to Logan, who gave her a smile and nod. With a hesitant step, she moved closer to Joan to return the handshake.

"Now." Joan stood up, not letting go of Charlie's hand as she walked toward the door. "You're going to want to sit with me at dinner. The cook knows to skip the vegetables on my plate, give me twice the potatoes and three times the dessert. I requested his special french fries tonight so we can pig out."

When Charlie giggled, I let out a huge sigh.

Joan had the same presence as Logan and his father did. They shared an air of confidence and command. But Joan's was warmer. And she still hadn't acknowledged anyone else in her family because she was so focused on my daughter.

Logan chuckled as he came to my side, placing his hand on the small of my back as we left the parlor. "Watch out. Granny might try and kidnap her."

"I don't think Charlie would mind."

Ahead of us, Granny was hunched to the side, listening as Charlie told her about something, most likely her fort.

I glanced over my shoulder to see Logan's parents behind us. Lillian and Thomas were both watching me. Behind them, Aubrey was rolling her eyes at Alice and Sofia, who were *still* giggling.

"I'm sorry," Logan whispered as we walked. "I had no idea Alice would be here."

"Ex-girlfriend?"

"She was never my girlfriend, just a mistake from months ago. But we dated and she's become friends with Sofia. I'm sorry."

I shrugged. "It's fine. Let's just get through dinner." Then we could escape back to the guesthouse and hide.

We all entered the dining room and took our seats. Charlie and Joan were talking about soccer. Thomas was engrossed with his phone, occasionally asking Aubrey if she'd seen this or that email. And the rest of us sat quietly and ate the first course, a simple salad.

"So Thea," Aubrey said from her seat across the table as the main course was served. "Logan says you're a professional artist."

I shook my head and swallowed my own fry. "No. It's just a hobby."

"She's incredible." Logan leaned past me to look at Joan. "I'll send you some pictures of her work. I think you'd like some things for your collection."

"Pass those on to me too." Aubrey smiled at me. "What style of art do you do? Impressionism? Contemporary? Realism?"

"Um, modern, I guess?" I had no clue how to classify my art. Was trash a style?

"Modern!" Aubrey cheered. "Oh, I love modern. Tell me about your process."

I shoved a bite in my mouth, chewing to buy myself some time. Aubrey meant well, but her questions made me feel even more like an imposter. She probably thought I was some kind of starving artist, forced to work at a bar until my art career bloomed. In reality, I loved my job at the bar and had no desire to become a full-time artist.

"Mommy, can I have some ketchup?"

"Sure, honey." I scrambled for the glass bottle, hoping it would be a segue into a conversation as far away from my garbage art as possible.

Luckily, by the time I plopped a blob onto Charlie's plate,

Thomas had stolen Aubrey's attention again to discuss something about work.

"Logan, have you given any thought to enrolling Charlotte at Rotherchild Academy?" Lillian asked from the foot of the table.

"It's Charlie," Logan and I both corrected in unison. "And no, Mom. I haven't thought about Rothchild. She's not going to school all the way out here."

"Then what about Fairlane?" Lillian asked. "It's closer to the penthouse if you'll be staying in the city."

"We'll see," he said. "Let's talk about it later."

I gaped at Logan. Had he actually considered putting Charlie in some New York academy after I'd specifically told him I wanted her to go to school in Montana?

"Charlie goes to school *in Lark Cove*," I announced. "She won't be going to any academy."

Logan ran a hand through his hair and turned in his seat. "That's not what I meant."

I threw his words right back in his face. "Let's talk about it later."

"Charlotte is a lovely name." Lillian forked a piece of roast tenderloin, cutting it into a delicate bite. "Don't you think, Sofia?"

"Lovely," Sofia agreed. "Much more fitting for the family than Charlie."

Lillian nodded. "I'd really love to call her Charlotte. Would that be all right?"

I looked down at Charlie to see her frown.

Obviously, I loved the name Charlotte. I'd picked it out because it had sounded classy, like something Logan's daughter would be named. It was a name I would have picked for myself. So I'd been upset the day Charlie had come home from camp and declared she was no longer Charlotte.

But my frustration hadn't lasted long. Hazel had told me about a boy who'd come to the camp. His name was Ray, he had muscular dystrophy, and my little girl had bonded with him instantly. Ray was confined to a wheelchair and since he couldn't get down and play in the dirt, Charlie had brought the dirt to him. She'd found him sticks and rocks and pinecones. From what Hazel had said, that boy had had an incredible camp experience simply because of my daughter.

Ray had nicknamed her Charlie.

So if that name was special to her, then she could go by it whenever she wanted. And I'd be happy to enforce it with Logan's mother.

"I'm sorry, Lillian. No. Charlie prefers her nickname and she's old enough to make that decision."

Lillian's eyes went wide, surprised that I'd deny her. She opened her mouth to protest, but before she could, Logan intervened. "Enough, Mom. It's Charlie. End of discussion."

"Shall we change the subject?" Joan offered. "Thea, remind me what you do in Montana."

"I manage a local bar and restaurant."

God, just saying it out loud sounded pathetic. How was it that in one dinner, these people had taken away something I'd always been proud of?

Well, forget that. I wasn't going to be ashamed that I made a living serving drinks. The waiters coming in and out of the dining room tonight had nothing to be ashamed of and neither did I.

"The bar has been in my family for years."

"Your family?" Thomas asked, tuning into the conversation. "What family?"

My head whipped to his end of the table. His expression

was knotted in confusion—Thomas knew I didn't have family. Because he'd looked into me. He probably knew more about my heritage than I did.

Did Logan? Had he had one of his assistants dig into my past too? He'd been so patient and understanding, letting me dodge the subject of my childhood. But maybe that was because he'd already learned everything there was to know.

I couldn't confront him about it now, not with his father's question hanging in the air.

What family?

"*My* family." Hazel and Jackson might not share my DNA, but they were my family.

"So you run a bar." Alice polished off her third glass of wine. The waiters had been refilling it constantly. "No wonder you jumped all over the chance to trap Logan."

"Excuse me?"

"Alice," Logan shot across the table, "one more word and I'll have you escorted out."

Sofia shushed her, scooting her water glass closer, but even Logan's threat didn't stop her loose tongue.

"Oh, Logan. Don't you see this is all just a trick? She's obviously a gold digger. Are you sure this kid is even yours? I mean, look at her." She flung out a hand, nearly knocking over her water as she snickered. "The least you could do is cut her hair if you wanted to pass her off as his kid. She's like a wild little animal."

Bitch.

Charlie's entire body flinched and I instantly took her hand.

The waves of anger coming off Logan crashed into my shoulder. "Get her out of my sight."

From nowhere, Phil the butler appeared along with one of his helpers. It took them all of twenty seconds to hoist drunk Alice out of her seat and away from the dining room. Her protests echoed down the hall for a moment until they stopped with the sound of a slammed door.

"What were you thinking, inviting her here?" Logan snapped at Sofia. "Why would you do that?"

"I just wanted to have a friend over." Sofia huffed. "This is my house too."

"Your taste in friends is worse than it is in husbands."

Sofia gasped. "Alice had a point. How do you know she's not just out for our money?"

The look on Sofia's face was full of regret as the words filled the room, but it was too late. She'd said them and Logan was not going to be forgiving.

I *almost* felt bad for her.

The glare Logan sent his sister gave me chills. "Say one more word and I'll revoke your ability to withdraw from your trust fund. Maybe if you went with a little less from now on, you'd be more respectful of the people in this room."

"What?" Sofia screamed, shooting up from her chair, teetering to the side from her own cosmo buzz. "You can't do that! Dad is in charge of the trust funds."

"Not anymore."

She held his gaze, her face paling when he didn't falter. She spun to Thomas. "Daddy?"

Thomas frowned, but before he could intervene, Aubrey spoke up. "Is this true?" she asked, looking just as stunned as Sofia.

Thomas nodded, his serious demeanor not cracking a bit. "Logan will be taking over some of the family responsibilities. Overseeing the trust funds is part of that. Until your funds are released, he'll be approving your withdrawals."

Or not approving their withdrawals.

"But I don't get my money for another three years!" Sofia

shrieked, now looking to her mother for help. "Mom?"

Lillian's mouth was slightly open. "Logan, you can't be serious."

He didn't respond to his mom. He just kept glaring at Sofia.

"Why are we just learning about this?" Aubrey asked Thomas. "I work with you every day, but you couldn't bother telling me that my brother is now in charge of my personal finances?"

"Don't be dramatic, Aubrey." Thomas waved her off. "We transferred it over just last week. Besides, you haven't taken a disbursement in years. We all know you're living off your salary. Or are you saying that I'm not paying you enough?"

"That's not the point."

"Then what is the point?" he fired back. "This was a decision that I made, and I don't require your approval. Don't forget your place."

"My place? I thought I was your daughter and colleague but apparently I'm just another employee." Aubrey shot out of her chair and started yelling at her father about all the work she put into their company. Meanwhile, Sofia ran to Lillian's side, sobbing as she cursed at Logan.

The room was chaos. Even the waitstaff had disappeared.

This was no place for my daughter.

I kept Charlie's hand and stood from my chair. Logan grabbed for me, but I slid free. With a nod to Joan as she mouthed, *Sorry*, I took my daughter straight out of the room.

We wasted no time escaping the dining room or the house. I opened the first door that led to the patio, breathing in the freedom of the night air.

I swung Charlie's hand at my side as we walked down the pathway to the guesthouse. "That wasn't much fun, was it?"

"No." She scuffled her feet. "They didn't like me."

When I heard her sniffle, I stopped and bent in front of her, catching a tear with my thumb, holding back tears of my own.

"I love you, Charlie. Just the way you are. Who cares what those mean people think?"

She sniffled, wiping her nose with the back of her free hand. "Do I have to cut my hair?"

I pulled out her headband, setting her brown strands free. There was *nothing* wrong with her hair. It was thick and soft and hung long down her back. Millions of little girls would love to have her hair.

"Of course not."

"Good," she whispered. "Can we go home now, Mommy?"

"Pretty soon. We're almost done with this place." I stood back up and kicked off my nude heels. "Let's forget about dinner and have fun. Take off your shoes."

"Why?" she asked as she kicked them off.

"Because we're going to have a race. Guess what I saw in the freezer earlier when I was poking around?"

She handed me her shoes. "What?"

"Ice cream. The first person back to the house gets to pick the flavor."

Without a moment's hesitation, she shot off the path, running as fast as she could through the grass. I laughed and did the same. She was giggling as she ran, looking over her shoulder to make sure I wasn't too close.

Her precious smile lit up her face.

Logan had asked me what I wanted last night. It was simple: a happy child.

I loved that Charlie was wild. I loved that she ran free. New York and Logan's family might kill her untamed spirit. I couldn't risk her suffocating here.

So I was taking her home.

twenty-five

LOGAN

SITTING AT THE DINING ROOM TABLE, I'D NEVER BEEN SO disappointed in my family. This dinner seemed more like a nightmare than reality. I'd wanted to follow Thea and Charlie out the door, but there were things to be dealt with here first.

Sofia had finally calmed down after her outburst. She was sitting back in her chair, sniffling like a toddler in timeout. Aubrey was fuming in her seat, throwing glares at Dad. Clearly, things at Kendrick Enterprises were not going as smoothly as I'd thought given Aubrey's overreaction. I'd have to discuss it with her later, but for now, I needed to right things for Thea and Charlie.

"What is wrong with you?" I asked the room. "How could you treat them that way? That is my child and the woman I'm going to marry."

"Marry?" Mom asked. "You can't be serious. You hardly know her, Logan. She's—"

"She's what?" I cut her off. "Kind. Talented. Loving. Beautiful. Are those not desirable traits these days?"

"That's not what I meant." Mom sighed. "She's . . . she's come out of nowhere. How can we be sure she isn't trying to manipulate you?"

Granny scoffed. "Please, Lillian. Thea isn't trying to

manipulate anyone. You're just being paranoid."

"I'm just looking out for my son," Mom told her. "And I have a right to be paranoid. Let's be honest here. My children don't have the best taste in romantic partners."

We all looked at Sofia, who sank deeper into her seat.

"This entire thing is suspicious," Mom said. "You went to Montana for a business meeting and found a long-lost child. Then she refused to give you a paternity test—"

"No, *I* refused."

"Because she's convinced you that the girl is yours. You've obviously fallen in love with them both, but Logan, that's the problem. Love has made you blind. How do we know that this all isn't a trap if she won't give you proof that Charlotte is your child?"

"Charlie." I fisted my hands on the table, trying to keep my cool. "Her name is Charlie. And she is, without a doubt, my child. I won't hear another thing about it. Understand? *Do not* mention the words 'paternity test' to me ever again."

"But—"

"Logan," Dad stopped Mom's rebuttal, "your mother has a point."

"Does she?" I clipped. "Because to me, it seems like Thea and Charlie had to pay the price tonight for Sofia's poor choice in husbands."

"We're just—"

"Looking out for me?" I finished Dad's sentence. "I don't need you to look out for me. What I do need is for you to be supportive of the choices I make, right or wrong. I need you to embrace my daughter and welcome her into this family, because whether or not you want to accept it, she is a part of this family. Thea will be too."

I stood from the table. "Now if you'll excuse me. I need

to go find my daughter. She deserves an explanation for dinner, though I'm not quite sure how to explain to a six-year-old that her grandparents don't like her because they think her mother's a gold digger."

"Logan, I . . ." Mom's shoulders drooped.

Her actions stemmed from love. I knew that. But it didn't change the fact that she'd crossed the line tonight.

"Charlie's not a pawn in some manipulative game, Mom. She's a little girl. *My* little girl. And she's your granddaughter. Maybe tomorrow you could try not to be so cold and indifferent?"

Her face paled as she nodded.

"Good night." I tossed my napkin on my unfinished meal, then I turned for the door and marched down the hall. I only made it a few feet before Dad called my name.

"Logan, we need to talk."

"Not tonight."

"Just give me five minutes before you run off. Please."

I sighed and turned, following him down a few doors to his office. As much as I wanted to get the hell out of this house, I needed to get this over with and hear whatever he had to say.

We entered the office and Dad went straight for his mahogany desk. This was the one room in the house that Mom wasn't allowed to redecorate every few years, so it was the same as it had been when I was a kid.

There were dark bookshelves on every wall. A liquor cart sat in the corner. His desk rested on a Persian rug in the middle of the room. A leather couch faced a gas fireplace. The smell of his last Cuban cigar lingered in the air. Every time I walked into his office, it brought back memories of me doing my homework on the couch while he worked every evening.

Dad had always worked, and until tonight, I hadn't thought

anything of it. As kids, if we'd wanted to spend time with him, it was in this room.

Was that how Charlie had felt this last week? I'd brought her and Thea here for a vacation but had basically abandoned them in favor of work. Did they feel like second place to my job?

Shit. Was I becoming my father? I loved the man. I admired him. But he wasn't the type of dad to coach soccer games, read bedtime stories or play in forts. If I wanted all of that with Charlie, things had to change.

I had to cut back at work.

"I need to check on Thea and Charlie," I told him.

"This won't take long." He slid a file folder to the edge of his desk, then ran a hand through his hair. It was a habit I'd also picked up from him long ago. Granny had always told me that when I did it, I looked just like Dad. "Read that."

I picked it up, opening it to a large photo of Thea working at the bar. *What the hell?* "Where did you get this?"

"I hired an investigator to look into Thea."

"You're kidding me." The corner of the cover's folder crumpled in my fist. "Why? Isn't it enough that I trust her?"

"Logan, be reasonable. Your mother wasn't entirely wrong earlier. You don't know this woman."

"But you do?" I held up the file. "I'm not looking at this." I tossed the folder on the desk. I trusted Thea to tell me about her past when she was ready.

"Then I'll tell you what it says." I turned to leave, but his words stopped me. "She was dumped as a newborn. Did you know that? She was found in a Dumpster in Harlem, strung out on heroin. According to the notes in her hospital records, she went weeks without a name because they didn't think she was going to live. I guess one of the nurses finally named her."

My dinner almost came up, but I swallowed it down and let Dad continue. I should walk away. I should leave this for Thea to explain. But I couldn't move my feet.

"She grew up in an orphanage in Brooklyn. From what the investigator could tell, that place should never have been left open. But it looks like the director had some sort of connection with the city to keep her funding. From what he could dig up, he thinks most of the money she got went into her own pocket."

Dad came around the desk, swiping up the folder as he approached. He rifled through it and held out a picture.

I took it from his hands, finding Thea immediately in a group of ten young children. She was the smallest, probably close to Charlie's age, and standing on the concrete steps of an old brick building. Her pants were three inches too short. Her shirt was too small. And damn she was thin. So thin it made me want to scream.

A large woman, the director most likely, was standing off to the side. Her smile was wide while the kids were all forcing it.

Thea had learned that fake smile much too young.

"The director kept about ten kids on average in that orphanage. I'm guessing that was done strategically. Enough kids to keep the place open, not so many to take away from her own profits. She let some turnover happen, just so she could say she was trying to get kids adopted. Not too much though. The investigator found out that three different families tried to adopt Thea when she was a baby. Each time their applications were denied."

The temptation was too much and I yanked the file from Dad's hands. He stood by watching as I thumbed through grainy pictures, school records and notes from the investigator.

As the pictures progressed, there were fewer and fewer

children in them. Except for Thea's face, consistent in them all. "Was she by herself?"

Dad nodded. "We're not sure, but I suspect the director made some sort of arrangement to keep the orphanage open until all the kids turned eighteen. They probably didn't want to uproot the kids who'd lived there all their lives. Thea was the youngest, so it closed down after she graduated. She lived there alone for about a year."

I stared at the last picture in front of the orphanage. Only Thea, the director and Hazel were pictured on the steps. "Was Hazel in on it?"

"The cook? No."

My shoulders sagged. I wouldn't have been able to tell Thea if Hazel had betrayed her. I wouldn't have had the guts to take Charlie's gran away from her.

"You're sure?"

He nodded. "We suspect she was the one to file a few of the anonymous complaints about the director."

Anonymous. Hazel had probably been too nervous about losing her job and access to the kids to file with her name on them.

"When the complaints didn't go anywhere, she started using her personal funds to supplement the food budget. Hazel's parents wired her money for years. The money stopped the day Thea turned eighteen and left the orphanage."

I went back to the file, thumbing through the rest. There wasn't much. Just a picture of a seedy apartment complex where Thea had moved after the orphanage. Another of the outside of the hotel where we'd met. All landmarks that gave me a glimpse into the life she'd led before.

She was too good for it all.

I handed Dad back the file before I could rip it in half. "You had your investigator go deep."

"He always does. Hell, I doubt Thea even knows some of the things in his report. She's probably never seen her hospital records."

She probably didn't know how close she'd been to death. Hazel had been right the first day I'd met her. Thea had been fighting her whole life.

"What do you want me to do with all this, Dad? It doesn't change anything." I looked him in the eye. "I love her."

"I know." He nodded. "I admire Thea for making something of her life. Over half the other kids in this picture are strung out on drugs, in jail or dead. But before you decide to marry her, ask yourself if that's right *for her*. It seems to me she worked hard to get away from her old life. Will she be happy coming back here for yours?"

"She could be." I could make her happy here.

"Maybe. But if not, what then? You two get divorced and she takes Charlie back to Montana. Where does that leave you?"

In the same place I was now—two thousand miles away from my daughter. "I could leave New York."

It wasn't the first time the idea had crossed my mind, but it was the first time I'd said it out loud. The words tasted bitter and my stomach churned.

"Not an option," Dad declared. "You can't abandon your responsibilities to this family. Before too long, I'm handing everything over to you and Aubrey."

I'd always known his position at the head of the Kendrick family would one day be mine. And though Aubrey might run the business side of things, we all knew I was the one who'd fill Dad's shoes as leader.

I'd be the one to solve problems or family disputes. I'd oversee the foundation. I'd ensure all of the Kendricks got their fair share. Aubrey would manage the business. I'd get everything else.

Dad was right. Leaving New York wasn't an option. I couldn't just quit my job at the firm; partners were owners too. Plus, I couldn't shirk my responsibilities with the family.

"Is this all? I need to get back to Thea and Charlie." The urge to convince Thea to move was stronger than ever. When Dad nodded, I started for the door.

"Oh, and Logan?" he called, causing me to pause and glance back. "I'm sorry about tonight. Your mother and I will do better tomorrow."

"I'd appreciate that." I turned again but stopped as Sofia hurried into the office.

"Logan?" Her eyes were puffy from crying. Her shoulders were hunched forward and her eyes downtrodden. It was the innocent, "poor me" look she'd perfected by thirteen. "Did you really mean it when you said you'd take away my money?"

No. But I was still pissed she'd brought Alice up here just to cause drama, so I wasn't going to tell her that tonight. "You went too far."

She sniffled. "I'm sorry."

"Are you? You and your *friend* condemned Thea because of her profession. Ironic, considering you've never had one. Maybe if you actually had to get a job, you'd appreciate the money you were born into."

Something I'd make sure Charlie knew was a privilege, not a right. My daughter would value the trust fund I'd set up for her weeks ago. Though, I doubted I'd be the one to teach her that lesson. Thea would do a better job than I ever could. After all, she actually knew what it was like to go without.

"You're serious?" Sofia's jaw dropped. "You'd really cut me off?"

I shrugged. "I guess that depends on you. Grow up, Sofia."

With that parting shot, I left her standing with her mouth agape in the office and darted down the hall. I opened the back door to the patio, finally escaping the house, but was stopped short when I spotted Granny sitting on a rocking bench by the pool.

"I figured you'd be long gone by now to escape the drama."

She smiled and patted the seat next to her. "I'll be off soon enough."

Granny lived just down the road in a house slightly smaller than ours. As kids, Aubrey, Sofia and I had spent our time alternating between her pool and our own each summer.

"So, dinner was interesting."

She laughed. "It always is."

"I'm not sure what to do here, Granny."

"What do I always tell you when you're stuck?"

"To sally forth."

Except pushing harder didn't feel right. Not this time. It would be like forcing together two puzzle pieces that had never been meant to fit.

"I can't lose them. I *refuse* to lose them."

There had to be a way to have it all. Somehow, I had to find a way to keep my job and uphold my family responsibilities while having Thea and Charlie by my side.

Granny patted my knee without another word of advice, then stood. "Come and visit me tomorrow. Bring my little Charlie and Thea along too."

"I will." I stood too to kiss her cheek and say good night.

After she disappeared inside, I jogged down to the guesthouse. According to the wall clock in the entryway, it was still early, only eight, but all the lights were off except one over the stove in the kitchen. I went straight down the hall toward the bedrooms, hoping Charlie wasn't already asleep.

I grinned at the light glowing from underneath her door. I reached for the knob but stopped when I heard Charlie and Thea giggling. I leaned in closer, savoring the sound.

"What else should we do when we get home?" Thea asked.

"Let's go fishing with Uncle Jackson."

"Oooh. Good idea. It's my turn to catch the biggest fish."

Charlie laughed. "Nuh-uh. You caught the biggest one last time. It's my turn."

"Oh, right. Sorry." Thea was smiling. I heard it in her voice. "Well, then I guess it can be your turn. What else?"

"Hmmm, I don't know."

"How about we do something special with Gran? I bet she's missed us almost as much as we've missed her."

"Yeah!" Charlie cheered. "We should go to our special waterfall."

"Definitely. We'll pack a picnic and make it a whole afternoon. Then we can tell Gran all about our trip."

Charlie giggled. "I'm going to tell her it always smells like poop."

Ironic that my daughter would think New York smelled bad when I'd told Nolan the same thing about Montana.

When she stopped laughing, the bed moved and Charlie yawned. "I can't wait to go home."

"You and me both, my love," Thea whispered. "You and me both."

The pain in my chest was staggering. I backed away from the door, leaning against the wall and sinking down to sit on the carpet. This dread was achingly familiar. It was the same one I'd felt when Emmeline had decided to move, except this time, it was a hundred times worse.

The woman I loved—the love of my life—was leaving me

for Montana. She was taking my daughter with her, and there wasn't a damn thing I could do to stop it.

All along, I'd believed that we could make this work. I'd believed that I could convince them to move. But as I listened to Thea and Charlie talk about going home, my beliefs slipped into the night.

Because I knew, deep down, the right thing to do was to let them go where they would be happiest.

twenty-six

THEA

CLOSED THE DOOR TO CHARLIE'S ROOM AND ALMOST SCREAMED when I saw Logan sitting outside it. My hand flew to my pounding heart. "Oh my god, you scared me."

"Sorry."

"What are you doing?" I whispered.

He shook his head, staring at the floor. "Just listening. Is she asleep?"

"Yeah. She's exhausted. It's been a long week." I held out a hand to help him up.

He took it, standing quickly and yanking me into his arms. We stood there for a few minutes, clinging to the other in the dark hallway. Finally, he broke away and took my hand, leading me to our bedroom. Logan flipped on the light, then ran a hand through his hair as he sat on the end of the bed.

I crossed the room and plopped next to him, our hunched shoulders touching.

"I'm sorry, baby. I never would have brought you here if I'd thought they'd act like that. I just can't believe . . ." He shook his head. "I'm so sorry."

"Don't be sorry. It's not your fault." He might not have expected them to act so suspicious, but I hadn't been entirely surprised. Disappointed, yes. But not all that surprised.

Logan took one of my hands, his long fingers easily wrapping over my palm. Then he turned it over, studying my knuckles. I felt his next words before they came out. "Don't leave."

"I have to," I whispered.

"Why?"

I turned to meet his pleading gaze. "I need to go home. This life . . ." I stood from the bed, swinging an arm to indicate the expensive room. "This life isn't for me."

"It could be."

I took a deep breath, willing myself not to cry. If even a single tear fell, I'd never be able to finish. And Logan deserved an explanation.

It was time for the conversation I'd been dreading for days. "Your dad looked into me, didn't he?"

He nodded. "I didn't know, but he told me tonight. There are some things he found. Things you should know."

"Did he find my mother?"

He shook his head. "No. It's about the orphanage and the director. She—"

"Don't tell me." I cut him off. "I don't want to know." I'd said good-bye to that chapter of my life earlier this week at the orphanage.

"Are you sure?"

I nodded. "I might ask you one day, but not now."

"All right."

"It's probably easier that way." I was glad I didn't have to explain it all. "Now you know that I come from nothing. All I have from my childhood were those photos you found and some old tattered baby booties that a nurse made me while I was detoxing in the hospital."

"I don't care where you came from."

"I know. But can you understand how big of a change this

is? You have so much."

"And you can too." He stopped me. "You can have anything your heart desires."

"It's not about the things, Logan." I started pacing. "Or money. It's about our lifestyle."

"And I'm telling you that we can have any lifestyle you want. If you don't want to live in the penthouse, we'll move. If you want to live where there's more space, we can buy a home out here, and I'll commute to work. Whatever you want, we can have it here."

"But that's just it. I don't want *here*." I pointed to the floor. "I don't want to live in New York."

His forehead furrowed. "Why?"

"Because I hate it here." My hands came to my heart as the truth came out. "Everything about New York just makes me feel like less. It makes me small. It reminds me of how powerless I was back then. No matter how hard I worked, I just couldn't get ahead."

No matter how nice or polite or happy I appeared, no one would ever give me a home. Every young couple who came into the orphanage left without a backward glance. Yet each time someone came in, I'd been foolish enough to hope that they'd pick me.

Years of shattered hopes had finally crushed my spirit. If Hazel hadn't come along, I doubted I'd have even a shred of it left.

Logan reached for me but I kept pacing. "It doesn't have to be like that ever again, Thea. You don't ever have to work. You can do your artwork here. We'll get your pieces into a gallery. You don't have to mix a drink ever again or pour another beer."

"No." The burn in my throat was choking me, but I swallowed it down. "It's not about my job. And I don't want to be in galleries. I don't want art to be my job. I do it for me, and that's it. It's about living a life I created. One that I'm proud of."

"And you couldn't be proud to live with me here?" The pain in his voice gutted me.

"I'm always proud to be with you." I walked to the bed and put my hands on his face, making him look me in the eye so he knew how true that was. "Always. But this isn't about you. It's about me."

I let him go and sat back down by his side, this time taking his hand in both of mine.

"I have three thousand, seventy-four dollars and fifty-one cents in my checking account." I'd memorized the number this morning, just like I did every day. "Every penny came from mixing drinks and pouring beer. Running the Lark Cove Bar isn't just my job. It's my passion."

His eyebrows came together. "Your passion?"

"My passion." I nodded. "When I left the city, I had nothing. Not in the literal sense, though I didn't have much, but I had nothing in here." I placed his hand on my heart. "No confidence. No strength. I was so lonely and broken and tired. The only thing keeping me going was Charlie. Knowing that she was growing inside of me and needed me to keep pushing."

His face softened and he placed his free hand on top of mine.

"She saved me, in so many ways. She gave me this ambition and this drive to give her everything in my power. She made me fearless. Because of her, I built us a life that I'm proud of and it all started at the bar."

When I'd gotten to Montana, I think Hazel had taken one look at me and known I needed a project. I'd always been a hard worker, at school or at whatever job I'd been in. But I'd had no ownership in them. Hazel had handed over the keys to the bar and led me to the office. She'd stood in the doorway, pointed to a desk buried in papers and said *fix it*.

Three days after that, I'd come home to find her cleaning out the garden shed so I could have it for my art. She'd given me a proper place to create instead of the orphanage's kitchen table where she'd watched me draw so many years before.

I leaned into Logan, who was waiting patiently for me to continue. "That place means a lot to me. I've taken it from barely paying expenses to making money for me, Jackson and Hazel. I didn't have a fancy education. Charlie learned things in kindergarten last year that I didn't learn until third or fourth grade. But I worked my ass off, researching and experimenting and running that business. I'm proud of what it's become."

"You should be." He kissed my forehead, his praise making it even harder not to cry. "If you want to run a business here, we can make that happen. I'll buy—"

"No, Logan." I stopped him. "Not here. I know I'm not doing a good job of explaining it, but I feel different here. Like the past is weighing me down. All those self-doubts and insecurities have come back."

"It won't always be like that. Give it time," he pleaded.

"Maybe. Maybe this all seems silly and after a year or two here, it wouldn't be like that anymore. But it's more than just bad memories. If we left, I'd have to say good-bye to Hazel and Jackson, and I honestly don't think I can. They're my family. I worked . . ." I choked back more tears. "I worked so hard to find a family, Logan. I don't want to give them up."

I didn't want to be thousands of miles away if Hazel's health started to fail or if Jackson finally found love.

"I'm worried that if I stay and I'm unhappy, I'll start to resent you." I held tighter to his hand. "And so would Charlie."

He hung his head. "She's miserable, isn't she?"

"She loves you. I think she'd put herself through all the

dresses and uncomfortable shoes in the world if you asked her to. But . . ."

"But I won't," he whispered.

And that was why I loved him completely. His love for our daughter. He'd known Charlie for weeks and already put her happiness first.

I'd do the same. If I truly thought she'd be happier here than in Montana, we'd stay. I'd sacrifice my home and job and family so she could be with her dad. But I knew deep in my soul that my girl needed open space and big skies.

"She's all that matters."

He brought a hand up to my cheek. "Not all."

A tear fell onto his thumb. "I wish—"

"I know." His eyes were still full of pain, but there was understanding too. "Me too."

Logan blew out a deep breath and stood from the bed. "I don't know what to do."

I shrugged. "There's nothing to do. We move forward. We make Charlie's life as happy as it can be."

"And what about us?"

I looked at my lap and let a few more tears fall onto my dress. "I think it would be better to end it now. Before it gets even harder."

"Even harder?" He scoffed. "Thea, I am in love with you. I have a ring in my suitcase that I'd hoped to give you tonight. How could it get any harder?"

My shoulders began to shake. "I love you too."

"Just not enough to stay."

My entire body flinched. The pain burned hot for a moment until anger took its place. "You could move. Why are we the ones who have to make the huge life change?"

He shook his head. "I can't. My career is in New York. My

family too. You're not the only one who's proud of what they've accomplished and doesn't want to give it up."

"Okay. Then we're back to where we were." I swiped my eyes dry. "The impossible."

He stopped pacing, his balled fists relaxing. "I don't want to fight."

"Me neither."

I didn't want us to end on bad terms. We had years ahead of us as Charlie's parents, and they'd be easier if we could end this amicably. We had to find a way to move past the pain and just focus on raising a happy child.

Logan crossed the room to take my hands and pull me to my feet. Then he wrapped me in his arms, breathing in my hair. "I don't want to let you go. Being with you. Having Charlie. It's the happiest I've ever been. But my family. My career. I can't—"

"It's okay." I relaxed into his chest. "I understand."

And I did. I didn't blame him for needing to stay. But we'd hit a dead end on our conversation and there wasn't anything more to say.

I leaned back, standing on my tiptoes to press my lips against his.

He returned my kiss without hesitation, taking charge like he always did.

I melted into him completely, telling him through my touches how desperate I was for things to be different.

We stripped each other bare and fell into a tangled mess of limbs under the bed sheets. Neither of us wanted to break away to turn off the lights. Logan made love to me with his weight bearing down hard, like he wanted to keep me pinned to this place. He moved over me with a ferocity I'd never seen before. The despair in his eyes never really gone, just masked by heat.

And through it all, I held him tight, whispering the three

words I'd never say to another man, memorizing the way he said them in return. *I love you* didn't scare me now.

It was just . . . the perfect end.

"Hello."

I looked up from my lounge chair as Thomas and Lillian came out to the patio. "Hi."

Charlie and Logan were swimming in the pool, enjoying the cool water on a hot afternoon. The overcast skies and cool breeze from yesterday had disappeared, so this morning, Logan and I had decided to let Charlie just play. We wanted to give her a fun last day with her dad because he wasn't sure when he'd be able to get to Montana next.

So we'd camped out by the pool this afternoon to soak up the sun.

"May we join you?" Thomas asked.

"Of course." I sat up and swiped Charlie's clothes off the chair next to me. Then I did a quick check to make sure my bikini top hadn't slipped down.

Lillian sat in the lounge chair next to me, while Thomas pulled up a regular seat from a table under an umbrella behind us.

I looked down the pool for some rescue, but Logan was too busy watching Charlie to notice his parents had come out. Instead, he was treading water while she stood at the end of the diving board, psyching herself up to jump.

"We owe you an apology," Thomas said, his eyes fixed on my daughter. "Our behavior last night was intolerable. On behalf of the entire family, I'd like to assure you it won't happen again."

I blinked a couple of times, glad they couldn't see my shocked eyes behind my sunglasses. "I, um, thank you?" When my ears registered that it had come out as a question, I cleared my throat and tried again. "Thank you."

"We'd like to get to know Charlo—" Lillian caught herself, swallowing. "Charlie."

"I'm sure she'd like that." It was a lie, but if these people were trying, then so could I.

There'd come a time when Charlie would come out here to visit Logan without me. Any bond she made with her grandparents while I was here would make those future trips easier.

"Have you all eaten lunch?" Lillian asked.

I nodded. "We went down to visit Joan this morning and she invited us to stay."

After a few hours with Logan's granny, I loved her even more than I had last night. Joan had showered Charlie with affection, constantly hugging or kissing her cheek.

"Well, if Mom got to enjoy your company at lunch, we get dinner," Thomas declared. "Is there something you and Charlie would prefer? Our chef can make just about anything. Or we can get takeout."

"We're pretty easy to please. Charlie loves your typical kid food. Macaroni and cheese. Pizza. Corn dogs."

"Corn dogs!" Thomas clapped once. "I haven't had a corn dog in ages. Let's have him make those and more of those fries. She seemed to like them last night."

I smiled, glad he'd noticed. "She'll love it."

"Look," Lillian gasped, sitting up straighter in her chair.

My eyes tracked hers to where Charlie was plugging her nose and Logan counted to three. She screwed her eyes shut and pushed off the board, splashing water all over her dad as she disappeared under the water.

Logan was right there as she came up for air, holding her to his side while she wiped the water from her smiling face.

The patio broke out in cheers as we all stood to clap for Charlie. She looked at us, then ducked her head into Logan's neck at the sight of Thomas and Lillian.

Logan just glared, swimming for the edge of the pool. He hoisted Charlie out first, then himself. The water glistened as it slid down his sculpted chest and abs in steady streams. A shiver rolled down my shoulders and I shut my eyes, committing that image to memory. It was one I'd use to keep me company on the lonely nights. I'd probably draw it in a sketchbook as soon as I got home.

With Charlie trailing behind him, Logan strode down the pool to our chairs. He swiped a towel off another lounger, handing it to Charlie, before getting one for himself.

"Mom. Dad." He nodded to his parents, then looked at me from underneath his towel, giving me the *Are you okay?* look.

I smiled. *All good.*

"We were just deciding on dinner plans," Thomas said. "Charlie, do you like corn dogs? I was hoping we could have them for dinner. Is that okay with you?"

She nodded, sliding closer to Logan's leg.

"Hi, guys!" Aubrey came out onto the patio, her face split into a wide smile aimed at my daughter. "Charlie, want to swim with me?"

Logan looked down, giving her a grin. "Aunt Aubrey is scared of the diving board."

Aubrey rolled her eyes. "I'm not scared. I just don't like water going up my nose."

"You should plug your nose." Charlie pinched her nostrils together. "This is how my daddy taught me."

"Hmm." Aubrey tapped her chin, pretending like she'd

never heard of the idea before. "Maybe you could show me?"

Charlie smiled, tossing her towel on the deck and wasting no time scurrying her little butt back to the diving board.

Aubrey smiled and followed close behind just as Logan's phone rang on a table.

"I'll be right there," he called to their backs, then took the call.

Thomas stood from his seat. "I haven't been swimming in ages. I think I'll change and join them."

"And I'd better let the kitchen know our dinner choice." Lillian gave me a genuine smile as she stood and followed Thomas into the house.

I let out a deep breath, relieved at how painless that had been. With Sofia having left for the city already, it might actually be an enjoyable Sunday afternoon. And I couldn't help but feel excited for Charlie that she might actually get to know her extended family.

Her shyness was gone with Aubrey—and the diving board—as she catapulted herself into the water. One by one, Charlie would warm to these people and pull them into her circle. If they were anything like Logan, which I suspected they were even with last night's events, she'd have more than just me and Hazel and Jackson in her family.

"That was Sean." Logan sat by my feet, blocking my view of Charlie and Aubrey. "He tried to track down the owner of that email account but is having trouble, which is just pissing him off. Sean thinks the guy is a hacker too and is blocking him."

I frowned. "This is not a big deal, Logan. Let it go. It's just some guy being a jerk. The emails will stop."

"I'm not willing to take that chance."

We went into one of our stare-downs, but I finally gave in. Even behind my sunglasses, he was winning. "Fine. If you want to waste Sean's time, that's your choice. But I don't want to talk about it. Not today."

Today, I just wanted him to be close. To have this last day together before everything changed tomorrow.

"Okay. Not today." The tension in his face disappeared and he scooted closer. His hand skirted up my knee to my thigh and he leaned down, giving me a gentle kiss.

I relaxed into him, leaning my forehead on his shoulder.

We held one another without another word until he wrapped his arms tight around my hips.

"Logan, that's too ti—"

I couldn't get the words out. One second I was sitting, the next Logan had scooped me off the chair and was hurling us both toward the pool. I screamed as we crashed into the water, laughing as I came up for air.

"You'll pay for that." I splashed Logan's smug grin.

"Oh, yeah? What are you going to do about it?"

I smiled, just as Aubrey and Charlie came up from behind him and dunked his head in the water.

And that was how we spent our last day.

Playing with our daughter. Getting to know his family. Eating corn dogs. And saying good-bye with every gentle touch and chaste kiss.

We spent the day savoring every moment. A calm understanding had cleared the worry between us and given us the liberty to just . . . be.

As heartbreaking as it would be to say good-bye tomorrow, we both knew it was the right decision. The fairy tale was over. The glass slipper was coming off. Charlie and I needed to go home.

Where we belonged.

twenty-seven

LOGAN

THE DAY I DROVE THEA AND CHARLIE TO THE AIRPORT WAS the worst day of my life, without question. We rode in solemn silence back to the city. Charlie's sad eyes often found mine in the rearview mirror. Thea held tight to my hand as I drove, keeping us connected for just a bit longer.

The entire time, I contemplated my options. I wanted to tell Thea I'd find a way for us to be together, but I couldn't make that kind of promise, not if I couldn't keep it.

So when we pulled up to the hangar, I took a long breath and prepared for an awful good-bye.

I got out first, waving to the pilots and crew as they approached from the base of the jet's stairs. They came over and took the luggage, then backed away as Charlie and Thea climbed out of the SUV.

"We're ready anytime, sir." The pilot smiled to Thea. "Just come on up when you're ready and we'll be off."

"Thank you." She nodded at him, then let go of Charlie's hand, motioning her to my side.

I dropped to a knee, tipping up Charlie's chin with my finger. "I'll see you soon, peanut."

"Okay, Daddy," she told her feet.

My heart broke as the tears welled in her eyes. I yanked her forward, pulling her to my chest and hugged her tight. "I love you," I whispered into her hair.

"I love you too." Her small frame shook as she cried into my shoulder.

I breathed through the crushing ache in my chest, getting my emotions under control. But when I looked up to see Thea swiping tears off her cheeks, a whole new wave of pain hit my center.

The idea floating in my head had to work. *It has to.* Seeing these two in tears was more than I could bear.

I stood, picking Charlie up off the ground, and took Thea's hand, tugging her into my side. The three of us held tight to our small huddle. None of us were in a hurry to break apart, but when I saw one of the crew checking their watch, I knew my time was up.

"Call me when you get home."

Thea nodded, sniffling as she stood back. "We will." Thea rubbed our daughter's back and I set her down. "Okay, Charlie. Time to go."

They linked hands and took a step away.

"Wait." I stepped forward, taking Thea's face in my hands. "I love you."

Her eyes filled with new tears. "I love you too."

Thea's explanation for leaving hadn't been easy to hear. I'd lain awake with her draped over my side for two nights now, replaying her words. And after all those hours of sorting it out and putting myself in her place, I came to a conclusion.

She loved me.

But she also needed to love herself.

If New York made her feel like less, then I wouldn't ask her to stay. If she needed to be with her family, I had to let her go.

She loved me enough to be honest. I loved her enough to

want her to have it all.

I pressed my lips to hers in a hard kiss. "I promise to see you soon," I whispered against her lips.

She nodded. "You know where we'll be."

At home.

I let her go, watching as she led Charlie to the plane. My daughter looked over her shoulder, giving me a tiny wave as she climbed the stairs. Thea never looked back.

She still didn't believe in promises.

But she would.

It took me two weeks to unravel my life.

Two weeks, and I was no longer a partner at Stone, Richards and Abergel. I was no longer the Kendrick prince, preparing to be king. And soon, I'd no longer be the chairman of the foundation's board of directors.

"How did brunch go?" Nolan asked, leaning back in his chair as I came into his office.

I collapsed in a leather club chair across from his desk, loosening the knot in my tie. "About as well as I expected. Dad thinks I'm fucking up my life and Mom can't fathom why Thea doesn't just move here."

"They'll come around. Give them a couple more grandkids. Buy them a lake house in Lark Cove. Once they spend some time there, they'll understand. Besides, it's not like you can't manage the Kendrick fortune from Montana."

I shrugged. "We'll see."

My parents thought abandoning the career I'd worked so hard to build was reckless. They'd been *disappointed* in my decision to move, especially Dad.

He wasn't concerned about me managing logistics for the family from Lark Cove. He knew location didn't matter when it came to handling finances, taking phone calls and returning emails. Dad *was* convinced that I'd never be seen as a leader if I was living thousands of miles away. He had a point.

So I'd handed over my crown.

Aubrey could take his place because I wasn't changing my mind. Two weeks without Thea and Charlie and I was coming out of my skin.

"Any word from the firm?" Nolan asked.

"No. I don't expect to hear from them again."

The day I'd dropped off Thea and Charlie at the airport, I'd called for an impromptu meeting with the senior partners at the firm. I'd gotten lucky that it had been on a Monday and none of them had been out golfing. Though I'm pretty sure all three of them had wanted to take a club to my head after the first five minutes of the meeting.

"Are they still pissed?"

I shrugged. "I think they're chagrinned that I outsmarted them. But they got the better end of the deal, so they'll get over it as soon as they cash a few Kendrick checks."

Nolan grinned. "Remind me to have you review any and all contracts before I sign them."

"You got it."

When I'd bought into the firm as a partner, I'd signed their standard partnership contract. It was fairly boilerplate, outlining the responsibilities of the partnership and the consequences if expectations weren't met. It also included a nepotism clause, stating that no partner could be in a relationship with other employees. Immediate family members were allowed to work at the firm, but not in the chain of command with the related partner.

All standard.

Including the clause where a partner's spouse and family members were not allowed to be clients of the firm.

That had been my loophole.

When I'd been offered a partnership, Kendrick Enterprises had been with another firm across town and it was well known that Dad was loyal to them. Since there was no shot at winning the Kendrick business, the senior partners had taken the next best thing: me. I'd become their star, bringing in clients they wouldn't have earned without my last name.

So my proposal to Stone, Richards and Abergel was simple: they buy me out of my partnership and I bring them the Kendricks. Aubrey had been more than willing to shuck their existing firm, which was full of lawyers who continually double-checked her directives with my father. It was in her authority to change firms, and after I'd asked her to consider it, she'd agreed immediately.

I was letting her deal with Dad's reaction to the change.

The senior partners had put on a good show, hemming and hawing for at least five minutes before agreeing. They'd even held back their excitement until after I'd left the conference room.

I'd spent two weeks on the phone and in meetings, notifying clients and getting the other partners up to speed on my former portfolio. Finally, yesterday, I'd packed up my office and handed in my keys.

"What do you have left to do?" Nolan asked.

"Not much. Sean has my personal belongings all packed up and ready for shipment to Lark Cove. Most everything else is staying since I'm keeping the penthouse. Now all I have left to do is step down as chair and I'm free."

"I think this is a mistake." Nolan frowned. "You can do this job from Montana."

I chuckled. "If I didn't know better, I'd say you were going to miss me."

"You're trained. If you leave, I'll have to break in someone new."

"I'll miss you too."

"Listen, I've been thinking about this and I have an idea. Let me bring Piper in so we can pitch it." He picked up the phone, dialing her extension. Not thirty seconds later, she waltzed into the office and took the chair at my side.

She looked me up and down. "You look like hell."

"Thanks," I muttered, knowing she was just saying it out of concern. The circles under my eyes were darker than any I'd sported during law school, but I hadn't slept much in two weeks. Without Thea in my bed, I'd been restless.

"Okay, so we've got an idea." Nolan leaned his forearms on his desk, nodding to Piper.

"I've been playing with the org chart and job descriptions." She handed me a piece of paper, showing me the current structure of the foundation.

The circle at the top was me, the chairman of the board. Below that, a row of the other board members. Beneath them was Nolan, followed by a row of vice presidents. Next to each bubble was a brief description of job responsibilities.

It was the same as it had been for decades.

"Now look at this." She handed me a new sheet.

The structure of the circles was the same except one vice president bubble had been removed and its job duties placed with me. With this new structure, I'd be taking over the team responsible for sorting through donation proposals.

My eyes snapped to Nolan and his smug grin. "What about Mike?" He was the current vice president in the role they were proposing to eliminate and had worked with us for a decade.

"He wants to retire. He talked about waiting a year, but I already spoke with him and he's on board with leaving early. We'll cut him a check and he'll move to Florida a year earlier than expected."

"But what about everything else? The events. The trips. I can't be here to split them with you."

"I've got them covered. With you weeding through proposals, it will take less time for me to review them. Mike does a great job, but I still spend a lot of time going through everything, mostly so I can get you up to speed. I won't have to do that anymore. We can either ask other board members to become more active, or we can cut down on some of the events. Worst-case scenario, I go to them all."

I sighed. "That's going to cut into your time with your family. I can't ask you to do that."

"Not necessarily. If I'm hitting more events at night, then I'm going to cut back at the office. Spend more time at home in the mornings. I can take Tyler to school, hang with Kayla until lunch, then come in for the afternoons and attend the functions when they happen in the evenings. All of that's possible if you take over Mike's job."

"Kayla would be okay with that?"

He nodded. "She's one hundred percent on board."

God, this would be amazing. More than quitting my career, one that I'd poured thousands of hours into building, I hated losing my place at the foundation.

It was my passion. It was my connection to my family. And more so, I could do this job and be home every night for dinner. I'd never miss a soccer practice or game. I'd have the chance to make up for the time I'd already lost with Charlie.

The last two weeks had taught me a lot. My eighty-hour workweeks were over. I was trading up for Thea and Charlie.

But if I could keep this tie to the foundation, to my family's legacy, then maybe I could have my cake and eat it too.

"I love it," I told Nolan and Piper. "But I just don't see the board approving the change."

The chairman of the board had always been a Kendrick, picked purposefully to be the face of the family. Before me, it was my uncle. When he'd been ready to retire, I'd taken over. I didn't see how the board would want it any other way.

"It's worth asking," Piper said. "If they say no, then you can step down like you'd planned."

"True." My original plan had been to move and settle in to Lark Cove. When I got bored, I'd find a low-stress job. If this didn't work out, I could always fall back on Plan A.

But damn, I wanted Plan B.

"The meeting with the board doesn't start until ten." Nolan checked the clock on the wall. "We've got thirty minutes. Let's prep to pitch this, instead of the list of recommended chair candidates we came up with last week."

I grinned at them both. "It's worth a shot."

Two hours later, the three of us were back in Nolan's office, celebrating.

The board had agreed to try this new structure temporarily and see if it worked. They weren't crazy about the CEO not being in the office from nine to five, or the chairman living in Montana, but we'd somehow managed to convince them that there were more benefits than costs on this one.

"I knew they'd go for it!" Piper hadn't stopped smiling since the board meeting had adjourned. "And I bet it will be less than two months and they'll vote to make this permanent."

I chuckled. "You realize this means you're going to have to deal with me a lot more frequently now."

"I'll adjust." She winked. "Besides, this means I get to take regular 'work trips' to Montana. Didn't you say you bought a boat?"

Nolan laughed. "We're just pawns, Logan. Little pieces on her chessboard."

Piper gave us both a diabolical smile.

"What's Thea going to think about all this?" Nolan asked.

I ran a hand through my hair and sighed. "I haven't told her anything yet."

"What!" Piper shrieked as she punched me in the arm. "You haven't told her what you're doing? Oh my god, why not? What is wrong with you?"

"Ouch." I rubbed my bicep. "I didn't want to get her hopes up if something came up. There was no guarantee the firm would let me out of my partnership. And I wasn't going to make her a promise that I wasn't one hundred percent sure I could keep. She's had enough people let her down. I won't be one of them."

"Oh." Piper relaxed. "Well, everything is all set here. What are you waiting for?"

I grinned and checked my watch. "My flight."

"Hi," I answered Sean's call as I beeped the locks on the rental car waiting for me outside the airport.

"Did you make it?"

"Yeah. I just got in." The six-hour flight from New York to Kalispell had put me back in Montana right before dark, thanks to the favorable time change and tailwind. I'd landed with just enough time to call Charlie and say goodnight, then talk to Thea while the plane had taxied off the runway.

"Good." Except he didn't sound good. "I've got some news."

The hairs on the back of my neck stood up as I opened the door and slid into the driver's seat, tossing my bag in the back. "Did you find him?"

Sean had been trying to track down Thea's email harasser for two weeks without luck. And since the emails to Thea had stopped, it had made his hunt that much harder. But I'd told him to keep digging, no matter the cost. So after hitting one dead end after another, Sean had called in one of his underground hacker friends to help.

"We found him. Does the name Ronny Berkowitz ring any bells?"

Ronny Berkowitz. I replayed it a few times as I turned on the ignition. "No."

"He's a local, but from what we can tell, he lies low. He works from his house, building cyber security systems."

Which explained why Sean had such a hard time tracing his identity. "What else?"

"He's originally from Dallas but moved to Lark Cove about five years ago. Ronny's not someone you want around Thea, Logan."

"Fuck." I shoved the SUV into drive and floored it out of the parking lot. "Why?"

"He was arrested about seven years ago for stalking a bartender in Texas. Things got fairly intense. He ended up breaking into her house and scaring her pretty bad. Luckily, her boyfriend got home early before Ronny could hurt her."

My jaw clenched as I swerved around a semi-trailer to get on the highway. Its horn blared as I zoomed past, gunning the engine faster.

"I've got a picture of that bartender. Her name is Angela Peters. And she looks a lot like Thea."

"Call the cops. Now. Send them everything you've found,

plus the emails you pulled from Thea's account."

"I already did. The sheriff is fully briefed."

"Call them back. I'll be at Thea's in thirty minutes, maybe less if I hurry. Until I get there, I want someone outside her house."

"Will do. What else?"

"Ruin him," I growled.

"Same drill as last time?"

The last time being when I'd discovered Emmeline had a stalker. Sean had arranged for someone to scare him off. This time around, a few punches to the face weren't good enough. I wanted Ronny Berkowitz destroyed.

"No. I want him broke. Zero out his bank account. Max his credit cards. Have his car impounded. Get him fired from his job. Expose him as a stalker to the local media. Whatever you can think of. I want Lark Cove to be the last place on earth this guy wants to stay. Can you do that?"

Sean chuckled. "And then some. Now that I'm into his network, I can bring it all down."

"Do it." I hung up the phone and immediately dialed Thea. When she didn't answer, I tried her again. And again.

"Answer the phone, Thea."

She didn't. By my fourth attempt, I was doing twice the speed limit down the highway.

Because my gut was screaming that we'd found Ronny too late.

twenty-eight

THEA

WITH MY PHONE RESTING ON MY LAP, I STARED ACROSS the yard toward the lake. The water was glassy tonight, much like my eyes.

Logan had called, but I'd ignored it. After the ringing stopped, I put it on mute.

We'd already spoken once tonight, and as of now, I was going to start cutting down on phone calls. I lived to hear his voice, but after each one, I felt miserable. It hurt too much.

He'd been busy these last two weeks, per his usual schedule. Maybe he was using work to hide from the pain of our split. Maybe he just wanted to return to his regular routine. Either way, he always seemed to be in the middle of something when we talked. But, to his credit, once he answered, we had his full attention. In the two weeks since we'd left, he hadn't missed a single call to wish Charlie sweet dreams.

Tonight, though, he'd sounded different. Still just as busy, but almost in a hurry to end our call. A quick hello. A faster good-bye.

Would this become the new normal?

I'd worked hard the last two weeks, catching up at the bar. Charlie had gone right back to days with Hazel at the camp, and for the most part, I was glad for the routine. Except for nights like this, when I wasn't working. Free time was my new enemy.

I was an emotional wreck when left alone with my thoughts, which was probably why I hadn't set foot in my workshop. I knew once I got in there and pictured Logan in his spot by the cabinet, I'd completely lose it, something I had yet to do.

One of these nights I'd go in there and have an ugly cry. Until then, I was toughing out the blurry tears and stinging nose.

Footsteps sounded behind me in the kitchen and I blinked fast to clear my vision. I didn't want Hazel to know I'd been on the verge of crying. So as the screen door creaked, I forced a smile when she stepped onto the porch.

"Figured I'd find you here."

I nodded. "I thought I'd better enjoy the evening before it gets too cold."

As soon as the snow fell, Hazel and I traded our porch visits for living room campouts. Each winter, we'd pick a new show to binge after Charlie was asleep. Though Hazel would still brave the cold to smoke.

She slid a cigarette from its box and pulled out a lighter from her jeans pocket. After a heavy drag, she took her spot on the railing, blowing the smoke as far away from me as she could. "I think Charlie's more nervous about first grade than she was kindergarten."

I sighed. "I think you're right." Charlie was struggling because one of her friends from kindergarten had moved away and because Logan wasn't here.

As expected, Charlie had been withdrawn these past two weeks. She was definitely happy to be home, but she missed her dad.

Just like me, she was torn.

"How are you doing?" Hazel asked.

"I'm good," I lied. "Glad we're going to be getting into the fall routine."

She laughed. "Try again."

"I knew you wouldn't buy that," I muttered. "I guess I just wish things could be different."

"But they aren't."

My gaze went back to the lake. "No. They aren't."

On the plane, I'd wondered if I'd feel the same sense of home—of peace—when I got back to Lark Cove. There'd been a niggling feeling that I'd built up Lark Cove as a sanctuary when it really wasn't and that without Logan in our lives, it would feel different. By the time the captain had announced we were landing, I'd all but convinced myself that Montana wasn't everything it had been before.

But the moment I'd stepped off the plane, breathing in the clean mountain air, the worries of the last week had vanished. A deep contentment had settled the anxieties from the city.

It just felt like . . . home.

Charlie's smile the moment we'd pulled up to the cottage had been impossible to ignore. She'd been so happy to be back in her safe place that I knew we'd made the right decision.

So now I was holding out hope that with time, the ache in my heart would lessen.

"I know I've told you this already, but it's worth repeating," Hazel said. "I'm proud of you for going. It couldn't have been easy to go back, but I think it's good you faced the past."

"Thanks." It hadn't been easy, but it had been a chance for me to confront those old demons. The wounds from my childhood cut deep, but they'd healed more in the past two weeks than they had in years.

"Why don't you go to your workshop and paint or something? It's better than you sitting out here, dwelling on the things that cannot be."

I shrugged. "I'm just not feeling it. But you're right. I shouldn't just sit here. Maybe I'll go for a quick walk."

Hazel frowned. "It's almost dark."

"I've still got thirty minutes or so. I'll be back soon but call if you need me."

I stood from my seat and turned my phone off mute. Logan had called again, but I cleared the notification, willing myself to stay strong and not call him back until tomorrow. Then I tucked my phone into my jeans pocket.

"Okay." She didn't press too hard for me to stay, likely knowing that some movement would clear my head. "See you in a bit."

I hurried down the stairs and around the side of the house, setting a fast pace on the sidewalk. I didn't follow my normal route past the bar and through town. Instead, I turned down a small dirt road that wound along the lake.

It took a while for my mind to quiet, but by the time I reached a small bend in the road, I'd found the calm I'd been seeking all evening. From there, I let my flip-flops lead the way as I watched the sun lower on the horizon. Its lingering rays cast an amber glow over the lake's surface.

As the light began to disappear behind a mountain range, I turned around to go home but stopped as I recognized my surroundings.

I'd walked right to the house that Logan had bought in Lark Cove.

The gleaming windows reflected pastel pink and sherbet orange from the sunset. The lawn was a deeper green under the fading sky. And the cedar shakes were so warm and inviting, I found myself crossing the grass to take a closer look.

I was jealous that Charlie had gotten a full tour. When he'd been here, Logan had driven us by it again, showing us the lot.

But since the purchase hadn't gone through yet, he hadn't had a key to take me inside. As I peeked inside the windows, I wished I'd taken him up on his offer to call the realtor.

There wasn't much I could see from outside, so I gave up my snooping and walked over to the driveway, testing the side entrance of the garage, just in case. I smiled when the door opened.

I didn't hesitate to go inside and flick on the lights. The two empty garage bays were the cleanest I'd ever seen. The concrete floors weren't marred with a drop of oil. Fresh paint hit my nostrils and I pulled in a deep breath. Since this property had been built about six years ago, Logan must have arranged for a crew to come in and paint. One of them had probably forgotten to lock the door.

I crossed the room, walking toward a row of cabinets at the back. The sound of my footsteps echoed in the bright space, bouncing off one white wall to the other, while the fluorescent lights hummed over my head.

I knew I was invading Logan's space, but I couldn't resist opening up a couple drawers and cabinets. As I opened the last drawer, a man's voice echoed in the garage.

"Hello, Thea."

I screamed, spinning around so fast that I slammed my hip into the corner of the counter. My heart was in my throat as I tried to regain my breath. "Oh my god," I heaved. "Ronny? You scared me to death."

"Sorry about that." He reached behind him and pulled the door closed. When he turned the deadbolt, every muscle in my body tensed.

Nothing about this situation was right. Nothing about Ronny was right. Whoever this was, it wasn't the sweetheart who came into the bar almost every weeknight and occasionally on Sundays to keep me company. This wasn't the quiet, polite and shy Ronny I knew.

His movements were aggressive, stiff and hard. His normally slouched shoulders were pulled back like he was preparing for a fight. And his jaw was clenched and angry.

Every hair on my body stood on end, affirming with their prickles what my gut was screaming. *This is not right.*

Ronny's gaze ran up and down my body, hovering too long on my chest. His eyes were narrowed with a predatory stare. He was the cat. I was the stupid mouse who'd gone for a walk in her safe, small, trust-everyone town.

"I, um . . ." I swallowed the fear clogging my throat. "What are you doing here?"

"I'm here for you." He said it like I should have known it already. Like the next word out of his mouth was going to be *duh*.

I needed to get the hell out of here, but Ronny held his position by the door.

Stay calm, Thea. Don't panic.

"Well, I'd better get going." I plastered on a wide smile as I shuffled down the cabinets. "Hazel's probably wondering where I went."

"You're not going anywhere." Ronny shook his head. "Not until we talk."

With Ronny standing by the door, I didn't have any choice but to go past him to get out. The buttons for the garage doors were right next to the light switches too, so I couldn't escape through one of the bays.

Relying on years of dealing with creeps and jerks at the bar, I dropped my shoulders away from my ears, hoping he'd take it as a sign I was relaxing. "Sure. I'd love to talk. But would you mind if we went outside? The paint fumes are getting to me."

He frowned. "Do you think I'm stupid?"

"Of course not! You're the best, Ronny. My favorite customer." I was laying it on thick, but I didn't care. I had no idea what Ronny's intentions were, but I was sure they were nothing wholesome or friendly. And I had a little girl waiting for me at home. She needed her mother to stay in one piece.

"You have—"

My phone rang in my pocket. I reached for it but stopped when Ronny took three fast steps my way.

"Don't," he barked. He held me captive with his angry glare until the phone finally stopped ringing. "You aren't going to ignore me this time. Now that you're back, we're going to have a long overdue discussion."

Ignore him? When had I ignored him? "Ronny, I don't understand. What's going on?"

My phone rang again, stopping him before he could explain. His nostrils flared as his face turned red.

I went for my pocket again. "Let me just put it on silent."

"I said don't touch it!" His roar filled every inch of the garage.

I flinched hard, nodding as I whispered, "Okay."

Ronny's entire body was shaking with fury. His hands were balled by his sides. The red from his face seeped across his fair skin, coating his neck, staining his ears and tingeing his arms. He had light-brown hair buzzed short, and even his scalp was turning crimson.

What was happening? Who was this man? Because he sure as shit wasn't the regular at my bar who I'd known for years.

My body was shaking from head to toe and I sucked in a hitched breath. Then I balled my own fists, fighting the panic away. "Ronny," I said quietly, "I don't know what I did to make you so upset, but I'm sorry. Let's talk about this. We're friends, right?"

His face was still red, but his hands relaxed. "Friends? We're more than friends. We're meant to be together. I knew it when I saw that drawing you did of me last year. I knew you thought about me as much as I thought about you."

My head spun as I thought about all the drawings I'd done of Ronny. There had to be at least twenty in all of my notebooks. Not because he had a particularly interesting face or anything, but because he was just . . . there. I'd drawn all of the regulars that many times because some nights, they'd been the only ones around.

"I'm so sorry," I lied, scrambling for anything to say to calm Ronny down. "I didn't mean to lead you on. I draw everyone. It's just a hobby. I didn't know you had feel—"

My phone rang again, cutting off my apology.

"Give me that phone!" Ronny exploded, storming across the garage in a flash.

I backed up, trying to get away, but he trapped me against the cabinet. He grabbed my arms, his fingers digging into my biceps, as my phone kept ringing.

"After all the nights we spent together." He shook me as he spoke, the jolts accentuating his words. "After all the hours I kept you company so you wouldn't be alone. After *everything* we had, how could you turn your back on me just because *he* showed up? Were you thinking of me when you *fucked* him at the motel? Or in your *shed*? How could you do that to us? How could you leave me for *him*? You really are just a filthy *cunt*."

Bile rose in my throat as I recalled the last threatening email I'd gotten, the one that had set Logan off.

Ronny was Anonymous743.

He'd been watching me. He'd been watching me with Logan.

He was off his fucking rocker.

Ronny wasn't much taller than me, maybe an inch or two, but he was stocky. He outweighed me by at least fifty pounds. The grasp he had on my arms was so tight, there was no way I could wiggle free. My only shot was to get him to let me go long enough to make a dash for the door.

I relaxed, completely, letting my shoulders go limp. The move caught him off guard just enough that he stopped shaking me. And the moment he did, I shoved my knee right between his legs.

The second I made contact with his balls, Ronny doubled over, his hands going slack. I wasted no time dashing around him and going for the door. That was lucky. *So goddamn lucky.* Elation swelled until panic set back in.

Ronny recovered more quickly than I thought and his boots thudded on the cement behind me. I had twenty feet on him, maybe less, but I kept running. My palms slammed into the door and my fingers scrambled for the lock. *Open, dammit. Open!*

The deadbolt flipped easily and I gave the knob a hard turn. I yanked the door open and flew through but kept my grip on the knob. Once I was clear, I whipped the door closed, watching over my shoulder as it slammed shut. Then I made a break for it, turning for the road just in time to collide with a solid chest.

I screamed as two arms wrapped me tight.

"Thea!" Logan pulled me closer, holding me so I wouldn't fall.

I blinked, looking up at a familiar chin. "Logan?"

"Thank god." He breathed in my hair. "Are you okay?"

I shook my head, trying to spin back around to the garage. "It's Ronny. He's in there. He's crazy, Logan! He's been—"

"You can't run from me, you fucking bitch! I want to talk!" The garage door flew open and Ronny rushed around the corner. He skidded to a stop on the driveway when he saw Logan.

Logan moved faster than I'd ever seen a human move. He let me go, took two long strides toward Ronny and started throwing punches. His arms were like snakes, striking Ronny's face, then recoiling only to strike again. It didn't take more than two seconds for Ronny to drop to the ground in a bloody heap.

I swayed on my feet, unable to process what was happening, when two sheriff's deputies flew past me. They went right to Logan, ready to drag him off Ronny, but Logan was already backing away.

"We got him, Sheriff," one of the officers said into his radio while the other fished out a set of handcuffs.

Logan's breath was coming hard as he turned and came back to me. His hands ran up and down my torso in a frenzy. "Are you hurt? Did he touch you?"

"No." I shook my head as my eyes took him all in.

He was wearing a suit, sans the jacket. His tie had come askew underneath his vest and his sleeves were rolled up his forearms.

He was gorgeous.

He was here.

If this was a dream—if I'd fallen asleep on the porch—I didn't want to wake up. Crazy Ronny and all, I'd take this dream every night.

Logan finished his inspection, and when he was convinced I was fine, he wrapped me in his arms. Then he held my head to his heart. My ear was pressed right against its frantic rhythm.

Behind him, I could hear handcuffs being clicked around Ronny's wrist.

"He came after me," I whispered. "He was *watching* us. He sent the emails."

"I know. Sean tracked him down this afternoon." His arms banded tighter. "Thank god, you're okay."

The adrenaline was fading and my muscles were shaking. The sides of my arms throbbed where Ronny had grabbed me. The strength in my legs was seeping into the concrete. So I clung to Logan, letting him hold me up. "You're here?"

"I'm here." He kissed my hair. "And I'm not going anywhere."

twenty-nine

LOGAN

SEATED AT THE KITCHEN TABLE WITH HAZEL AND THEA, I sipped my coffee in silence. Hazel was staring blindly at her own coffee, letting everything Thea had just told her about last night sink in.

I'd never forget the feeling of helplessness I'd had last night. First on the drive to Lark Cove, when I hadn't been able to get ahold of Thea. Then getting here to find out she was gone.

By the time I had arrived in Lark Cove, the sheriff was already at the house to warn Thea. Except Thea was on a walk. Hazel panicked and tried to get ahold of her numerous times, but every call went unanswered. When she called Jackson at the bar and no one had seen Thea, I immediately called Sean.

Within two minutes, he triangulated her cell to my house. It was a miracle that I found her in time and that nothing had happened to her. I wasn't letting myself even consider the unthinkable.

After I knocked that psychopath Ronny unconscious, Thea and I spent the rest of the night at the sheriff's department. We stopped by briefly to assure Hazel that Thea was okay, then went into the station right afterward to deliver our statements.

Even with everything Sean had already sent the officers—emails, prior records, photographs found on Ronny's computer—it took hours before we could leave.

So when Thea and I got back to the cottage, we collapsed into bed for a few quick hours of sleep until we woke up to explain to Hazel what had happened, then take Charlie to her first day of school.

"Daddy?"

I spun around. Charlie was standing in the doorway wearing her pajamas.

I smiled and set down my coffee mug. "Hi, peanut."

She blinked, then flew across the room, launching herself into my lap. Then she wrapped her arms around my neck, hugging me with all her might.

"I missed you." I ran a hand up and down her back. I wanted so badly to tell her that I'd never be far again, but since Thea and I hadn't talked about it yet, I kept my mouth shut and just held my girl.

"Good morning, honey." Thea stood from her chair and came to kiss Charlie's hair.

There were tears in her eyes, a mix of emotion and exhaustion. She'd tossed and turned against my side last night, until I'd held her so tight, using my arms and a leg to trap her down, that she'd finally fallen asleep for a couple of hours.

But even with dark circles under her eyes, she was heart-stopping.

After she'd hugged me enough, Charlie leaned back and smiled. "Can you take me to school?"

I nodded. "I wouldn't miss it for the world."

I wouldn't miss any of her first days of school again. Hell, if she wanted me with her for her first day of senior year, I'd walk her to class.

"Okay." Thea sniffled. "We'd better get ready."

The morning turned into a blur of activity as we had

breakfast and got Charlie ready for school. Then, dressed in her new jeans, new shoes and new shirt, Charlie walked to her first day of first grade, accompanied by Hazel, Thea and me.

She kept ahold of my hand until we took her into her classroom and she put her backpack in her cubby. She'd been anxious on the walk, tugging on her hair and chewing her lip. But when two of her kindergarten friends and soccer teammates rushed up to her, all the nervous butterflies flew away. My peanut gave us a huge smile and wave, then disappeared into the classroom to pick her desk.

"Is it always that hard?" I asked Thea and Hazel as we headed back to the cottage.

I hadn't expected a first-day-of-school drop-off to be so difficult. Charlie had been ready to let go, but I hadn't.

"Yes," Hazel and Thea answered together.

I took Thea's hand, lacing her fingers with mine. Then I brought it up to my lips for a kiss. "I'm glad I made it."

"Me too."

"So what else happened last night?" Hazel asked as we turned down their road. "When will we know what's going to happen with Ronny?"

Thea took a deep breath before summarizing our discussion with the sheriff last night. "They're going to charge him with assault and criminal stalking. I've put in for a restraining order, just in case Ronny gets out of jail, but the sheriff thought the district judge would work quickly on this one. It's likely Ronny won't get bail and he'll be sent straight to sentencing. We've got a meeting with the county attorney's office at two to discuss it all."

With this being Ronny's second stalking offense, the chances of him getting jail time were high. Prison was going to be hard on a sick bastard like Ronny Berkowitz. My money would make sure of it. And when, or if, he was released, he'd be coming home to a life in ashes.

Sean had been up all night, digging into Ronny's system. I doubted we'd ever know for sure, but it appeared that his obsession with Thea had all stemmed from his obsession with Angela, the bartender in Texas.

Because of their physical and occupational similarities, Ronny had latched onto Thea. He'd actually known Angela as a kid. They'd gone to elementary and middle school together. From early on, he'd formed an attachment to her, one that had turned sour when Angela hadn't returned his affections and began dating someone else instead. The same emails that Ronny had sent Thea, Sean had found to Angela. He was still emailing her, even after years of living in Lark Cove.

He'd just added Thea to his routine too.

None of us were sure why he'd come to Montana after he'd been arrested for stalking Angela in Texas. As far as we knew, he had no personal connection here. Sean's theory was that Ronny had come up here for a vacation after being let out of jail in Dallas and had stumbled across Thea at the bar. Since he couldn't have Angela, he'd settled here instead.

If not for me showing up, he might have gone on as a quiet, unsuspecting citizen. He might have just admired Thea from afar, never progressing to the extreme.

"I hope they put him away for a good long while," Hazel said, stopping as we reached the sidewalk leading up to the front door. She stepped closer to Thea, placing her hands on her shoulders. "No more late-night walks."

Thea nodded. "Never again."

"And no more scaring me to death. My heart can't take it."

"Neither can mine."

Hazel pulled Thea in for a tight hug, then kissed her cheek.

"I'm going to take a nap."

As Hazel went inside, I tugged Thea's hand. "Come on."

I led her around the house and across the lawn, straight to the dock. We walked down the worn planks and stood at the end, looking out across the water. The morning air was crisp and fresh. It was the next best smell besides Thea's hair. The sky was a cloudless blue, bright with the early sun.

"It's beautiful this morning." Thea yawned. "But I'm going to need a nap too."

"Same here."

"I'm glad you're here." Thea leaned into my side. "How long are you staying?"

"For a while."

I grinned and patted my jeans pocket. Inside was the ring I'd stashed there this morning.

Proposing today hadn't been on my agenda. Thea and I were both exhausted, physically and emotionally. I had a lot I needed to explain. I'd only grabbed the ring so Thea wouldn't find it accidentally. But I couldn't stop my hand from slipping into my pocket just to touch the delicate band.

Should I? Should I ask her?

Marry me. The words were right there, practically leaping from my lips. I wanted to start building our life together *today*, and when I told her I was moving, I didn't want her to have a shred of doubt that I'd ever leave her again.

I should wait.

Fuck it. I wasn't waiting any longer.

I dug out the ring and spun Thea away from the lake to face me.

"Thea Landry." I took her hand, then dropped to one knee. She deserved a proposal on one knee.

"Oh my god," she gasped as panic flashed across her face.

She probably thought I was here to beg her to move back to the city. "Logan, what are you—"

"Let me go first," I said. "When I asked you what you wanted, you said the impossible. But I don't believe anything is impossible, not for you. I'll do everything in my power to make sure you never have an impossible again. Including living our life together in Lark Cove."

Her eyebrow quirked. "Really?"

"I love you. I want you to be my wife and for us to be a family. Marry me?"

She nodded, a tear sliding down one cheek. "Yes."

Yes. Fireworks exploded in my chest as I slid on her ring. As soon as it was nestled against her knuckle, she dropped to her knees, nearly tackling me in a kiss.

I smiled against her lips, stroking them gently with my tongue. When she opened for me, I slid inside slowly, savoring her taste and the feel of her in my arms. It didn't take long for the spark to ignite and the two of us to get lost in a kiss I'd never forget.

We poured everything into that moment. Love. Passion. Hope. Excitement for the unknown we'd face together.

When we finally broke apart, I looked up to the sky and said a silent *thank you* to the angel who'd led me into her hotel bar all those years ago. The same angel who'd brought me to Montana and back to Thea's side.

"I can't believe it," Thea whispered, studying her ring. I'd gotten the best solitaire in Manhattan and set it in a diamond-studded gold band. From here on out, Thea would live a life full of sparkles. "I just . . . I can't believe it."

"This is real, baby. Me and you and Charlie. It's as real as it gets. I'm not going anywhere."

Her forehead furrowed as she met my eyes. "Are you sure?

What about your job? And your family? I can't ask you to give it all up."

"You didn't. I made this decision because it's the right one. I'd never be happy without you or Charlie, so if this is your home, then it's my home too."

"What about the firm?"

I shrugged. "I quit."

"You quit?" Her jaw dropped. "How can you quit? You love your job."

"Yes, I did. I loved working hard. I loved the challenge. At the time, I needed that in my life. Now, I don't. I don't want a job that keeps me from you at night. Or makes me miss breakfast and bedtime with Charlie. Being a lawyer isn't at the top of my priorities anymore."

My first priority was watching her and Charlie shine.

I'd finally realized what mattered.

The dock planks were digging into my knees, so I shifted Thea, moving us so we were seated and looking out across the water.

"So what are you going to do?" she asked.

"I'm sure I won't be bored. Nolan and I are juggling some responsibilities around at the foundation so I can play a more active role. I'm going to spend some quality time on my new boat. And I'm taking over coaching for Charlie's soccer team."

She laughed. "Are you now?"

"Next year, we're going all the way." I put my arm around Thea's shoulder, tucking her close. "I'll be able to do ninety percent of my work from home here, but there will be times I'll have to go back to the city for family things and such. Foundation meetings I can't miss. But it won't be often."

"I can live with that."

"Maybe one day, you'll want to come with me. I understand

it might take time, but I'd love the chance to show you the part of the city I love. We can make our own memories there, good ones to overshadow the bad. If it takes ten years, then I'll wait. If it never happens, then that's okay too."

She thought about it for a moment. "I think I'd like that. One day. What does your family think about all this?"

"They'll come around." And if they didn't, then it wasn't my problem. If I had to give up the Kendrick family responsibilities to ensure that *my* Kendrick family was happy, then I'd do it every day of the week and twice on Sunday.

"You're sure?"

I kissed her hair. "I'm sure."

We sat there for a while, watching as a flock of birds flew over the water. Across the bay, a woman was walking her dog. A few houses down, someone was mowing their lawn.

My phone rang in my pocket and I shifted my weight to dig it out. "Sorry. It's Granny."

"You should take it. I don't mind." She leaned away, but I pulled her right back in as I answered the call and put it on speaker.

Other than Charlie, I couldn't think of anyone else I wanted to tell about our engagement.

"Hi," I answered.

"Hello, Grandson. What are you up to today?"

"Not much." I grinned. "I was actually going to call you today to tell you that I figured it out."

"Figured what out?"

"The secret to life."

Granny's laughter rang through the speaker. "I take it you're in Montana?"

"I am." Right where I belonged.

"Well, it's about time. Hello, Thea."

Thea giggled. "Hi, Joan. How are you?"

"Much better now. I'll let you two go, but please have Charlie call me tonight. I'd like to hear about her first day of school. And Logan?"

"Yes?"

"You have two weeks to get your house set up for guests." With that, she hung up the phone.

"I guess we have some work to do," Thea muttered. "We can't have police tape by the garage when Granny shows up."

"Hey." I took her chin, turning it so I could see her eyes. "If you don't want that house, we'll find another one." I'd never force her to live there, not after what had happened last night.

"No." She shook her head. "I think it will be fine. It's such a pretty home and in the best spot. It will probably take me hours to clean, but I don't want to let it go just yet. Maybe we could go over later and you could give me the full tour. See how that goes and then move forward from there."

"All right."

I let the cleaning comment go for now. She'd never clean or cook or wash clothes another day in her life unless she wanted to. But we'd work into that after the dust from last night's drama had settled.

The two of us went back to watching the lake, both yawning from time to time but neither making a move to leave. A fish jumped not far off and I made a mental note to take the boat out tomorrow. Maybe Thea could come with me and we could break it in properly. I wanted to talk her into forgetting the condoms from here on out. Call me a barbarian but getting her pregnant was the next item on my to-do list.

I just hoped she was as eager as I was to expand our family. Because this time, I wasn't going to miss a thing. I'd be here for the pregnancy test, the doctor's appointments and the midnight feedings. Every moment for the rest of my life, I'd spend with Thea.

"Logan?"

"Hmm?"

She looked up at me. "I love you."

"I love you too."

"It's hard to believe this is really happening."

I smiled. "Believe it. Always believe."

epilogue

THEA

Three years later . . .

"WHAT ARE YOU DOING HERE?" JACKSON SNAPPED AS he walked into the bar and spotted me mixing a drink.

"What am I doing here?" I poured a shot of vodka into my shaker. "Working. Obviously."

"You're not supposed to be here." He turned his glare to Logan. "Why is she here?"

Logan chuckled and held up his hands. "I tried to get her to go home, but she threw a beer bottle at me."

I winced. I hadn't been able to help myself with all of Logan's nagging to take a break. One minute the beer bottle was in my hand and the next it was flying across the room. Pregnancy had stolen my sanity.

Lucky for me, Logan had fast hands and caught it before it broke.

"Sorry, gorgeous."

He walked up behind me, putting his arms around my enormous belly and kissed my neck. "It's okay, baby. I know you're miserable."

"I am." Tears flooded my eyes, something that happened

every five seconds. "I just want her to come out."

"She will. We just have to give her a little more time."

Easy for him to say. He wasn't nine months and five days pregnant. I hadn't slept in days and I was on the verge of a complete meltdown. Exhausted and uncomfortable, my temper flashed on and off faster than a strobe light. If I wasn't crying, then I was snapping at people.

The doctors said nothing was wrong with the baby, she just wasn't ready yet. *Take it easy. Enjoy this quiet time. Be patient.*

Fuck patience. I'd spent the last two days in bed trying to relax without luck. I'd finally gotten so fed up that I'd come to the bar in hopes that work would distract me from my swollen feet, aching back and raging heartburn.

"What are you doing here?" Logan asked Jackson as he took a stool. "It's our weekend at the bar."

He shrugged. "I just thought I'd come and keep you company for a while. I didn't know *she'd* be here. Go home, Thea. Or for fuck's sake, at least sit down."

My hands shot across the bar, stretching for Jackson's neck. But Logan held me back before I could strangle my best friend.

"Why are you tormenting my wife?" Logan asked.

Jackson just grinned. "Maybe if I get her fired up a bit, that kid will pop out and she'll turn back into Nice Thea. We can't afford to keep scaring customers away just because they ask for a lemon wedge in their water."

"It wasn't just a lemon wedge!" I shouted. "She already had ten! Ten lemons in one glass of water. Who does that? And I didn't scare her away. I just reminded her that we served lemonade."

Logan's chest shook against my back as he laughed. "Baby, you told her the only way she was getting another lemon was if she found a lemon tree and plucked one herself."

"We don't need customers like her," I muttered.

The woman had come in with a couple of friends about a month ago. Every time I'd waddle over, she'd need just one more thing. Lemon wedge after lemon wedge, followed by a glass of ice, a cocktail napkin and two more straws. The final lemon wedge had pushed me over the top.

"So where's Charlie and Collin?" Jackson asked.

"With Hazel." Logan let me go to get Jackson a beer. "They're spending the evening with her and then having a sleepover at the cottage tonight."

Hazel loved the weekends when Logan and I were at the bar. It was an arrangement we'd made with Jackson not long after Logan had moved to Lark Cove.

It had taken us less than a month to get pregnant with our son, Collin. I think we conceived him one lazy afternoon out on the boat. When we found out I was pregnant, Logan and I agreed it was time to cut back at the bar.

With Jackson's agreement, we hired our first employee.

Dakota had been new to Lark Cove at the time, so he'd been more than willing to take some of my evening and weekend shifts. Our weekend rotation just worked out naturally from there. Dakota had one weekend. Jackson another. Logan and I the next.

He was always my weekend partner.

Not once in the last three years had Logan suggested I give up my job at the bar. It wasn't like we needed the income. But he'd embraced the Lark Cove Bar as part of our family. On our weekends, we worked here together. If I had a new idea, I ran it by him before anyone else. He'd even helped me establish a partnership so Jackson and I could buy Hazel out and fund her retirement.

My husband was so damn smart it amazed me.

In the last three years, he'd grown the Kendrick Foundation considerably, especially their influence on the West Coast. It gave Logan an outlet to channel his brilliance and ambition. It gave him a passion.

Everything we did was for our own happiness.

"Guess what?" Logan handed Jackson his beer. "I got a call from that indoor soccer league up in Kalispell this morning. They agreed to let us add a Lark Cove team if we can get enough players."

"Yes!" Jackson pumped his fist. "We'll get enough. I'll start making calls."

The two of them had thrown themselves into Charlie's soccer life, something she loved almost as much as them. Any of the old animosity between Logan and Jackson had vanished the night Ronny came after me. They'd both gone over-the-top protective for a few months and come out as friends.

They co-coached Charlie's soccer team each summer, and now they'd coach the winter league, even if that meant shuttling kids up to Kalispell once a week for indoor games. I wouldn't be surprised if Logan had an indoor field built here, just so they could host.

Logan didn't flaunt his money, but when it came to the kids or me, he didn't skimp. He took me on a vacation twice a year because he wanted to show me the world. And slowly, he was making New York a place I didn't mind visiting.

We still had the penthouse, but we mostly spent time in New York with Joan and his parents. Thomas and Lillian had come around to Logan living in Montana, and they'd even bought a place a couple of miles away for their vacations in Lark Cove. Aubrey was an incredible aunt to the kids, even though she lived so far away. But she called every week and was always sending over gifts.

Sofia eventually came around too, just in time to attend the small wedding we'd had in the backyard of our house. I doubted we'd ever be best friends, but I was glad to see that she'd been working hard lately to rid herself of the toxic people in her life, including Alice.

"Hey, Thea." Wayne, my one and only regular these days, sidled up to the bar.

"Hi, Wayne." I smiled at him and went to the tap for his favorite beer. It had hit Wayne hard to learn about Ronny's stalking. The two had been friends, or at least he'd thought so. Now Wayne sat by himself when he came in each night and I made it a point to spend more time chatting with him.

That was after Logan had instructed Sean to do a full background check on every person he and Jackson had deemed a "regular."

It had taken me a while to get over the garage incident with Ronny. But eventually, I let it go. Logan had originally intended for the garage to become my art studio, but it was too big and, well, clean. So we used it for the cars and he'd had my old shed moved over from the cottage.

"Are you sure you should be working, Thea?" Wayne asked as I set down his beer.

I shrugged. "I can't stay at home anymore. I'm going crazy."

"Want me to go buy you some castor oil? My sister says it was the only way she could get her kids out."

I gagged. "No, thanks. I tried that with Charlie when she was late and it was awful."

"How about some spicy food? I'll split a jalapeno pizza with you."

"Let me throw some sausage on there and you've got yourself a deal."

He smiled. "You're on."

I turned to go to the kitchen, but Logan was right there. "I'll make your pizza. Why don't you sit for just a minute?" When I frowned, he just grinned. "Please, baby? Just sit for a few minutes. For me."

"Okay." I sighed. My feet *were* getting tired. I gave him a quick kiss and shuffled around the bar, taking the stool between Jackson and Wayne.

The three of us chatted for a while until the pizza came out. I didn't have much room for food, with the baby taking up so much space, but I managed to eat two pieces. I was picking at the crust of the third when the front door flew open.

Charlie ran through first with a huge smile on her face. Collin was right on her tail, doing his best to keep up.

"Hey!" I slid off my stool and stood just in time to catch Charlie at my side. Collin collided with my legs next. "What are you guys doing here?"

"We went to check on you at home but you weren't there," Charlie said. "Gran thought you'd be here with Daddy for dinner."

Hazel came through the door with a scowl on her face. "You're supposed to be resting."

"So I've been told," I muttered.

"Who do I hear?" Logan came out from the back, where he'd been putting in another pizza. The instant Collin spotted him, he abandoned my leg.

"Daddy!" Collin giggled as Logan scooped him up and tossed him into the air.

My heart melted at the sight of them together. Charlie looked more and more like Logan every day while Collin was the two-year-old version of me. But he and his dad shared a special bond. They were inseparable.

Logan had vowed not to miss a moment of Collin's life, and

he hadn't. The same was true with Charlie. Every step of the way, he was the most engaged and loving father I ever could have hoped for. And I knew he'd be the same with our baby girl.

I stroked my belly, hoping that spicy pizza would do the trick. Then I sat back down and spent the rest of the evening talking with my husband while he bartended and my kids ate some pizza before going to the cottage with their Gran.

Jackson left to go home not long after dinner, and by eleven o'clock, it was just me and Logan in the bar.

We were sitting in a back-corner booth. Both of us were crammed in on one side because this spot had the best view out the front windows. From here, you could see outside and across the highway where the lake peeked out between a grove of trees. Tonight, the moonlight was dancing on the rippled water.

"I'm so tired." I leaned deeper into Logan's side and yawned.

"I know you are, baby. I wish there was something I could do."

I smiled. "Just love me. Even when I'm acting crazy and hoarding lemon wedges."

He chuckled. "I love you no matter what." With his arm around me, he hugged me closer. "We need to get you home. Let's close up early."

"Good idea."

But neither of us made a move to leave. Instead, we sat together enjoying the peaceful moment until my first contraction squeezed. Then the second. During the third, Logan was racing down the highway toward the hospital in Kalispell.

And by nine the next morning, Logan and I were cuddled together in a hospital bed with Charlie, Collin and our baby girl, Camila Hazel Kendrick.

My family.

Finding them had been so worth the wait.

Want more Logan and Thea?
Sign up HERE to receive a bonus epilogue!

dl.bookfunnel.com / wfmpw0d261

acknowledgments

First and foremost, thank you, my reader! I am so grateful for your love and support.

Thanks to my unbelievable editing and proofreading team. Elizabeth Nover. Ellie McLove. Julie Deaton. I would be lost without you. Thank you, Sarah Hansen and Stacey Blake, for making my books beautiful, inside and out. And to Danielle Sanchez, my incredible publicist, for everything you do.

To all of the bloggers who have helped spread the word about this book, thank you from the bottom of my heart. To my ARC and street teams, thank you for all the excitement and energy you bring to every release. To Kaitlyn and Jenn, thank you for reading the first drafts, middle drafts, last drafts, and all the other drafts in between. To Ana, Karen and Jennifer, thank you for being my sounding board and number one fans.

And lastly, thank you to my husband and two incredible boys. Thanks for understanding when I get lost in a book. For not caring when the house is a mess. And for loving McDonald's cheeseburgers when I don't have time to cook. I love you.

also available from
DEVNEY PERRY

The Birthday List

Jamison Valley Series
The Coppersmith Farmhouse

The Clover Chapel

The Lucky Heart

The Outpost

The Bitterroot Inn

Lark Cove Series
Tattered

about the author

Devney is the *USA Today* bestselling author of the Jamison Valley series. Born and raised in Montana, she loves writing books set in her treasured home state. After working in the technology industry for nearly a decade, she abandoned conference calls and project schedules to enjoy a slower pace at home with her husband and two sons. Writing one book, let alone many, was not something she'd ever expected to do. But now that she's discovered her true passion for writing romance, she has no plans to ever stop.

Don't miss out on Devney's latest book news. Subscribe to her newsletter!
www.devneyperry.com

Devney loves hearing from her readers.
Connect with her on social media!

www.devneyperry.com
Facebook: www.facebook.com/devneyperrybooks
Instagram: www.instagram.com/devneyperry
Twitter: twitter.com/devneyperry
BookBub: www.bookbub.com/authors/devney-perry

Enjoy this preview from *Timid*,
book two in the Lark Cove series.

timid

prologue

WILLA

"D AD, IS IT OKAY IF I GET TWO—"

The Snickers bar in my hand slipped out of my grasp and dropped to the floor. My jaw was down there too, thanks to one glimpse at the man walking through the gas station door.

He was, without contest, the most beautiful man in the world. *No, the universe.* He'd stepped straight out of my *Seventeen* magazine and into the Lark Cove Gas 'N' Go.

His golden-blond hair was buzzed short to his scalp, a cut seen regularly in the hallways of my high school because most boys in Lark Cove had their moms whip out the bathroom clippers once a month. Except nothing about this man's haircut was boyish. On him, it was rugged. A little dangerous even. This guy couldn't be bothered to style his hair. He had more important things to do, like bench-press cars or battle zombies or rescue kittens from treetops.

Hidden in the candy aisle, I peered around a display of Doritos as he grabbed a bottle of water from the cooler by the register. He set it on the counter and dug out a wallet from his back jeans pocket.

"Just the water?" the clerk asked.

The man nodded. "And the gas on pump two."

A shiver ran down my spine at his low, rumbling voice. He made the word *gas* and *pump* sound hot.

The clerk punched in some numbers on the till. "Anything else?"

The man leaned back from the counter, eyeing the row of candy bars placed below for impulse buys, then grabbed a Snickers.

We liked the same candy. That *had* to mean something. Like . . . fate.

He handed the bar to the clerk before casually leaning an elbow on the counter. His shoulders pivoted my way, enough so I could get a better look at his face but not enough he could see me spying. With a smile, he nodded to the lottery ticket machine. "I'll take a Powerball too. Maybe it's my lucky day."

My knees wobbled at that smile. *Wowzah.* His soft lips stretched over straight, white teeth. His sky-blue eyes brightened. The smile softened his square jaw just enough that he became a whole different kind of dangerous. It was the kind that made me want to do stupid, embarrassing things just to get a fraction of his attention. It was a smile that vaporized the two-year crush I'd had on Brendon Jacoby, my lab partner in biology.

I couldn't like a boy now that I'd seen this *man*.

Who was he? He had to be a tourist passing through town. I'd lived in Lark Cove my entire life and never seen this guy before, which meant I'd probably never see him again.

My stomach dropped. Doing the only thing I could think of, I closed my eyes and said a prayer that we'd get a freak July snowstorm and the man would be trapped here for at least a week, preferably without a place to stay other than my house.

"Hey there, Jackson." My eyes popped open as Dad walked up to the register with his hand extended. "Nice to see you again."

"You too." A frenzy of excitement shot through my veins as

the two shook hands. "It's Nate, right?"

"That's right." Dad smiled. "My wife, Betty, and I were down at the bar last week."

"For your anniversary." Jackson snapped his fingers as he put it together.

"Right again. Are you getting all settled into town?"

"I am. I didn't have much to move so it made unpacking easy."

Jackson said something else to Dad, but my heart was beating so hard I couldn't focus on their conversation.

Jackson. His name was Jackson. And he lived in Lark Cove.

"Willa."

Jackson and Willa. Willa and Jackson. Our names went together like peanut butter and jelly.

"Willa."

Maybe people in town would merge us into a nickname. *Will-son. Jack-illa*. Both were terrible, but I'd think of something better tonight.

"Earth to Willa!"

I flinched, my eyes whipping up. "Huh?"

Dad shook his head and laughed. "Lost in outer space again?"

"Yeah." Heat crept up my cheeks as I bent to pick up my fallen Snickers. With it in hand, I came out from behind the aisle.

"Jackson, meet my daughter." Before Dad could finish his introduction, the clerk stole his attention, asking if he wanted his weekly scratch ticket too.

"Hey." Jackson waved. "I'm Jackson."

"I'm Willa," I mumbled. Articulating words was impossible standing in front of him.

"Nice to meet you, Willow."

"It's, um . . . Willa."

But Jackson had already turned away. The clerk had his

attention again, joking with both Jackson and Dad that if either won the lottery, he wanted a kickback.

With his purchases in hand, Jackson said good-bye to Dad and went right for the door and pushed outside.

"Ready to go?" Dad asked.

I nodded and handed him my Snickers.

As the clerk rang up my candy bar, Dad's ticket, a bag of M&M's and two cans of Coke, I peered outside, hoping to get one last glimpse of Jackson. But with the front windows stacked full of beer boxes and a rotating rack of maps blocking the only other free space, I couldn't see anything past our car parked right outside the door.

I drummed my fingers on the counter, willing the clerk to make change faster. Finally, he handed Dad a dollar and some coins, and I bolted for the door, stepping into the bright, summer sunshine just in time to see Jackson slide into an old Chevy truck.

"Did you forget something, honey?" Dad appeared at my side, handing me my Snickers and Coke.

"Whoopsie. Sorry, Dad."

He just laughed. "It's okay."

I took my things, then slowly walked toward our car, keeping one eye on Jackson's truck as it pulled onto the highway. When it disappeared behind a patch of trees, I sighed and resumed normal speed, opening the passenger door and sliding inside.

Luckily for me, Dad didn't comment on my strange behavior. He just popped the top on his Coke, took a sip and backed us out of the parking lot to go home.

"Um, Dad? Who was that?"

He pulled onto the highway, going the opposite direction of where Jackson had turned. "Who was who?"

"That guy you introduced me to in the gas station. I haven't seen him around before." I added that last part hoping I sounded more curious than desperate for information.

"That's Jackson Page. He just moved to town to work with Hazel down at the bar. I think he's from New York or New Jersey? I can't remember."

"That's good." *More like freaking fantastic.*

Dad gave me a sideways glance. "Is it?"

Uh-oh. Maybe I hadn't hidden my crush as well as I'd hoped. "Totally!" I came out too loud as I scrambled for a recovery. "It's, um, good that Hazel has some help. Don't you think she's kind of old to be working at the bar all by herself?"

Dad frowned as he turned down the street toward our house. "Old? Hazel isn't all that much older than me and your mom. But I guess teenagers think anyone past thirty is old."

I giggled. "Ancient. You're practically fossils."

"Ouch." He clutched his heart, pretending to be hurt as he pulled into our driveway.

"Just kidding."

Dad smiled. "Try to save part of your candy bar until after dinner."

"Deal." I hopped out of the car, escaping inside while Dad went to check on Mom's progress in her vegetable garden.

I yanked my diary out from underneath my mattress and got comfortable on my bed. Then I tore into my Snickers bar, chewing as I opened to a blank page. My pen flew across the paper, leaving a trail of purple ink as I recounted every second at the gas station. When I was done, I closed the book and clutched it to my chest, smiling at the last line I'd written.

One day, I am going to marry Jackson Page.

I just had to get him to notice me first.

one

WILLA

Nine years later . . .

"THERE'S ONE," I WHISPERED, POINTING TOWARD THE shooting star that streaked across the midnight sky. Even though I was alone, pointing them out had become a habit. My dad had been my stargazing partner for as long as I could remember. As a kid, he'd taught me about the constellations and galaxies. We'd have contests to see who could spot the most shooting stars.

These days, he preferred to sleep at night unless there was a special stellar occasion, like a comet or a lunar eclipse. So my nights counting falling stars were done alone. I'd come out to the playground behind my house, sit in the same swing with my eyes to the sky, then report to Dad the next morning how many I'd counted.

Sending some wood chips flying, I kicked off the ground and got my swing moving. My hands gripped the chains as I pumped my legs for some speed. When I had my momentum built, I let my head fall back. The tips of my long, blond hair nearly touched the ground as I smiled at the Milky Way.

Today had been a good day. No, an *incredible* day.

Months ago, I'd petitioned a charitable foundation in New

York to buy the Flathead Summer Camp, the children's camp where I worked as the director. It was owned by a local church, but after years of barely covering the overhead and maintenance costs, they'd decided it was time to let it go. The church had wanted to sell it to someone who'd continue it as a camp, but with no buyers, the camp would have to be closed down permanently and the land sold off for private development.

But kids needed that camp. They needed a place to escape for a week every summer without toys or iPads or video games. So I'd written a proposal and sent it to various charitable organizations around the country, then wished on a hundred shooting stars for a miracle.

I still couldn't believe my wish had come true. Earlier today, the Kendrick Foundation from New York City had agreed to buy my camp. And as a bonus, they were keeping me on as director.

Tonight, I wasn't wishing on falling stars. I was simply grateful.

My swing slowed to a stop. I pulled myself upright and took in the quiet night. Behind me was Lark Cove School. Its cream cinderblock walls glowed with reflected moonlight. The school and the long playground took up the whole block, except for five houses—three straight ahead and two to the left, one of which was mine.

My parents had never needed to build an outdoor play area. Instead, growing up, I'd just cross the invisible boundary that separated our lawn from the playground's and use the same swing set and jungle gym that I played on during recess.

All of the houses were dark tonight, the only light coming from across the street where a few porch lights were on. I was admiring a hanging basket of flowers when a dark figure strode onto the sidewalk.

I gasped, nearly falling off my swing as he stepped off the

cement and onto the grass.

My fingers slipped into the right pocket of my navy sundress, palming the small canister of pepper spray Dad had bought me for nights when I came out here alone. He'd also given me the whistle I was wearing around my neck.

I contemplated jumping off my swing and hurrying home, but stopped short.

I knew that stride. No, that *swagger*.

It belonged to the man who'd made my heart race and cheeks flush since I was seventeen.

Jackson.

Was he coming over here? I looked over my shoulder, expecting someone behind me, but there wasn't.

Forgetting the pepper spray, I used both hands to smooth down my hair. It had a natural wave that looked great for the first eight hours of the day, but somewhere between hours nine and ten, it grew exponentially in volume and frizz. With it sort of tamed, I swallowed the nerves in my throat just as Jackson stepped off the grass and into the wood chips surrounding the swings.

"Hey, Willa."

Oh. My. Goodness. He'd called me by the right name. Finally! After years of correcting him each time he called me Willow, hearing my name in his deep voice gave me wings.

Heat broke across my cheeks and I managed a breathy "Hi."

"Is this swing taken?"

I shook my head.

He grinned, then somehow fit his large frame into the small black rubber seat. His broad shoulders extended past the chains by at least five inches on each side, his jean-covered legs too long for the short seat.

"Nice night."

I nodded. "Yeah."

It came out quieter than I had intended, probably because I'd stopped breathing. So I ducked my chin into a shoulder and pulled in a long breath through my nostrils, hoping he couldn't hear me shaking.

The chains on his swing creaked as he dug a heel into the wood chips and propelled himself backward. "It's probably not safe for you to be out here at night."

"I have this whistle." I held it up so he could see it. "And some pepper spray in my pocket."

"Is that what you were reaching for when you spotted me?"

"Sorry." Mortification crept up my face, flaming my already hot cheeks. The last thing I wanted was for Jackson Page to think I was scared of him. Well, I was scared. More like terrified. But only because I'd crushed on him for basically my entire teenage and adult life.

"I'm just teasing you." He chuckled. "I'm glad you have the spray. Though I'd feel even better if you were behind a locked door at night, not sitting alone in a playground."

I gripped the chains on my swing tighter so I couldn't jump up and start dancing around. He was concerned about me. *Me.* Willa Doon, the girl who'd been trying to get his attention for nearly a decade.

Jackson pushed off the ground again, letting the silence of the night surround us.

Too shy to say anything, I resumed my swinging too. The color in my face drained away in the cool rush of air. Every time Jackson swung forward and I swung back, I'd catch a whiff of his spicy scent, cloves mixed with forest moss.

A combination that shouldn't have smelled so good, but boy did it ever.

"Crazy day."

"What?" I asked as it clicked what he was talking about. "Oh! You mean with Thea. Yeah. That was crazy."

Two executives from the Kendrick Foundation had flown to Montana today to check out my camp. I'd taken them on a tour and that's when they'd agreed to buy the place and keep me on as director. To celebrate, I'd taken them down to the bar for a drink.

The Lark Cove Bar was where Jackson had worked for years alongside his childhood friend, Thea. I'd gotten to know Thea and her five-year-old daughter, Charlie, over the years. They were awesome, but I'd never had the courage to ask about Charlie's father.

It turns out, I hadn't needed to ask. I'd had a front-row seat as Thea had dropped the bomb of a lifetime on one of the executives I'd brought to the bar.

Logan Kendrick, the chairman of the foundation and now my boss, had met Thea years ago in the city. I hadn't gotten the dirty details, but I'd deduced from the show that they'd hooked up without sharing important info, like last names or phone numbers. She'd gotten pregnant and come to Montana as a single mom. He'd come out today to buy a camp and gotten a daughter as a bonus.

It was the biggest drama we'd had in Lark Cove in ages.

"How is Thea doing?" I asked.

"I dunno." He went back to his swinging.

I pushed off the ground, swinging back and forth too, stealing glances at Jackson as our swings crossed at the bottom.

That was the story of my life, watching Jackson Page. It sounded like the title for a made-for-TV movie.

I'd been watching him for years, ever since the first day I'd seen him.

As a teenager, I'd search for him or his truck everywhere.

Occasionally, I'd see him at the gas station filling up. Or sometimes I'd spot him at the town grocery store or eating at Bob's Diner. There weren't a lot of places to go in Lark Cove, and since he didn't go to our church and had no reason to come to my school, I'd been forced to settle for chaste glimpses every month or so.

My diaries had the exact dates and times.

I'd seen Jackson even less after high school. I'd moved two hours away to attend college in Missoula, and my infrequent trips home had meant six or more months between sightings. By the time I'd come back home, I'd been certain I would be returning to news that he'd gotten serious about a woman.

No sirree. He was still the same playboy he'd been for years.

Despite all the floozies and bimbos, I'd never stopped crushing on Jackson and I'd never stopped watching for him. It was just easier to do now that I was old enough to go into the bar.

Tonight was different though. Tonight, it was just the two of us. Not once in nine years had we shared a space alone. And because he wasn't putting on a show for his customers or flirting with every woman in Flathead County—well, except me—I saw something in his eyes I hadn't seen before.

Loneliness.

Deep, dark, empty loneliness.

I wanted to jump off my swing and hug it out of him.

Had Jackson always been lonely? Had I been so mesmerized by his handsome face that I'd missed this all along?

Outside of Thea and Hazel at the bar, I'd never seen him around town with a buddy. He'd never had a passenger in his truck or a partner in his fishing boat. The few times I'd seen him at the diner, he'd been eating alone.

Year after year of watching, it was sufficient to say that I'd become an expert on all things Jackson Page.

So how had I missed this loneliness he wore for all the stars to see?

I let my feet dangle and my swing slowed. Jackson gave his a few more pumps but then stopped too. As the two of us rocked back and forth, I took a deep breath and mustered the courage to speak.

"Are you okay, Jackson?"

His shoulders sagged, digging into the chains. He looked over with a sad smile. "I'm having a rough night."

"Want to talk about it? I'm a good listener."

He looked out over the grass. "It's crazy, don't you think? That after all these years, this guy shows up and all of a sudden Charlie has a dad?"

I didn't know if Logan's appearance would spell *miracle* or *disaster* for Thea and Charlie. But I did know that Jackson loved that little girl like his own. "For what it's worth, I spent some time with Logan today. He seems genuinely nice."

Jackson shrugged. "We'll see. Thea never said anything bad about him, but I don't trust the guy. I just . . . don't want things to change."

I didn't have anything wise to say or advice to offer. So I shuffled my feet, scooting my swing a bit closer to his before reaching over to give him a reassuring touch.

The moment my hand settled on his forearm, an electric shock zapped my fingers. What was that? I almost pulled back to examine my palm but stopped, not wanting to let him go. I'd never touched Jackson before, not even to shake his hand.

His face whipped to mine, his eyes widening. Focusing.

My breath caught at the intensity of his gaze, but I still didn't remove my hand. Instead, I wobbled a smile and stroked his skin with my thumb.

His eyes softened. "Thanks for listening."

"Anytime." With my cue to let go, I picked up my feet and swung back to my groove.

He pushed off the ground, resuming an easy swing. "What are you doing out here?"

"Just counting shooting stars." My eyes tipped up to the sky just in time to see another. "There." My finger shot in the air. "Did you see it?"

"Yeah."

"Aren't they pretty?"

"Beautiful." But he wasn't staring at the sky. He was looking at me.

I blushed and dropped my arm as my heartbeat raced. Had Jackson just called me beautiful? Because it seemed like it. I didn't have a lot of experience with men. None really. But that definitely sounded like flirting. And *gosh,* I liked it.

"Sure are a lot of stars. You don't see stars like this in the city."

I nodded. "I love it out here. I come out as much as I can in the summer to enjoy them. I live right over there." I pointed past him to the back of my parents' house. "Above the garage." Yes, it was borderline loser to live twenty feet from my parents, but it was free and there wasn't a huge rental market in Lark Cove.

Jackson's boots skidded on the wood chips as he stopped his swing and stood. With his hand extended, he nodded to my place. "Come on. I'll walk you home."

I practically flew out of my seat. The minute my fingers slid against his palm, I got another one of those zaps. My breathing came in erratic pants rather than smooth ins and outs as he led me toward my house. With every step, I wished home wasn't so close and my mom's garden miles away, not just yards.

I tried not to wiggle my fingers, keeping them still in his grip so he wouldn't let me go. But I was so excited to be holding

Jackson's hand, it was nearly impossible. Every atom in my body was buzzing. Never before had electrons whirled around protons and neutrons so fast.

Much too soon, we reached the base of the staircase that ran up the backside of the garage. I'd expected him to let go of my hand, but he didn't. He towered over my five-five with an odd stare.

Maybe it was the light, or lack thereof, but his eyes seemed duller than usual, the blue clouded by a slight haze, and they looked tired.

I would stand here forever holding Jackson's hand, but as exhaustion rolled off his wide shoulders, I reluctantly slipped my hand free. "I, um . . . thanks. Maybe we could—"

One moment I was trying to find the words to ask him out to dinner. The next, he was kissing me.

Jackson Page was kissing me.

On the lips.

His thick hands came to my cheeks. His calloused fingers slipped into the roots of my hair. And his tongue ran over my bottom lip.

My eyes went wide. Was this happening? His eyelids were closed. His nose was brushing mine. Our mouths were touching.

Jackson Page was kissing me. *On. The. Lips!*

I couldn't *not* smile. When I did, he took advantage of the part in my lips and his tongue slid inside, tickling the inside of my cheek.

I gasped and turned to mush. Gripping his forearms so I wouldn't fall, I relaxed completely into his kiss, letting my eyelids fall. His taste was incredible. It was minty with a hint of citrus. There was something else on his tongue too, but I wasn't sure what.

Hesitantly, I stroked my tongue against his. I had no idea if I was doing this right, but when Jackson moaned into my mouth, I did it again.

From there, whatever he did, I copied. When he crested his tongue over my top lip, I did the same to his bottom. When he nipped at the corner of my mouth, I gave him one right back. And when he sucked my bottom lip between his teeth, I waited until his was free, then did the same.

It was hot and wet and magic.

The scruff on his jaw made the skin around my lips the exact right amount of raw. An ache unlike anything I'd felt before curled in my belly. A throb pulsed between my legs. Without thinking, I shuffled my hips closer, brushing against the hardness in his jeans.

He hissed, sending a blast of air between us that cooled the wet skin above my lip. Then after one last lick, he pulled away.

"Sorry," he whispered, not letting go of my face. "I didn't mean—"

"Don't," I breathed. "Don't be sorry."

Because I'd never be sorry for that kiss.

My first kiss.

Something I'd avoided for years because I'd been waiting for *this* kiss with Jackson.

"I'd better go." His hands dropped from my face and he planted a soft kiss on my forehead. Then he backed away three steps before turning around. Even then, he glanced over his shoulder a couple of times as he walked through my parents' yard.

I waved and hurried up my stairs. The minute I closed the door behind me, I went to the window beside the door since it overlooked the playground. Crouched on my floor, hidden behind a curtain, I watched as Jackson passed the swings and the silver slide. It didn't take him long to step back onto the sidewalk and turn toward his house.

When he disappeared behind the corner of the school, I sank to the floor and let a happy grin stretch my cheeks.

After years of watching and waiting and hoping, Jackson had finally noticed me.

Me, the shy girl who'd loved him from a distance. Tonight, he'd made one of my dreams come true.

Sleep didn't come easy after my kiss with Jackson. I replayed it over and over and over, touching my swollen lips until eventually I crashed around four a.m. When my alarm went off at six, I jumped out of bed with a perky smile, like I'd slept for a day.

The smile stayed all day long. Every time I got weary, I'd think of Jackson's kiss and get hit with a fresh burst of energy.

By six o'clock, I was eager to get away from the camp. Not because I hadn't had a great day with the kids and my staff, but because I wanted so badly to see Jackson again. So instead of going home, like I normally did on Tuesday evenings, I steered my Ford Escape toward the bar.

The parking lot was full but I squeezed into a tight space in the last row. I did a quick check in my visor mirror, pulling my hair into a topknot and smearing on some lip gloss. Then I popped a piece of cinnamon gum. I doubted Jackson would kiss me while working, but he might and I wanted to be prepared.

I walked into the bar with a confidence I hadn't felt in years, maybe ever. I strolled right up to the bar, sliding into a rickety old stool next to Wayne and Ronny, two locals who came down to the bar most nights. Normally, I picked a table in the middle of the room or a booth in the corner, somewhere I wasn't conspicuous.

But not tonight.

Tonight, I was going to be front and center.

"Hi, guys."

"Hey, Willa." Wayne patted my shoulder. "How are you today?"

"I'm great. How are you?"

"Can't complain."

I loved that Wayne always had a smile. I'd known him my entire life and couldn't remember a time when he wasn't in a good mood. Even during his divorce. He was in his late fifties, like my dad, and worked at the school doing maintenance. He'd always walk the halls whistling a cheery tune.

"Um, is Jackson here tonight?" I asked, my eyes scanning the bar.

Wayne didn't answer because at that moment, Jackson came out of the back carrying a pizza pan. He delivered it to one of the tables, then came back around the bar.

The minute he made eye contact, my heart jumped into my throat. "Hey," I breathed as the smile on my face got impossibly wider.

Jackson grinned. "Hey, Willow. What can I get for you?"

My smile faltered. *Willow?* I stared at him, hoping he'd start laughing at his not-so-funny joke, but he just stood there, waiting to take my drink order.

"It's Willa. With an *a*," I snapped. "Will-a."

He winced. "Sorry. I suck at names. Did you want a drink?"

I suck at names. That's how he was going to play this? He was going to pretend that last night hadn't happened? Was kissing me really so bad that he'd resort to childish games?

"I'll get your drink, Willa," Wayne offered. "How about a Bud Light?"

I nodded, unable to speak.

"Coming up." Jackson whipped a pint glass from beneath the bar and took it to the tap.

"It's still weird to me that you're old enough to drink." Wayne chuckled. "I remember you coming into the school every summer when you were just a little thing, helping your daddy get his classroom all ready for the school year."

I faked a smile for Wayne as Jackson set down my beer.

He turned and grabbed a bottle of aspirin from behind the cash register, opening the cap and popping a couple of pills into his mouth.

"Not feeling good?" Ronny asked.

Jackson shook his head. "I haven't had a bitch of a hangover like this in years. The damn thing has lasted all day. Remind me never to do tequila shots, then smoke a joint with the tourists again. I'm a fucking dumbass."

Ronny and Wayne both laughed.

I did not.

Tequila and weed. That was the taste I couldn't pinpoint last night. That was the reason for the haze in his eyes. He'd been drunk and high during my first kiss.

"Did you stay out late?" Ronny asked Jackson.

He shrugged. "Not really. I closed up around midnight after the tourists left the bar. Walked home and passed out."

I stared at his profile, waiting for his eyes to at least flicker my way. He was forgetting a stop on his stroll home. Was that intentional? Did he not want Wayne and Ronny to know he'd even talked to me? Or had he forgotten me completely in his inebriated state?

"You just went home and fell asleep?" I asked.

He glanced over. "Pretty much. Had some crazy dreams though."

I narrowed my gaze, assessing his expression. He wasn't

lying. He wasn't pretending. He wasn't omitting pieces of his story.

He really had forgotten.

He'd forgotten the best night of my life. The best first kiss in the history of first kisses.

He'd forgotten me.

The pain nearly knocked me off my stool. Jackson continued to chat with Wayne and Ronny while I stared unblinking at my beer glass. The bubbles collected on the rim, then burst.

Like my heart.

Enough, Willa. Enough.

My friends had told me for years to move on, to forget my schoolgirl crush on Jackson and go after a man who actually knew I existed.

But I'd nurtured and coddled the fantasy for nine years.

I'd finally had enough. This was the kick in the rear I'd needed to let him go. In a way, I was glad this had all happened.

Yep, glad. Super glad.

G-L-A-D, glad.

He was just a silly dream.

And it was time to chase a new one.

Printed in Great Britain
by Amazon